The Ascent of Man
David Pilbeam

Primate Evolution
Elwyn L. Simons

The Macmillan Series in Physical Anthropology
Elwyn L. Simons and David Pilbeam, editors
other volumes in preparation

The constitution of the ape is hot, and since he is rather similar to man, he always observes him in order to imitate his actions. He also shares the habits of beasts, but both these aspects of his nature are deficient, so that his behavior is neither completely human nor completely animal; he is therefore unstable. Sometimes, when he observes a bird in flight, he raises himself and leaps and tries to fly, but since he cannot accomplish his desire, he immediately becomes enraged. Being similar to man, the (she-) ape also has a menstrual cycle governed by the moon, and since both aspects of its nature are unstable and weak, the creature has no medicinal value.

Saint Hildegard of Bingen ca. 1150

trans. Jansen, 1952

UNIVERSITY OF SUSSEX

THE EVOLUTION OF PRIMATE BEHAVIOR

The Macmillan Series in Physical Anthropology

Macmillan Publishing Co., Inc.
NEW YORK
Collier Macmillan Publishers
LONDON

Printed in the United States of America

Macmillan Publishing Co., Inc.
866 Third Avenue, New York, New York 10022

Collier Macmillan Canada, Ltd.

Library of Congress catalog card number: 73-160371

Printing 9 10 11 Year 8 9

for G. E. Hutchinson

who once defined ecology as
the study of the universe

Preface

In this book, I have attempted to survey current knowledge about primate behavior and its relevance to human behavior. This is obviously an impossible task, for it would have to begin with a perfect understanding of man. It is also impossible in a more mundane sense, as the amount of published data increases so rapidly that a year's lag in publication may mean covering only half the field. Add to these the author's shortcomings, and the result must be sketchy indeed.

However, the attempt seems worth making. The other primates resemble man in so very many aspects of their behavior that a general survey is overdue—not just of feeding or sex, aggression or intelligence, but all of them. Furthermore, our ideas about all these things depend so much on the present amount of data and its coverage—by no means an unbiased sample of the universe—that one must be particularly alert to sources and cautious about how quickly general conclusions can change.

Parts I and II, "Ecology" and "Society," present lines of thought that are common among zoologists and anthropologists. Part III, "Intelligence," is far more eclectic, and will be more controversial. Instead of a fair picture of the schools of primate psychology, I have chosen a few that seem relevant to the evolutionary, developmental approaches of Parts I and II. The evolution of intelligence is one of the most fascinating themes of primate behavior, but, starting as a biologist rather than as a psychologist, I feel that intelligence is only a part of the make-up of the animal as a whole, not an abstract entity to study in isolation.

There is no single conclusion to this book, no simple clue to man's difference from the other primates. We are not just oversexed apes or killer apes or grammatical apes. However, there is one recurrent theme: that the primates, including man, can only be understood as social creatures. Every aspect of our behavior, from feeding to reading (and writing) textbooks, depends on the nature and support of society. We are individuals, but our individuality evolved only within and through our interdependence.

I would like to thank all those who contributed ideas and criticisms to this text, in particular J. Bruner, S. Green, G. E. Hutchinson, and P. Marler. My thanks also go to the editors, Charles Smith and Ray Schultz, and to the designer, Wayne Ellis. I thank Mrs. William Hare, who made the book possible, and Margaretta, Susan, and Arthur Morris for their occasional forbearance. Above all, I thank my husband, Richard, for his enthusiasm, his criticism, and his conviction (he says insight) that primate behavior chiefly holds a mirror to the behavior of primatologists.

Contents

II / SOCIETY

Introduction

Man is a primate. We know this in every detail of our physical form, from our flat fingernails to our blunt big toes, and in the colors we see out of our eyes. Linnaeus (1735) classed man with monkey, lemur, and bat. When T. H. Huxley (1863) drew the anatomy of man and ape, he challenged his hearers to deny their kinship with the chimpanzee.

Does man behave as a primate? No. Chimpanzees probe twigs into holes; we analyze moon rock. Chimpanzees have destroyed their own children, but one of our species wrote *Medea.* However, the creationist who looks for absolute differences between ourselves and the ape is likely to be disappointed. Our love and hate and fear and curiosity, our birth and death, all our emotions, and even some of our logic stem from the primate past.

On present reckoning we have been placental mammals for 130 million years, and have been monkey-like, large-brained, possibly group-living creatures for 30 million years. Sometime in the past 5 million to 15 million years we became terrestrial hunters (the time uncertainty here is one of the major question marks in human evolution). Only for the final millennia have some tribes tilled fields, built villages, constructed human life as we now conceive it.

All written history is the chronicle of a *nouveau riche,* abruptly risen to dictatorship of his planet—not what we are, but what we have made ourselves. Our earlier history, the part without writing or artifacts, can only be deduced from what we do and what our primate relatives do—the hieroglyphics of the chimpanzee's whimper and the baby's smile.

ARGUING FROM PRIMATE TO MAN

The paradigm of evolution has embraced us. We are, in T. S. Kuhn's phrase, in the puzzle-solving phase of discovery, when each new fact fits, more or less, into an evolutionary picture. We believe that we know how natural selection and cultural transmission work. We can, with confidence and excitement, construct more and more of what the picture of primate evolution might have been.

On a smaller theoretical scale, however, the study of primate behavior is changing radically. The cruder classifications with which each discipline began are being reanalyzed and refined at every level. To take a few examples: We used to talk about the group size typical for a species—now we must specify group size at what population density, in what environment. We used to speak of linear dominance hierarchies—now it is a concept more like role playing, because different measures of "dominance" rarely rank the same individual in quite the same way. We used to list categories of displays—now we study how the components of each display may grade into each other, through a continuous series of intermediate forms. This is the common pattern of science: whenever enough is learned about an object, or type, it is analyzed into components that may vary somewhat independently of each other and be differently affected by their environment. The exciting part is that we are reaching a level of sophistication in analyzing primate behavior where we can use at least some of the same terms for the behavior of mankind. We can at last begin to speak of primates without doing too much violence to either scientific objectivity or human intuition.

It is a tenet of evolutionary theory that any species of animal is nearly perfectly adapted to its environment. Although the theory itself is a dynamic one, it begins from the cross section of animals one sees at the present moment. It is easy enough to show the results of artificial selection of fruit flies, milk cows, or pedigreed poodles, but mammalian generation times are too long for us to have observed the dynamics of change of wild populations under natural selection. Therefore, we assume that in stable habitat they are changing very slowly. Changing situations—invasions by alien species, islands with "empty" niches and successive colonizations, even the catastrophic changes caused by modern man—provide ecology with its most critical theories. However, among the primates, such examples have been only recently appreciated.

Thus, the zoologist can take a modern monkey in an "undisturbed" habitat and assume that the monkey evolved over millenia in a similar habitat. The shape of its limbs, the quirks of its mind, must be adjusted, to a very close approximation, to each other and to the trees it inhabits. This gives deep satisfaction—an intellectual confirmation of the zoologist's affection and respect for the animal he studies. The natural monkey (though not the natural man) has a kind of perfection.

Not the natural man. We ourselves are torn and divided. We have "original sin," or "innate aggression without innate control." We have "sparks of divine reason" or "cultural norms"—whatever the catchword, we have never been able to think ourselves either natural or perfect. When anthropologists seek out the origins of human behavior, they are after the beginnings of this imbalance, this divergence or emergence from the zoologist's world. (I did not say the animals' world. Animals might not suppose themselves natural either, were they to think.)

This leads into the dynamic aspect of evolutionary speculation, whereby we try to reconstruct the behavior of our fossil ancestors from that of living forms. What can be reconstructed is very obvious—in a sense, if there are clear similarities between the great apes and ourselves, the common ancestor quite probably shared them as well. If there are clear convergences among savanna-living primates, or among hunting mammals, perhaps our ancestors evolved similar behavior when hunting in savannas. But it becomes much more difficult when speculation runs: "the human environment changed faster than man's biological make-up, while cultural adaptation took over from biological adaptation to meet the changing environment." To be consistent with the logic that applies to monkeys, we should have to say that we are in fact adapted, by the mere fact that we are not extinct (yet) and that culture is our speciality, foreshadowed in bees, birds, and mice as well as other primates. If we have conflicting and sometimes individually destructive impulses, so do limpets and lemmings.

Reconstructing the origin of man then becomes an exercise in relative rates of change: the *relative* importance at each stage of hunting, speech, extended female receptivity, intergroup conflict, tools, magic. And speculation on these points, although it is carried out in the context of evolutionary theory, is not much helped by available zoological data. There are a few experimental studies aimed at changing one aspect of the social behavior or ecology of a group of nonhuman primates, but we are only starting to tease out the strands that make up their behavior, not yet the relative importance or relative rates of change.

What we need are data. We need far more data on primate species that have not yet been studied, and more on different populations in different habitats. Oddly, the species for which we need data most is man. So far, we know so little about the primates that we cannot confidently predict even the grouping tendencies of a primate that has not yet been studied. Therefore, we need data on man to tell us about man: Is the pair bond universal (Stephens, 1963)? Are there constant traits in the societies of hunting peoples (Lee and DeVore, 1968)? We can hardly expect to reconstruct the behavior of protohominids from the behavior of primates alone when we cannot extrapolate from a North Indian langur to a South Indian langur!

In the circumstances, all this book can do is describe and compare the primates themselves. Where man *resembles* other primates, the morals are clear, and we can see how our present capacities evolved in the ecology or society of a primate forebear. Where man *differs,* we can only speculate backward along our divergent path.

FIELD STUDY

Imagine a forest canopy 80 to 120 feet above ground, with emergent giant trees towering to 150 feet. The canopy is so dense that little light reaches the forest floor, and there is almost no undergrowth—except where a tree has fallen to make a "clearing"—a solidly braided tangle of vegetation, plants locked together in the light, racing each other upward before the canopy roof shall close again. In the tallest trees, often invisible to a ground-based observer, sit the howler monkeys. And sit. And sit. An individual howler rests for 80 per cent of his day. They are black lumps on the branch, without expression, individuals distinguished mainly by the goitrous swellings made by botfly larvae on their throats. They may reward, and threaten, the observer with dramatic howls—or they may simply pick themselves up, drifting from tree to tree by several paths, so it is even difficult to count the animals, while the observer stumbles down and up the ravine-slashed forest floor in their wake.

This is not a picture of the selfless heroism of the primatologist—he is usually enjoying himself. But it attempts to show how he wastes his time. He cannot find his animals, or he cannot see them, or, when all else is perfect, they "do nothing." Finally, when they do do something, it is so complex that he knows he needs another year in another site even to be confident he has seen typical behavior for the species.

This method of study has important results for the distribution of data. Easily visible inhabitants of open savanna are much better known than forest species, and in the forest sedentary species are better studied than those that agilely disappear. Nor is there an adequate amount of data. Many species are "known" by the counts of one troop—or two or ten. Few species have been studied for more than 1 year, few in more than one site. Finally, even among those that are "well studied," the differences in observation conditions mean there are few objective standards for comparison among species. Although it is instantly obvious that African baboons are more active than Panama howler monkeys, different observers may have no measures to quantitatively compare primates' activity in the field, let alone the complexities of their social interactions.

THE BACKGROUND OF PRIMATOLOGY

Scientists of many disciplines have converged on primate behavior: anthropologists seeking the nature of man, psychologists seeking the nature of thought, zoologists challenged by the most complex of animals. These three disciplines bring their traditional attitudes and techniques with them. Psychologists have usually studied primates in cages, under controlled conditions, in hopes of finding logical answers to abstract questions. Zoologists, whether their subjects are in cage or field, have often been fascinated by the communication of emotion, and, once the communication system is understood in part, the individual relations it reveals. Anthropologists, who have done many field studies, have seized on the grand format of ecology and social structure. Of course, techniques and interests have blended, and anyone now might study the social communication of a learned skill within a wild troop.

Modern primate field study began with Robert Yerkes. He did not go into the wild—not further than to watch his chimpanzees climb birch trees in his yard in Connecticut (1943). However, Yerkes collected all that was known about the great apes, from Aristotle's fascinated description of a gorilla's foot up to the 1920s (Yerkes and Yerkes, 1929). He was amazed at how very little factual study there had been. To supplement his own observations, and psychological rearing and testing of captive animals, he sent out students into the field. First, Bingham (1932) and Nissen (1931) went to observe gorillas and chimpanzees—difficult quarry in impossible terrain, for people who had no idea what primate research would mean. Then, Clarence Ray Carpenter (1934 in 1964) made the breakthrough, with 2 years' observation of the howler monkeys of Barro Colorado. This remains one of the great qualitative descriptions of a wild primate. Yerkes, and Carpenter, founded one tradition of primatology—delight in the animal for its own sake and meticulous observation of it in natural setting.

In the year that Carpenter left for Barro Colorado, Sir Solly Zuckerman (1932, 1933), a zoologist, founded the second tradition of primatology—as a direct clue to the origin of man. Observation of chacma baboons on the cliffs near Cape T[illegible] and hamadryas baboons captive in the London Zoo led him [illegible] theory of the beginning of human social behavior. H[illegible] prolonged female willingness to mate) was th[illegible] holding together the primate troop. Zuckerman's successors have since disproved the theory in this form—but because they followed his initial leap of imagination, his considering what we could learn about humanity from the baboon.

Even before these field studies, during World War I, Wolfgang Köhler (1927) sought out "insight learning" in his captive chimpanzees. This was the beginning of a third tradition—modern primate psychology and the search for structures of thought that would, on the one hand, simplify and explain and yet, on the other hand, be worthy of the complexity of the primate mind. Nadia Kohts (1923), also a psychologist, first raised a chimpanzee in a human home to learn the limits of its capacities.

And if the *Soul of the ape* (1969) can be believed, there was another early precursor, Eugene Marais, who studied a troop of wild chacma baboons just after the Boer War and wrote, in 1922, of the problems of natural selection in a creature governed by learning and social tradition. His manuscript was lost, and played no part in the subsequent rediscovery of his own main themes.

Nowadays, there are many field primatologists. Major schools of interest have begun with Sherwood Washburn in America, Miyadi and Imanishi in Japan, Ronald Hall in England, Bourlière in France. As in other scientific disciplines, knowledge increases at a geometrical rate. The gaps in the data are being filled year by year—which means that a textbook's conclusions are outdated while being written. Let the student beware!

CONTENTS OF THE BOOK

The book itself is divided into three parts. The first, "Ecology," deals with general adaptations of primate behavior to habitat. A chapter describes the primate order, its phylogeny, and our present data. Three chapters deal with locomotion, feeding, and defense against predators, which should give some notion of the environment and techniques of dealing with it. Three further sections relate social organization to habitat—partitioning the environment between species, the ecological pressures toward communal life, and then group structure and home range, which are ways of partitioning the environment within the species.

Part II, "Society," turns to experimental work as well as field study. Chapter 8 begins with a brief discussion of learned and innate behavior, as these terms are currently used. The next chapter deals with expression of the emotions—primate communication and how it fits (or does not fit) within the classical terminology. Then follow chapters on interindividual interactions as they compose the social fabric of the troop—dominance interactions, sexual ones, friendship. The ontogeny of social behavior concludes Part II with mother-infant relations, troop-young behavior, and juvenile and adolescent behavior. A final chapter summarizes some changes in mammalian behavior under crowding, stress, and confinement supposedly parallel to those of urban man.

Part III, "Intelligence," after a historical introduction, treats first the manipulation of objects, which has long had pride of place in discussions of the origin of man. Then, formal experiments of primate learning are set in the framework of Piagetian stages of child development. A chapter on language follows and, finally, one on social learning and social traditions. The book ends with a chapter on the evolution of intelligence.

Thus, the book attempts to move coherently from basic ecology, toes gripping tree limb and mouth full of cecropia leaves, to the evolution of logic and the heritage of culture.

I / ECOLOGY

Phylogeny and Ecology 1

Animals that resemble each other may derive their common traits from a common ancestor or may have evolved them in converging to a common way of life. Those derived from a common ancestor are called traits of common inheritance (Le Gros Clark, 1962; Martin, 1968b).

To speculate about the behavior of an extinct, ancestral form, we assume that it had the traits of common inheritance of its living descendents and neighboring collateral lines. We may also suggest that it adapted itself to its ecological habitat in ways similar to modern animals of the same ecology. The problem, of course, is to decide which characters are which—those due to common inheritance or to recent adaptation.

Take genus A and genus B, each with several species, and with three groups of traits. One group x is common to all of them. The simplest hypothesis is that x is a trait of common descent, from the ancestor of *both* genera (see Figure 1).

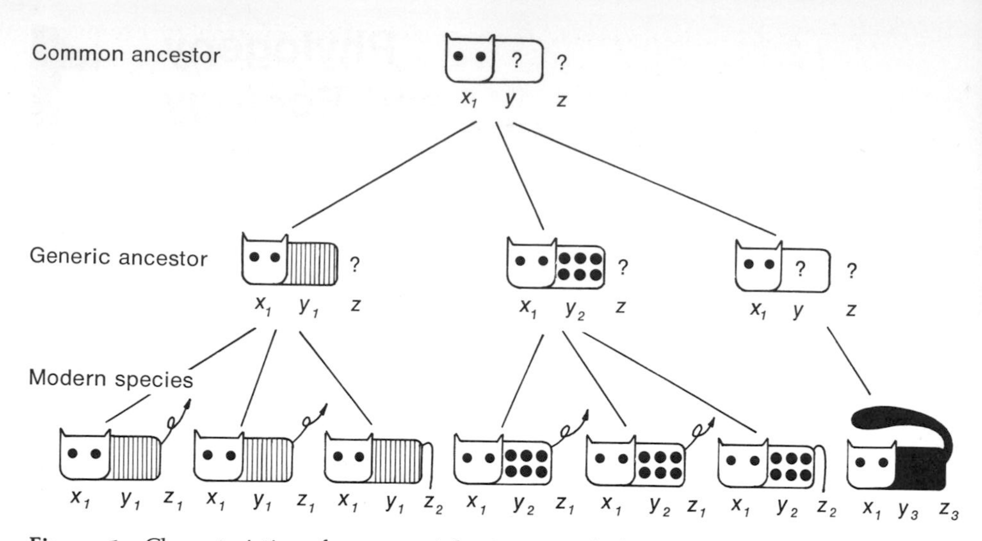

Figure 1 Characteristics of common inheritance and characteristics of recent adaptation. Taxonomy is agreed to depend primarily on *x* traits and secondarily on *y* traits. Even with agreed taxonomy, it may be difficult to decide the *z* traits of ancestral forms without fossil evidence or data on the habitat of the ancestors. The aberrant single species gives even less clue to its immediate ancestor.

A second trait group y_1, y_2 is consistently different in the two genera. Presumably, it was inherited, but only from the generic ancestor of each. A third z_1, z_2 is irregularly distributed among the species—but correlated with habitat differences. This is presumably a recent adaptation at the species level.

Of course, one must measure many traits and try to see which are functionally connected. Only this will give the basis for classifying y_1 species together as a single genus, not z_1 species. But, even if we start with a fairly reliable classification as a framework, how do we decide the nature of the generic ancestor? In this example, two lines of argument are open. Either the ancestor had trait z_1 that appears in most of its descendants, or else it had the *z* trait that corresponded to its ecological situation, either z_1 or z_2. With more information, it might be quite possible to decide, or make reasonable speculations, about the likelihood of z_1 or z_2 in the ancestor.

However, suppose there is another genus C, with only one surviving species. Then it becomes difficult even to distinguish *y* and *z* traits—even if the taxonomic classification is the same, it is harder to tell whether *y* or *z* adaptations were acquired earlier in the separate history of each line. This need not necessarily bother the taxonomist of modern species, but is crucial to the anthropologist or paleontologist whose goal is reconstruction of hominid behavior.

Thus, it is not enough for the argument that any two primate species (or families, genera, troops) are alike or different in certain traits—it is necessary to examine relatives of each to provide a baseline. This means that where there are not enough living relatives, the argument must remain incomplete.

In practice, then, the strongest arguments for ecological influence are taken between either widely separated species or conspecific troops. If leaf-eating monkeys of New and Old Worlds resemble each other as well as the leaf-eating lemurs of Madagascar in some traits more than they resemble their fruit-eating close relatives, then there is a strong case for the resemblances being adaptations to similar ecological factors. If the leaf eaters of the Old World resemble each other, it proves little, because they are probably descended from a common ancestor as well.

On the infraspecies level, if forest-living baboon troops differ consistently from baboons in dry savanna, again one could argue that the differences depend on environment. In this case, the troops of the species are the close relatives—if various populations respond in the same way to different environments, their behavior is presumably a direct response to the environment.

Thus, where there are many troops to compare, or many species of different lineages, arguments can be strong. If there are only single examples, the phylogeny versus ecology distinctions must be weak. As man is the single surviving species of his line, the comparisons are weak—or farfetched—as you please.

What data, then, do the primates offer us? (See Table 1 and Figure 2.) First, primates have evolved a wide range of living forms, in at least three major lines of descent. The Malagasy lemurs, Old World monkeys, and New World monkeys are each a relatively homogeneous phylogenetic group, whose members have radiated to fill comparable niches on three different continents. Arguments about ecological-behavioral similarities among tree-living, monkey-like forms can therefore be fairly firmly based, because one can compare species in three independent phylogenetic lines.

These "monkey-like" forms, which exist in all three major lines, are all diurnal, are predominantly vegetarian, and live in quasi-permanent social troops. This may be considered the "typical" higher primate pattern of existence. On the other hand, many prosimians are nocturnal, chiefly insectivorous, and solitary. Here, within the prosimians, the Malagasy lemurs may be compared with the more closely related lorisoids of Africa and Asia and the anatomically very distinct but ecologically similar tarsier. *Aotes*, the night monkey, fills the same sort of niche in the New World.

Unfortunately, inferences about behavioral adaptation to savanna or open-country life are much harder to make. The New World monkeys may never have invaded the savannas, and the ground-living lemur species are extinct. *Lemur catta*, the ringtail, is as terrestrial as "forest-living" baboons, but there are no surviving lemurs in open country. This leaves Old World monkeys alone occupying what was probably the habitat of early hominids. Within the Old World monkeys, one can compare two much more closely related taxa—the baboon group and the guenon group. These share the same subfamily, the Cercopithecinae, so the groups have not even the dignity of a Latin name to split them. However, it is clear that the forest-living drills and mandrills anatomically resemble the plains baboon, whereas the plains-living patas monkey and the forest-edge vervet are related to guenon species of the high forest. Thus where (or if) the savanna forms have converged in behavioral traits and differ from their forest relatives, again ecological influences may be argued against phylogenetic ones.

Monkeys, then, because of the wide variety of taxa occupying different habitats, give a fairly strong base for arguments. The great apes, on the other hand, are too few in number of species to provide this sort of check. The gibbons and siamangs, which on fossil evidence may only be very distantly related to the other apes, are highly specialized brachiators living in monogamous family groups. Both ecologically and socially they are set apart, in their specializations, from other primates. Orangutans' social behavior, at least under modern hunting conditions, seems to be that of solitary animals, or with mother and infant as a typical social unit, which is unique among the Anthropoidea. Gorillas conform far more to the usual primate pattern of relatively stable troops, but their huge size, sedentary habits, and near immunity from predation except by man are again unique.

Finally, the chimpanzee. Far from being unique, the chimp seems an extrovert parody of a human being in nearly every capacity—social structure, opportunist exploitation of its environment, mental and emotional development, and even many details of communication. However, in the absence of other comparable species we are still left with the dilemma of whether our mutual resemblance derives from a recent common ancestor or from our similar environments. We can only stop with the delight that chimpanzees exist.

This brief survey of the primates shows that one can be on fairly strong ground in comparing various nocturnal, solitary, "primitive" primates and also the diurnal, social, "advanced" ones. However, we do not as yet understand the influences of savanna ecology on behavior, in part because only a few species of Old World monkeys have invaded the savanna, and in part because data on the forest-dwelling relatives of these few species are only now being collected. Finally, the great apes, as our closest relatives, do not in fact prove much about ecological influences, because their four surviving types are so specialized.

However, chimpanzees can illuminate the effects of ecology, if we compare populations of the same species. This is a much riskier business than comparison of unrelated species, which have (if they are adequately sampled) had millenia to adapt to a reasonably stable environment. Two subspecific populations studied may, in fact, differ genetically. They almost certainly differ in the accidents of local culture and bias introduced by individual dominant animals. At any rate, unless the species is a wide-ranging opportunist, one habitat may be suboptimal and reveal mainly the disintegration of behavior rather than an adaptively selected response.

Text continues on page 22.

Figure 2 Taxonomy of Primates. (After J. R. Napier and P. H. Napier, 1967.)

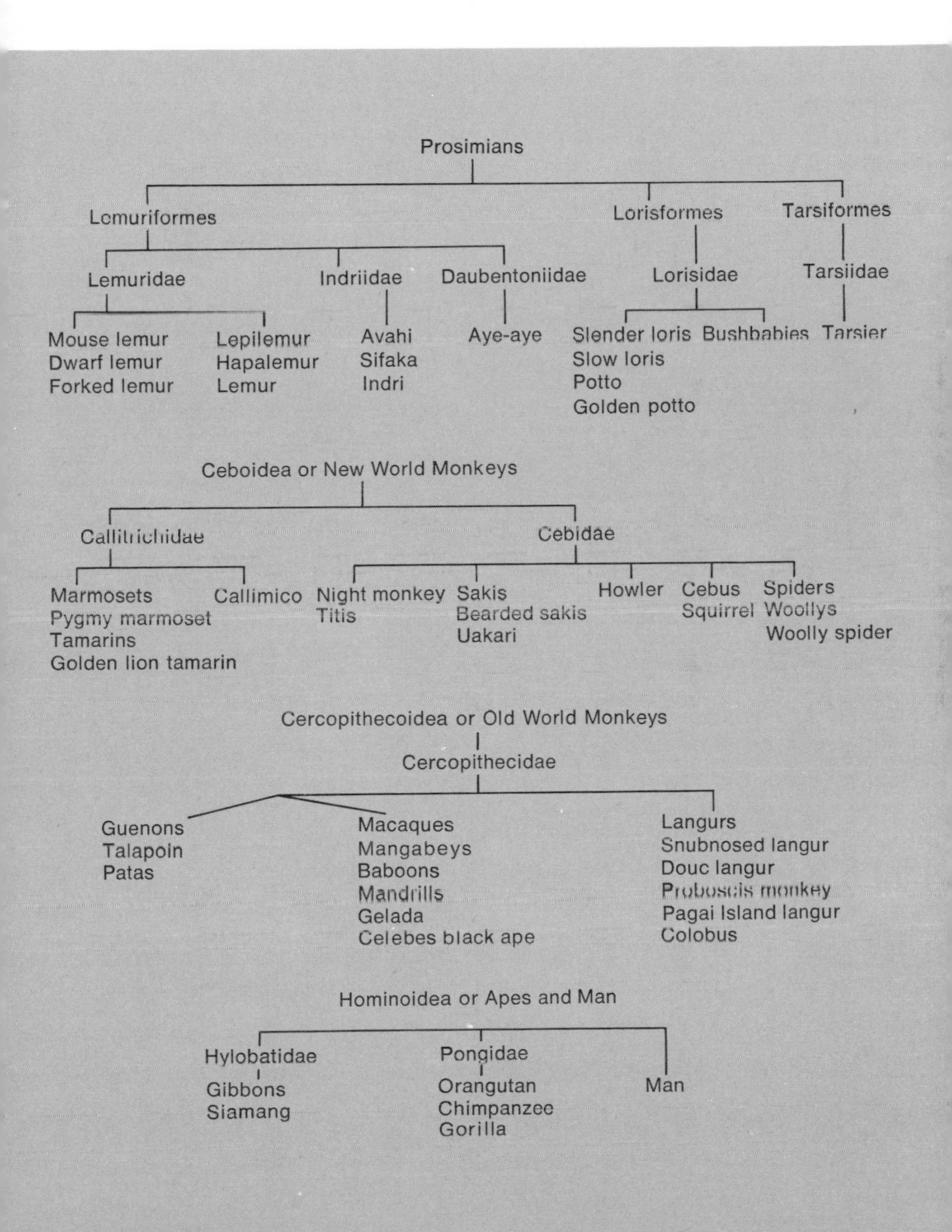

TABLE 1 TAXONOMY OF THE PRIMATE ORDER

Suborder	PROSIMII	PROSIMIANS
Infraorder	LEMURIFORMES	MALAGASY LEMURS
Superfamily	LEMUROIDEA	LEMUROIDS
Family	Lemuridae	
Subfamily	Lemurinae	
Genus	*Lemur*	lemurs
Species	*catta*	ringtailed lemur
	variegatus	variegated lemur
	macaco	brown or black lemur
	mongoz	mongoz lemur
	rubriventer	
	Hapalemur	gentle lemur or hapalemur
	griseus	
	simus	
	Lepilemur	sportive lemur or lepilemur
	mustelinus	
Subfamily	Cheirogaleinae	small nocturnal lemurs
	Cheirogaleus	dwarf lemurs
	major	greater dwarf lemur
	medius	fattailed dwarf lemur
	trichotis	hairyeared dwarf lemur
	Microcebus	mouse lemur
	murinus	
	coquereli	Coquerel's mouse lemur
	Phaner	forked lemur
	furcifer	
Family	Indriidae	
	Indri	indri
	indri	
	Avahi	woolly lemur, avahi
	laniger	
	Propithecus	sifakas
	diadema	diademed sifaka
	verreauxi	white sifaka
Superfamily	DAUBENTONIOIDEA	
Family	Daubentoniidae	
	Daubentonia	aye-aye
	madagascariensis	

Column 1 gives classification. Column 2 gives the *scientific* name (Latin nomenclature). Column 3 gives the *vernacular* for the scientific name. Underscored names are the vernacular for the *genuses.*

Abridged from Napier and Napier (1967) and Napier (personal communication).

Infraorder	LORISIFORMES	LORISES, LORISIFORMS, LORISOIDS
Family	Lorisidae	
Subfamily	Lorisinae	
	Loris *tardigradus*	slender loris
	Nycticebus *coucang*	slow loris
	Arctocebus *calabarensis*	golden potto
	Perodicticus *potto*	potto
Subfamily	Galaginae	galagos, bushbabies
	Galago (Galago)	galagos, bushbabies
	senegalensis	Senegal or lesser bushbaby
	crassicaudatus	thicktailed or greater bushbaby
	alleni	Allen's bushbaby
	Galago (Euoticus) *elegantulus* *inustus*	needleclawed bushbaby
	Galago (Galagoides) *demidovii*	Demidoff's or dwarf bushbaby
Infraorder	TARSIIFORMES	
Family	Tarsiidae	
	Tarsius	tarsiers
	spectrum	spectral tarsier
	bancanus	Horsfield's tarsier
	syrichta	Philippine tarsier
Suborder	ANTHROPOIDEA	MONKEYS and APES
Superfamily	CEBOIDEA	NEW WORLD MONKEYS
Family	Callitrichidae	tamarins and marmosets
Subfamily	Callitrichinae	
	Callithrix	marmosets
	jacchus	common marmoset
	argentata	blacktailed marmoset
	aurita	whiteeared marmoset
	flaviceps	buffheaded marmoset
	geoffroyi	whitefronted marmoset
	penicillata	blackeared marmoset
	humeralifer	Santarem marmoset
	chrysoleuca	golden marmoset
	Cebuella *pygmaea*	pygmy marmoset

TABLE 1 TAXONOMY OF THE PRIMATE ORDER (continued)

	Saguinus (Saguinus)	hairyfaced tamarins
	tamarin	negro tamarin
	devillei	De Ville's tamarin
	fuscicollis	brownheaded tamarin
	fuscus	
	graellsi	Rio Napo tamarin
	illigeri	redmantled tamarin
	imperator	emperor tamarin
	melanoleucus	white tamarin
	midas	redhanded tamarin
	labiatus	redbellied tamarin
	mystax	moustached tamarin
	pileatus	redcapped tamarin
	pluto	Lönnberg's tamarin
	weddelli	Weddell's tamarin
	nigricollis	black-and-red tamarin
	lagonotus	harelipped tamarin
	Saguinus (Oedipomas)	crested barefaced tamarins, pinchés
	oedipus	pinché, cottontop
	geoffroyi	Geoffroy's tamarin
	Saguinus (Marikina)	true barefaced tamarins
	bicolor	pied tamarin
	martinsi	Martin's tamarin
	leucopus	whitefooted tamarin
	inustus	
	Leontideus	lion tamarins
	rosalia	golden lion tamarins
	chrysomelas	
	chrysopygus	
Subfamily	Callimiconinae	
	Callimico	Goeldi's marmoset, callimico
	goeldii	
Family	Cebidae	
Subfamily	Aotinae	
	Aotus	night monkey, owl monkey
	trivirgatus	
	Callicebus	titis
	personatus	masked titi
	moloch	dusky titi, moloch
	torquatus	widow monkey
Subfamily	Pitheciinae	
	Pithecia	sakis
	pithecia	paleheaded saki
	monachus	monk saki

	Chiropotes	bearded saki
	satanas	black saki
	albinasus	whitenosed saki
	Cacajao	uakaris
	melanocephalus	blackheaded uakari
	calvus	bald uakari
	rubicundus	red uakari
Subfamily	Alouattinae	
	Alouatta	howler monkeys
	belzebul	redhanded howler
	villosa	mantled howler
	seniculus	red howler
	caraya	black howler
	fusca	brown howler
Subfamily	Cebinae	
	Cebus	capuchin monkey, cebus
	capucinus	whitethroated capuchin
	albifrons	whitefronted capuchin
	nigrivittatus	weeper capuchin
	apella	blackcapped capuchin
	Saimiri	squirrel monkey
	sciureus	squirrel monkey
	oerstedii	redbacked squirrel monkey
Subfamily	Atelinae	
	Ateles	spider monkey
	paniscus	black spider monkey
	belzebuth	longhaired spider monkey
	fusciceps	brownheaded spider monkey
	geoffroyi	blackhanded spider monkey
	Brachyteles	woolly spider monkey
	arachnoides	
	Lagothrix	woolly monkey
	lagotricha	Humboldt's woolly monkey
	flavicauda	Hendee's woolly monkey
Superfamily	CERCOPITHECOIDEA	OLD WORLD MONKEYS
Family	Cercopithecidae	
Subfamily	Cercopithecinae	
	Macaca	macaques
	sylvanus	barbary ape
	sinica	toque monkey
	radiata	bonnet monkey
	silenus	liontailed macaque
	nemestrina	pigtailed macaque
	fascicularus	crabeating monkey

TABLE 1 TAXONOMY OF THE PRIMATE ORDER (continued)

Scientific name	Common name	
mulatta	rhesus monkey	
assamensis	Assamese macaque	
cyclopis	Formosan rock macaque	
arctoides	stumptailed macaque	
fuscata	Japanese macaque	
maurus	Celebes or moor macaque	
thibetana	Thibetan macaque	
Cynopithecus	Celebes black ape	
niger		
Cercocebus	mangabeys	
albigena	graycheeked mangabey	
aterrimus	black mangabey	
torquatus	whitecollared mangabey	
atys	sooty mangabey	
galeritus	agile mangabey	
Papio	baboons	
cynocephalus	yellow baboon	savanna baboon
anubis	olive baboon	savanna baboon
papio	Guinea baboon	savanna baboon
ursinus	chacma baboon	savanna baboon
hamadryas	sacred baboon, hamadryas	
Mandrillus	mandrills	
sphinx	drill	
leucophaeus	mandrill	
Theropithecus	gelada baboon	
gelada		
Cercopithecus (Cercopithecus)	guenons	
aethiops	vervet	
sabaeus	green monkey	
cephus	moustached monkey	
diana	diana monkey	
lhoesti	L'Hoest's monkey	
preussi	Preuss' monkey	
hamlyni	Hamlin's or owlfaced monkey	
mitis	blue monkey	
albogularis	Sykes' monkey	
mona	mona monkey	
campbelli	Campbell's monkey	
wolfi	Wolf's monkey	
denti	Dent's monkey	
pogonias	crowned guenon	
neglectus	De Brazza's monkey	
nictitans	spotnosed monkey	
petaurista	lesser spotnosed monkey	
ascanius	redtail	
erythrotis	redeared guenon	
erythrogaster	redbellied guenon	

	Cercopithecus (Miopithecus)		
	talapoin	talapoin	
	Cercopithecus (Allenopithecus)		
	nigroviridis	Allen's swamp monkey	
	Erythrocebus	patas, red hussar	
	patas		
Subfamily	Colobinae		
	Presbytis	langurs	
	aygula	Sunda Island langur	
	melalophos	banded leaf monkey (langur)	
	frontatus	whitefronted leaf monkey (langur)	
	rubicundus	maroon leaf monkey (langur)	
	entellus	hanuman langur	
	senex	purplefaced leaf monkey (langur)	
	johnii	John's langur, nilgiri langur	
	cristatus	silvered leaf monkey, lutong	
	pileatus	capped langur	
	geei	golden langur	
	obscurus	dusky leaf monkey (langur)	
	phayrei	Phayre's leaf monkey (langur)	
	francoisi	François' leaf monkey (langur)	
	potenziani	Mentawai leaf monkey (langur)	
	Rhinopithecus	snubnosed langur	
	roxellanae	golden monkey	
	avunculus	Tonkin snubnosed monkey	
	Pygathrix	douc langur	
	nemaeus		
	Nasalis	proboscis monkey	
	larvatus		
	Simias	Pagai Island langurs	
	concolor		
	Colobus (Colobus)	colobus, guerezas	
	polykomos	King colobus	black-and-white
	guereza	Abyssinian colobus	colobus
	Colobus (Procolobus)		
	verus	olive colobus	
	Colobus (Piliocolobus)		
	badius	red colobus	
	kirkii	Kirk's colobus	
Superfamily	HOMINOIDEA	APES and MEN	
Family	Hylobatidae		
	Hylobates	gibbons	
	lar	whitehanded or lar gibbon	
	moloch	silvery gibbon or moloch	

TABLE 1 TAXONOMY OF THE PRIMATE ORDER (continued)

	agilis	dark handed or agile gibbon
	hoolock	hoolock gibbon
	concolor	black gibbon
	klossi	Kloss's gibbon
	Symphalangus	siamang
	syndactylus	
Family	Pongidae	great apes
	Pongo	orangutan
	pygmaeus	
	Pan	chimpanzees
	troglodytes	chimpanzee
	paniscus	pygmy chimpanzee, bonobo
	Gorilla	gorilla
	gorilla	
Family	Hominidae	
	Homo	man
	sapiens	

However, the latitude of possible responses, especially if several species modify their behavior in the same direction in similar environments, can be very revealing. In this sense, even highly unadaptive behavior, under artificial conditions or under stress, may tell us much about our own reactions to the artifice and stress of "normal" civilized life.

SUMMARY

Primate behavior, like primate anatomy, is derived both from inheritance of traits common to a phylogenetic lineage and from more recently evolved traits, adapted to the particular ecology of each species or population. Thus, we need to compare a two-way matrix of animals of widely differing phylogeny but similar ecology, such as leaf monkeys of the Old World and New World, or of similar phylogeny but different habitat, such as olive baboons in forest and savanna. We lack data and we lack species to make this comparison complete: there are no open-country, ground-living New World monkeys or lemurs to compare with the Old World lineages.

Habitat and Locomotion

The primates evolved as arboreal animals. The grasping big toe, thumb set at an angle, and flattened fingernails are all adaptations to life in the trees. Even the first mammalian stock may have been arboreal, for the divergent big toe develops briefly in embryos of many mammalian orders (Martin, 1969).

Not only limbs but also senses are adapted to the trees: binocular vision with its capacity for depth perception, and color vision with its added dimension for distinguishing branches in the daytime and ripe from unripe fruit. The arboreal gibbon and squirrel monkey are distracted by nearby cues in formal learning tests; they have to learn, against their inclinations, to look past a wire mesh or plexiglass lid to find relevant cues. It matters to arboreal animals if a branch will block their leap—their perception, or attention, must begin with the near (Rumbaugh and McCormack, 1969).

Life cycle as well is adapted to the trees. Ungulate babies may be precocious enough to run during the first day of life, but no mammalian newborn is steady enough to climb unaided on

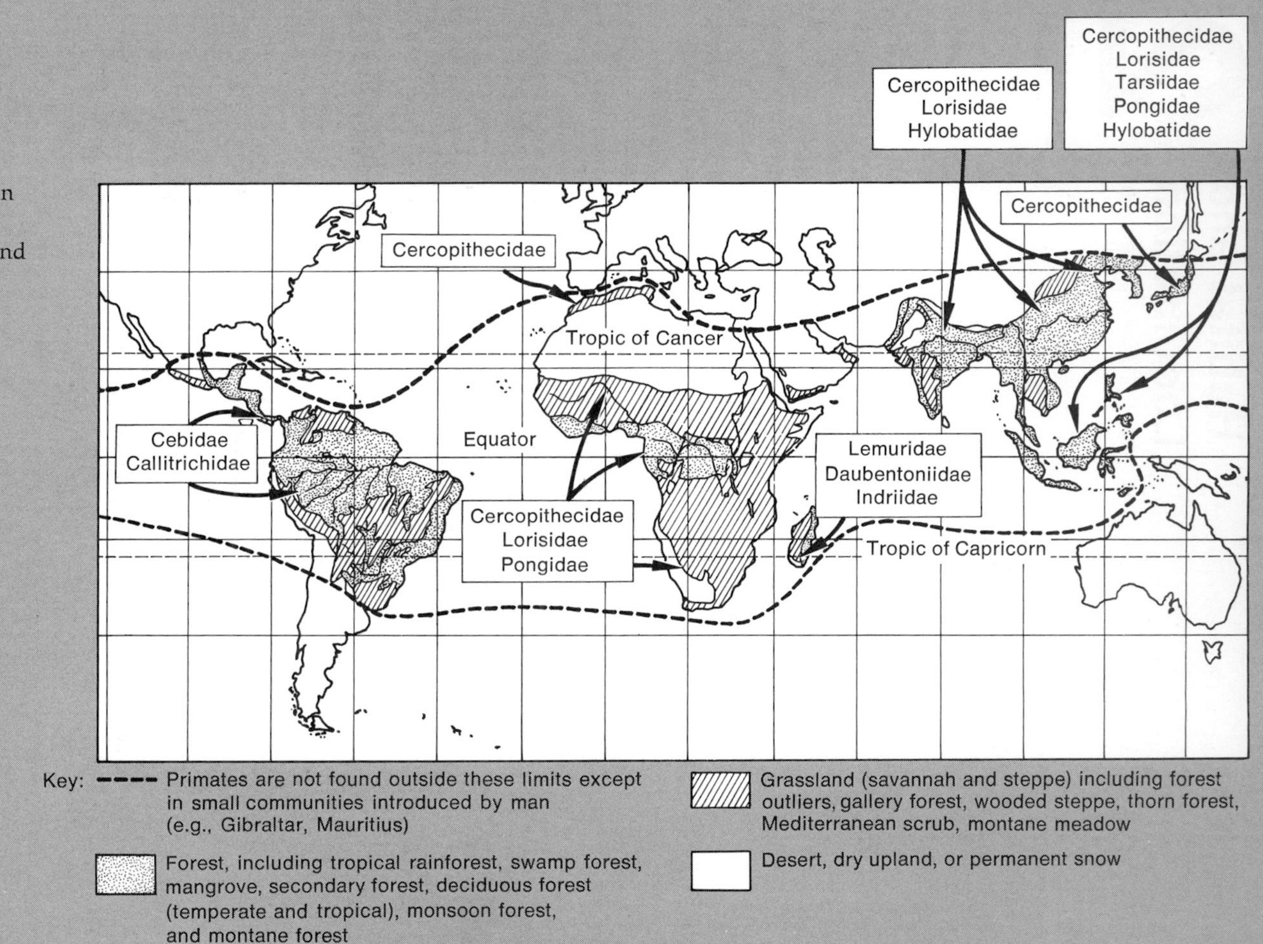

Figure 3 Nonhuman primate distribution. (After J. R. Napier and P. H. Napier, 1967.)

branches. A tree-living baby either needs a nest or else he must cling to his mother's fur, which means chiefly maintaining a grip, at any orientation, and often with some assistance from his mother. Martin believes the embryonic big toe not only shows that mammals were at first arboreal but that they carried their babies on their fur.

Many primates, including man, no longer live in the trees. But even the monkeys of open savanna retain much of this behavioral complex: limbs, senses, and clinging babies. Their behavior, adapted to different sorts of forest, different ways of moving in the forest, different degrees of independence on the ground, does not fossilize—but the limb and trunk bones do. Thus, locomotor patterns provide the most consistent single index to a primate's way of life.

FOREST, WOODLAND, SAVANNA

Figure 3 shows the distribution of tropical forests. High forest, or rainforest, forms a vast belt across equatorial Africa, as well as Southeast Asia and the Amazon Basin. To the north and south of the high forest belts lie woodlands, either drier or colder or both. Beyond the woodlands again are steppes or savanna, unsuitable for any but the most terrestrial primates.

Table 2 gives a more detailed breakdown of African forest types. As Moreau (1966) has shown, climatic changes in Africa during the Pleistocene have dramatically shifted the balance of montane forest and lowland forest, wet forest and drier woodlands. In cold periods, belts of montane forest were continuous with each other, and the present expanse of lowland forest was cut into blocks, or islands. In dry periods (which may have coincided with the cold ones), tongues of woodland or savanna cut through the West African coastal forest, as, for instance, the Dahomey and Volta gaps. Thus, there was every opportunity for speciation of the forest fauna, cut into isolated populations that could evolve in their own way, which then reunited to compete and perhaps diverge still further.

Within the lowland forest, swamp forest makes a specialized habitat. Swamp forest denizens include the guenon called Allen's swamp monkey, the whitecollared mangabey, and the little green talapoin in troops fifty to a hundred strong.

Secondary, or regenerating, forest is mostly provided by man. Even before human slash-and-burn agriculture, this existed where lightning or old age felled a forest tree and left a "clearing." Many primates, including the mountain gorilla (Schaller, 1963), thrive on the lush growth of secondary forest. Gallery forests along rivers and forest outliers in the savanna have less distinctive primates: mainly the usual inhabitants of wet forest or of woodland.

The forest edge and a variety of open woodlands have their

TABLE 2 A SUMMARY OF THE VEGETATIONAL

Vegetation zone		Subtype
Type I	**Tropical rainforest** Alternative terms: Moist forest Lowland rainforest Tropical high forest Forêt dense	
		Mangrove
		Secondary forest
		Swamp forest
		Montane rainforest Alternative terms: Highland forest Cloud forest
		Bamboo forest
Type II	**Savanna** Alternative terms: Sour veldt (S. Africa) High grass (E. Africa)	Woodland
		Open savanna
		Forest outliers Alternative terms: Bowl forest Kurmi Copses
		Gallery forest Alternative terms: Riverine forest Fringing forest
Type III	**Steppe** Alternative terms: Thornland Sweet veldt (S. Africa) Short grass (E. Africa) Desert grass Orchard steppe	Wooded steppe

After Napier and Napier (1967).

ZONES AND RELATED PRIMATE FAUNA OF SUB-SAHARAN AFRICA

Vegetation and climate	Genera
Three strata constituting an open and closed canopy with emergents Temperature—steady with narrow range Rainfall—high Relative humidity—high Specialized mangroves lining estuaries and creeks to tidal limits Tropical rainforest that has been cultivated and subsequently abandoned Similar but more open and irregular in structure	Guenons except vervet Colobus Chimpanzee Gorilla Mangabeys Mandrills Potto, Golden potto Bushbabies: Allen's, Demidoff's, needleclawed Talapoin De Brazza's guenon Allen's swamp guenon Whitecollared mangabey
3000 ft up to 8000 ft (depending on climatic conditions). Varies from evergreen forest to woodland with tree fern and bamboo thickets. Lianes 7000–10,000 ft. Stands of bamboo from 20–35 ft. Ground cover sparse	Chimpanzee Gorilla Colobus Savanna baboon
Trees 20–50 ft high, especially *Isoberlinia* Grass 6–15 ft high Trees widely spaced Grass 6–15 ft high	Vervet Patas Savanna baboon Bushbabies: senegal and thicktailed
Islands of tropical rainforest. Occurs in hollows and ravines where edaphic conditions are favorable Tropical rainforest on river banks	Vervet Colobus Savanna baboon Mangabeys Bushbabies Potto
Open and closed woodlands or thickets. *Acacia* and *Commiphora* Short grasses	Vervet Patas Savanna baboon Hamadryas baboon Gelada

Figure 4 (opposite) Tropical high forest, Uganda. The girl, 5 feet tall, gives scale. Many species of primate can live in the various vertical layers of such a forest. (Courtesy of C. H. F. Rowell.)

separate species. Savanna baboon, vervet guenon, and two species of bushbaby commonly live in woodland, or where grass and forest meet. Chimpanzees, at home in the forest, also range far into tree savanna.

However, few primates can do entirely without trees. The patas monkey, fox red and long legged, and the massive-maned hamadryas and gelada baboons range farthest into the arid zone, but even they climb trees, where there are any about to climb, as we do, at least when young.

Asia offers many parallels. Most of the primates live in high forest: the gibbon, and orangutan, most of the langurs, and many macaques such as the pigtail, the stumptail, and the liontail. The crabeating macaque may be particularly common in mangrove swamps.

The hanuman langur of India and Ceylon can live in high forest, but it also invades dry forest, scrub forest, and isolated stands of trees overhanging villages. It is the sacred monkey of India and takes full advantage of its position.

The Japanese and barbary apes (also macaques), and presumably the Chinese macaques as well, range through temperate-zone

Figure 5 Savanna, Amboseli Park, Kenya, with yellow baboons, impala, and zebra. (From S. A. Altmann and J. Altmann, 1970. By permission of the publishers, and S. A. Altmann, holder of the copyright.)

Figure 6 Temperate cedar forest, Morocco, habitat of the Barbary macaque. (Courtesy of J. M. Deag, from J. M. Deag and J. H. Crook, in press.)

Figure 7 Cliff habitat, Morocco. The Barbary macaque also lives on this sort of cliff. Many primates are extremely adaptable. (Courtesy of J. H. Crook, from J. M. Deag and J. H. Crook, in press.)

woods—at their northernmost limit, the deep-furred Japanese macaques winter in snow, chewing bark from the bare trees. Other macaques can survive among men: rhesus and bonnets in North and South India roost on the roofs of houses, temples, and railway stations.

In South America, the picture is somewhat simpler. There is no evidence that New World monkeys ever radiated a lineage of ground-living forms (Hershkovitz, 1969). Thus, all the species of New World monkeys, both the prosimian-like or squirrel-like marmosets and the more "monkey-like" cebids, live in forests. "Swamp forest," which occurs in patches in Africa, covers hundreds of square miles when the Amazon is in flood. Groups such as the uakaris and the talapoin-like squirrel monkey are specialized for swamp life, whereas the redhanded tamarin is especially fond of second growth.

In Madagascar, there is a band of rainforest up the eastern side of the island, where a mountain range catches the prevailing winds from the Indian Ocean. One genus of lemurs, the indris, is confined to the wet forest, whereas the nocturnal forked lemur is confined to the dry woodlands of the west. The other genera each have two or more forms, classed as species or subspecies, which are confined to the wet east or dry west. There were giant apelike lemurs and ground-running lemurs until the arrival of man. The aye-aye, aberrant in every way, apparently ranged over west and east, although it may now be wiped out in the western region.

VERTICAL SPACING

This horizontal spacing, as Napier and Napier (1967) say, is not enough to understand the distribution of primates. They not only live in different kinds of forest or savanna, but at different vertical levels. Figure 8 shows a profile of mature rainforest: the under story, middle story, and emergent giants. Napier, arguing from Booth's data in Table 3, points out that a number of species share the middle and lower stories of trees, from 5 to 120 feet, whereas life in the emergents, to 150 feet, seems more distinct. He reasons that the "lower" trees form a closed canopy, or at least their crowns touch each other, they are often bound together by thick lianas, and their foliage is fairly evenly distributed. Among the emergents, on the other hand, each tree opens to a vast umbrella, its crown distant from each neighbor, and its foliage at the farthest tips of slender twigs.

Therefore, it is possible to run quadrupedally among the tangled under story and the canopy. However, in the emergents, a primate must leap and/or swing, and be prepared to feed at the extreme periphery of a tree, often slung underneath a swaying branch.

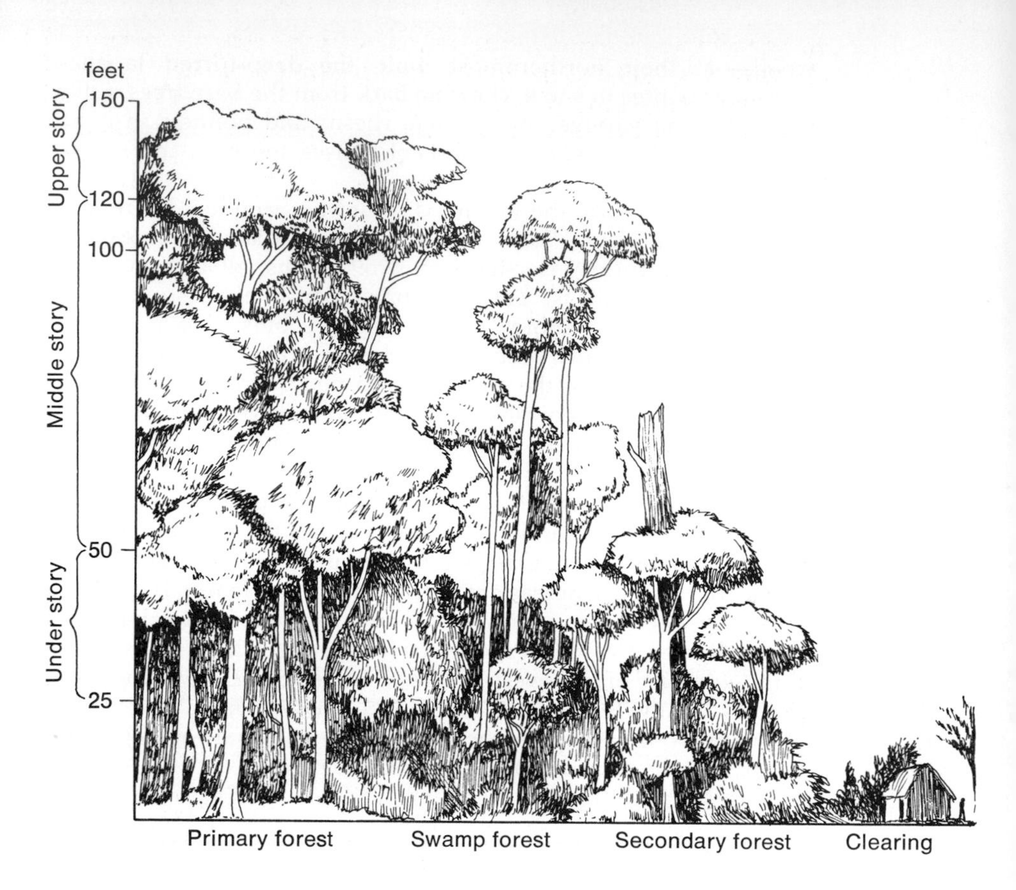

Figure 8 Tropical forest. (After J. R. Napier and P. H. Napier, 1967; R. E. Moreau, 1966.)

Finally, at the other extreme, many rainforest primates descend to the ground. Some species of African guenon and mangabey at times climb down. The forest baboons (drills and mandrills) and the forest macaques, like their open-country relatives, forage and flee along the ground. In Malaya, Bernstein (1967b) writes that only in 15 per cent of his contacts with traveling pigtailed macaques were they on the ground, but that this was far more often than the crabeating macaques or the langurs and gibbons of the same forest: "Animals leapt to the ground from as high as 10 meters .... [and fled] in a compact mass with individuals often shoulder to shoulder moving quietly and rapidly along the forest floor" (Bernstein, 1967b). Chimpanzees, even in the lush foliage of the Budongo forest, also come to the ground to flee, along their own chimpanzee trails (Reynolds and Reynolds, 1965). Thus, terrestriality as such, although correlated with the ability to invade forest edge or tree-savanna habitats, also plays a role among forest primate species.

TABLE 3 VERTICAL RANGE OF MONKEYS IN SOUTHWESTERN GHANA

	Red colobus	Black-and-white colobus	Olive colobus	Diana guenon	Campbell's guenon	Lesser spotnosed guenon	Sooty mangabey
Sleeping							
Upper	+	+	–	+	–	–	–
Middle	–	+	+	+	+	+	+
Lower	–	–	+	–	(+)	+	+
Traveling							
Upper	++	+	–	+	(+)	–	–
Middle	+	+	+	+	+	+	+
Lower	–	–	+	–	+	++	+
Ground	–	–	–	–	(+)	(+)	++
Feeding							
Upper	++	(+)	–	+	–	–	–
Middle	+	+	(+)	+	+	(+)	–
Lower	(+)	+	+	(+)	+	++	–
Ground	–	–	–	–	–	–	+
Food							
Fruit	–	–	–	+	+	+	+
Leaves	+	+	+	–	–	+	–

++ very frequent.
+ frequent.
(+) rare.
– almost never.

From Booth (1957) and Napier and Napier (1967).

LOCOMOTOR CLASSIFICATION

Table 4 gives a slightly modified version of the classification of primate locomotor behavior adopted by one leading authority, J. R. Napier (Napier and Napier, 1967). As Napier emphasizes himself, such a classification is not exclusive. Almost any primate may move in almost any fashion on a branch—above, below, creeping, or leaping. However, such a classification into broad categories fixes on single patterns of behavior: the most usual or most obvious and distinctive means of locomotion. Further, any one species may fall between, rather than within, major categories. Napier here is grading "the *degree* of these activities shown by different groups of primates: this involves an arbitrary segmentation of a continuous spectrum of activity."

A classification on these lines attempts to synthesize behavioral and morphological data. Morphological study is fairly refined: the shape of the limbs is itself the adaptive synthesis of the many conflicting requirements of the species' movements. Studies such as Ashton and Oxnard's (1964) of the shoulder girdle that take account of many diverse measurements (with appropriate statistical caution) can thus determine a series of forms, differently adapted, with which to compare fossil finds. On a cruder level, the intermembral index, or ratio of leg length to arm length, gives a rough idea of the relative importance of arm and leg in propulsion (*cf.* tables in Napier and Napier, 1967).

Behavioral studies, on the other hand, have been less extensive. Either the animal is provided with an artificial habitat in zoo or laboratory, which is limited or even inappropriate to an unknown degree, or else circumscribed questions are asked about the mechanics of a single movement. In the wild, there has been little attempt so far at quantitative description. Because Napier's (or any other) classification explicitly depends on the degree to which a primate uses various patterns, this leaves the behavioral side of the definitions still hanging in midair (Avis, 1962; Proust and Sussman, 1969).

The usual reaction of field observers is surprise that their animals can, in fact, do *everything.* In some cases, unsuspected patterns appear—an extreme "brachiator," the gibbon, and an extreme "leaper," the sifaka, both feed from the terminal tips of the branches, by slinging themselves underneath the flexible outer twigs. Their adaptations for fast movement must therefore be seen in the light of their equally specialized feeding behavior. However, on the whole, field descriptions do not usually add such a neat new category—instead they confuse the picture by realistically pointing out the variation among ages, activities, and even time of the day in the way primates treat their trees (Ripley, 1967b).

One very revealing study, by Rose (in preparation) (Table 5), summarizes his 4 months' observation of sympatric Uganda pri-

TABLE 4 LOCOMOTOR CLASSIFICATION

Category/subtype	Activity	Primate genera
1. **Vertical clinging and leaping**	Leaping in trees and hopping on the ground	Avahi, bushbabies, hapalemur, lepilemur, sifaka, indri, tarsier
2. **Quadrupedalism**		
(i) Slow-climbing type	Cautious climbing—no leaping or running	Golden potto, potto, slow and slender lorises
(ii) Branch-running and walking type	Climbing, springing, branch running	Mouse lemur, dwarf lemur, forked lemur, lemur, all marmosets and tamarins, night monkey, titis, sakis, uakaris, cebus, squirrel, guenons
(iii) Ground-running and walking type	Climbing and ground running	Macaques, baboons, mandrill, gelada, patas
(iv) New World "semi-brachiation" type	Arm swinging with use of prehensile tail, little leaping	Howler, spider, woolly spider, woolly
(v) Old World "semi-brachiation" type	Arm swinging and leaping	Colobus, all langurs, proboscis, snubnose
3. **Ape locomotion**		
(i) True brachiation		Gibbon, siamang
(ii) Modified brachiation	Arm swinging and quadrumanous climbing	Orangutan
(iii) Knuckle walking	Occasional brachiation, climbing, knuckle walking	Chimpanzee, gorilla
4. **Bipedalism**	Standing, striding, running	Man

Ape locomotion is defined as what each genus does. It is disputed whether to lump chimpanzee and gorilla with orang, or to separate as terrestrially adapted knuckle-walkers.

After Napier and Napier (1967).

TABLE 5 POSTURAL AND LOCOMOTOR ACTIVITY OF SYMPATRIC UGANDAN PRIMATES

	Per cent of time			
	Sitting	Walking	Running	Standing
Arboreal feeding				
Black-and-white colobus	95	3	1	1
Guenons, blue	94	5	1	1
redtail	95	4	1	1
vervet	94	5	1	1
Savanna baboon	90	6	0	4
Feeding in low bushes				
Vervet	72	22	2	4
Feeding on the ground				
Vervet	38	32	5	25
Baboon	30	30	5	35

From M. Rose (personal communication).

mates. He concludes that they average about 75 per cent of their day *sitting,* or nearly 90 per cent of 24 hours, including their sleep. Thus, they spend the bulk of the time in postural rather than locomotor activity. Both baboons and vervets walk while they eat on the ground, whereas they sit to eat in a tree. This in part accounts for terrestrial primates' larger ranges than those of more arboreal conspecifics.

VERTICAL CLINGING AND LEAPING

All the vertical clingers and leapers of Napier's classification are prosimians (Napier and Walker, 1967). They include the tiny, insectivorous Senegal bushbaby and the tarsier, as well as the 3-foot-high indri and sifaka. The hapalemur is an intermediate form, as often quadrupedal as vertical.

The leap itself may be prodigious. Hall-Craggs (1965) has measured an upward vertical leap of a Senegal bushbaby at 7 feet $4\frac{3}{4}$ inches. The bushbaby starts with its center of gravity only $1\frac{1}{2}$ inches above ground.

Another aspect of the leap is its necessary precision. A bushbaby pauses noticeably before each hop, fixing the prospective landing place with its eyes. It lands with the flexible fingers outstretched, ready to cling like a tree frog to the twig it aims at. Lowther (1939) records one downward leap of a pet bushbaby in which the animal sprang from a balcony to land, 20 feet away, on top of a door.

Similarly, the sifaka measures its leap visually, pausing and weaving its head from side to side before launching itself across a 20-foot gap to a neighboring trunk. It springs away from its perch with body almost in a straight line, then twists in midair to land feet first (Figure 10). Thus, the force of its landing is broken by the great jumping hind legs themselves.

However, the long dramatic leaps are not the commonest locomotor pattern of either animal. They are used during the few times of day when the animals change from one area to another, for instance, from sleeping to feeding trees. They are also conspicu-

Figure 9 The tarsier is a "vertical clinger and leaper." (San Diego Zoo Photo by Ron Garrison.)

Figure 10 The sifaka, a Malagasy "vertical clinger and leaper." The hind legs propel the sifaka into a straight-line take-off; then the animal turns in mid-air, to land again on its hind feet. (Courtesy of D. Attenborough.)

Figure 11 The sifaka hanging by its hind legs to feed. Almost any primate can at times move in any fashion. (Courtesy of J. Buettner-Janusch.)

Figure 12 The sifaka walking bipedally. (Courtesy of J. Buettner-Janusch.)

ously useful when escaping from predators, suddenly taking the animal out from under the descending claw, talon, or telephoto lens of its enemy. A succession of three or four silent leaps, in the case of the sifaka at least, can remove the troop from view into thick foliage, where they remain still. This means that the enemy must locate them over again, often overshooting in the apparent direction of their departure.

In ordinary feeding, either large or small "vertical clingers and leapers" hop short distances from branch to branch, especially upward or downward, or even make a succession of hops along a horizontal branch that is large in relation to the animal's body size. Much of normal foraging involves the hands, with straightforward quadrupedal locomotion, either vertically or horizontally, or at an angle.

In feeding, bushbabies sometimes pounce or drop on insect prey. However, it is as common in captivity, and probably in the wild, to see them stalk an insect on all fours, without alarming it, then catch it with a straight-armed grab with one hand. Sifakas, exclusively vegetarian, draw in a branch of fruit or leaves with one hand. On fine, terminal twigs, as mentioned above, they sling themselves slothlike under a bending branch and can feed to the buds at the outermost tips.

Thus, leaping is not consistently used, although it is distinctive. However, the predominantly vertical position of the body is common to the group.

Oddly, although vertical leaping can be correlated with insectivorous or slothlike feeding, it does not seem confined to particular habitats. Sifakas look appropriate leaping among the slender vertical stems of a rainforest or the thorn-studded vertical spires of *Euphorbia.* However, they seem equally adapted to temperate woodland, where tamarind trees with massive boles and horizontal branches, like ancient oak trees, give no special advantage to the vertical clinger. Similarly, the Senegal bushbaby may leap and pounce, but the still tinier Demidoff's bushbaby is no less insectivorous, yet scuttles among twigs and lianas like an arboreal mouse.

Napier and Walker (1967) believe, from fossil evidence, that Eocene vertical clingers and leapers were ancestral to modern monkeys and apes. The groups that are most likely candidates for ancestors have the limb proportions of leapers. Quadrupedalism would then have evolved, not only with relative lengthening of the forelimbs, but with habitual horizontal posture of the trunk, through intermediates like hapalemur and lemur, which usually run on branches but may hop on the ground and leap in the trees.

QUADRUPEDS

Moving quadrupedally, with equal-length limbs and trunk horizontal, includes a vast array of locomotor specializations. The cautious climbers, again all prosimians, are remarkable as much for their flexibility as for their tenacious attachment to support. The potto silently oozes along a branch, to clamp its hand on the back of an unsuspecting cockroach, or seize a roosting bird. The rolling gait, with only one limb free at a time, never shaking the branch, is again a feeding adaptation, not just a means of progress (Walker, 1969).

Branch runners include three lemur genera, all the marmosets and tamarins, seven of the Cebidae, and one genus, the guenons,

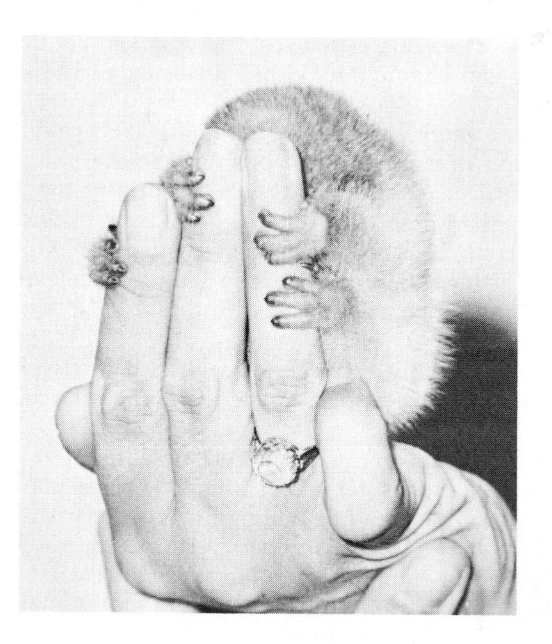

Figure 13 A baby potto, a quadrupedal "slow climber." Its hand has become a forceps with the index finger reduced to a small lump. Note the "toilet claw" on the hind foot that is used for scratching and as an earpick. (Courtesy of A. Walker.)

Figure 14 A small nocturnal quadrupedal branch runner, the dwarf lemur. (Courtesy of R. D. Martin.)

Figure 15 (above) The semi-brachiating or quadrupedal Old World colobus runs along branches, leaps between them, and uses its tail as a balance. (Courtesy of M. D. Rose.)

Figure 16 (at left) The quadrupedal New World cebus monkey uses its prehensile tail as fifth arm. (Courtesy of D. J. Chivers.)

among the Old World monkeys. Of these, the marmosets and tamarins have clawed hands and move squirrel-like on the branch tops or run upward on bark. However, they may leap between trees, or even cross a grove of saplings from one vertical to the next, like a vertical clinger and leaper (Thorington, 1967).

The other cebids show progressively more flexibility, in progress from the marmoset-like forms to those that often hang or clamber with arms over head, like the uakaris. The guenons, on the other hand, have less flexibility of movement (Grand, 1968).

"Semibrachiators," or more totipotent animals, use their arms for support, and tend to leap still more than the branch runners. However, there is considerable difference in the actual form of leap.

Figure 17 When the quadrupedal Old World blue guenon leaps between foliage banks, its shoulders, elbows, hips, and knees remain partially flexed, compared with the straight-line body of the leaping sifaka in Figure 10. (Courtesy of P. Aldrich-Blake.)

Figure 18 A spider monkey walks bipedally. The spider monkey, a "semibrachiator," often keeps its trunk erect, suspended by arms and tail. Note its residual stumplike thumb. (Courtesy of D. J. Chivers.)

Figure 19 A vervet (guenon) monkey, a semiterrestrial quadruped, rises to walk bipedally. (Courtesy of M. D. Rose.)

The Old World colobines are more apt to leap downward, landing on all fours among foliage and twigs, whereas New World monkeys may catch a branch and swing underneath, arms fully extended. The cebids' prehensile tails, as well, reach over their heads as they dangle to feed—not so much tripedal as tribrachial locomotion.

The ground runners, on the other hand, are true quadrupeds. Rowell (1966a) reports that savanna baboons seem as agile as "arboreal" monkeys when climbing forest trees. However, the baboon's hand and limb proportions, and even more the lengthened, gazelle-like legs and hands of the patas monkey, are marks of the savanna.

BRACHIATION AND KNUCKLE WALKING

The gibbon, flinging itself hand-over-hand through space, is itself the definition of a brachiator. However, Ellefson's (1968) recent field study emphasizes that, as with the leaping of sifakas, such long-distance swinging is relatively infrequent during the day, when the family moves in a coherent fashion from one area to another. The males also use magnificent acrobatic swinging and dropping in display against territorial neighbors. In many ways, however, the gibbons' ability to swing beneath branches may again be considered a feeding adaptation, which allows the animals to hang like fruit

Figure 20 (opposite) The siamang, a relative of the gibbons, is a true brachiator. It travels underneath branches suspended by its arms and swinging from one hand grip to the next. (Courtesy of D. J. Chivers.)

Figure 21 A gibbon, the typical brachiator, dangles to feed. (Courtesy of D. J. Chivers.)

in the swaying terminal twigs, without the need to keep their balance on top of a branch.

Ellefson believes that brachiation is intimately linked with, or even dictates, other aspects of the gibbons' behavior. Their very small size (an adult male lar gibbon weighs only 10 pounds) again is related to terminal-branch feeding. The high energy expenditure of brachiation may limit the distance that a single animal can economically travel and thus lead to families inhabiting small defended areas of forest—they could not form large, widely ranging social units. The fossil record indicates that the locomotor specializations of the gibbon line date from at least the Miocene. If Ellefson's logic is correct, the tendencies to small body size, small family size, limited range, and territorial defense may be as old.

The orangutan, on the other hand, does not brachiate but climbs cautiously, clinging, using its arms over its head for suspension. This leads to some of the same anatomical modifications as the gibbon, but without the same behavioral complex.

The gorilla and chimpanzee are called, in Napier's terminology, "modified brachiators." There are marked similarities among all the great apes, such as that arms are longer than legs, and hands are elongated with flexed, curved digits. The chimp and gorilla anatomy thus may reflect the build of a truly brachiating ancestor, which moved like the modern gibbon.

This theory has recently been challenged. Tuttle (1967, 1969) points out that the flexed fingers may be primarily adaptations to walking on the ground, with weight borne on the curled-under second phalanges. Their arms, like those of the orangutans, frequently have a suspensory function, but they probably never approached the habits of a real brachiator—if only on the argument that their body size would forbid brachiation under any but gigantic tree limbs.

The behavior of modern great apes supports this hypothesis. Mountain gorillas do climb trees, but quadrupedally and with extreme caution. Rambunctious juveniles, like their human counterparts, sometimes swing by their hands or slide down vines. However, Schaller's (1963) only glimpse of an adult attempting such a feat ended in comic disaster: "A silverbacked male suddenly swung free and hung by his arms alone. As he reached for another branch, the supporting limb cracked and slowly collapsed, dumping him on his rump in the vegetation 10 feet below."

Chimpanzees, like other species, use every possible form of locomotion—bipedal walking on the ground, knuckle walking, even very infrequent brachiating.

More interesting than the qualitative catalogue, though, are the independent estimates by van Lawick-Goodall (1963) and by the Reynolds (1965) that the chimpanzees they watched spent only 50 to 75 per cent of the day in the trees. Jane van Lawick-Goodall works in the deciduous woodland of the Gombe Stream Reserve, where the chimpanzees often cross open grassy spaces. The Reynolds, on the other hand, were in the Budongo, a closed canopy

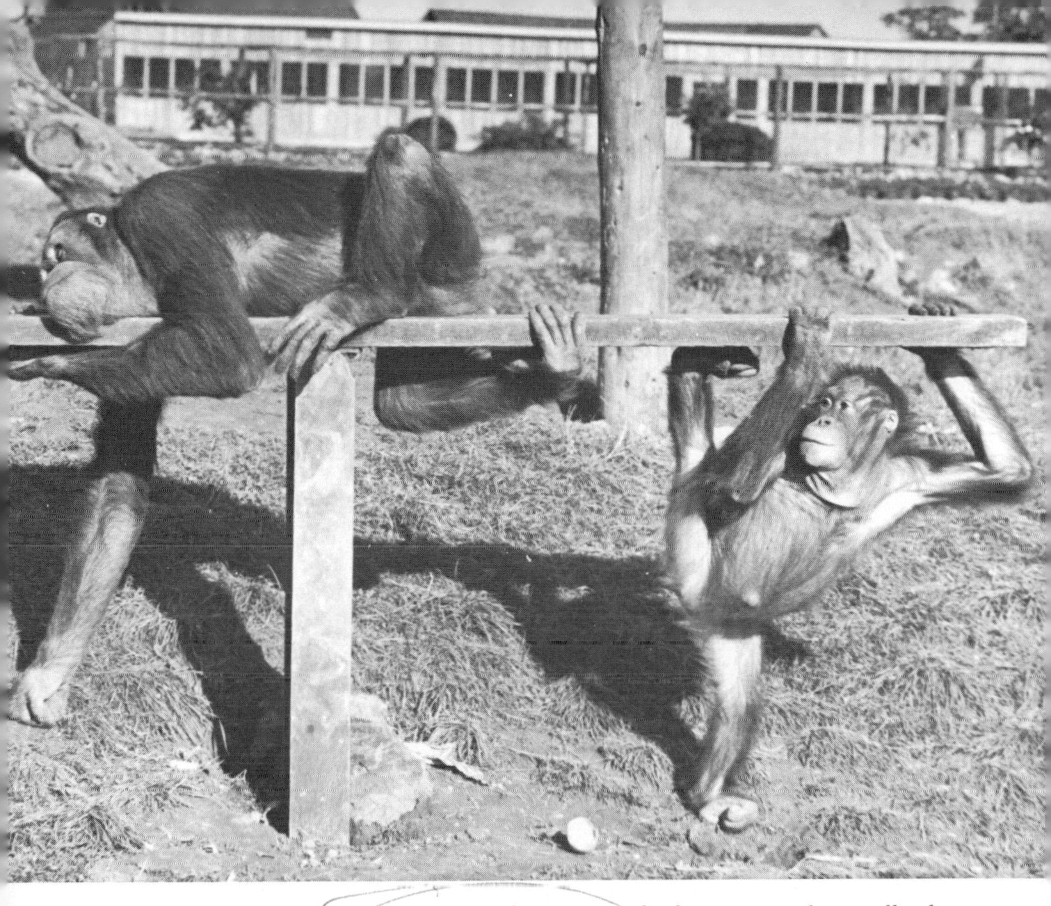

Figure 22 Orangutans, quadrumanous climbers, can and typically do do anything. (Courtesy of D. Sorby.)

forest. Even there, "to travel distances of more than 50 yards they usually came to the ground; they fled on the ground; and they had a network of tracks at ground level through the forest."

Thus, locomotion on the ground is a very important part of chimpanzee movement, and one might expect the "knuckle-walking" or terrestrial aspect of locomotion to have had considerable selective effect. Further, if one wants to push the analogy to the other categories, in each of the others the *fastest* mode of locomotion is diagnostic. Sifakas spring away from predators, baboons run away on all fours, gibbons brachiate away. By this criterion, the chimpanzee and gorilla are knuckle walkers (or perhaps knuckle trotters?), as this is their means of quickest progress or flight.

In summary, various semibrachiating and leaping adaptations could have evolved directly from vertical clinging and leaping without passing through a stage of complete quadrupedalism. Forelimbs would have lengthened in the semibrachiators but, with the trunk more usually vertical, would have retained their mainly suspensory,

Figure 23 Gorillas are highly specialized to walk on their knuckles on the ground. (Courtesy of D. Sorby.)

rather than supportive role, with accompanying flexibility of trunk and joints.

The true, extreme brachiators could only have come from some "semibrachiating" or totipotent intermediate. However, bipedalism could be derived at almost any point in the series. Perhaps, if the hominid line has been distinct since the Eocene, it could have come directly from a vertical clinging prosimian ancestor. More probably, it may eventually be traced to a totipotent fossil whose trunk was frequently erect and who never adopted either a true quadrupedal or extreme brachiating way of life.

EVOLUTION OF THE HAND AND PRECISE MANIPULATION

The primate hand, with fingernails and divergent thumb, originally evolved as an adaptation to arboreal locomotion.

However, not all primates have "the primate hand." Marmosets climb like squirrels with clawed digits. The New World monkeys, as a whole, have thumbs more or less in parallel with the other digits, not habitually divergent like either prosimians or Old World monkeys. Some "semibrachiating" monkeys—the spider monkey in the New World and the colobus in the Old World—have lost their thumbs altogether, and habitually hold on with the hooklike digits 2 to 5.

All species use their hands in feeding, as well as traveling.

Prosimian hands have a wide variety of anatomical shapes. Figure 24 reflects their various locomotor adaptations. The lorisoids can be divided into two groups: vertical clingers and leapers, and cautious quadrupeds. The leapers, the two galagos, have splayed-out hands, which grasp branches in nearly any direction that the animal may meet at the end of its leap. The quadrupeds show a progressive series of specializations from this splayed type to the "heavy forceps" of the potto, which tenaciously clamps the branch before letting go for another safe hold. In the lemuriform series, on the other hand, which also includes quadrupeds and leapers, larger forms hook around a branch with fingers 2 to 5 in parallel on one side of it.

When we look at the actual movement of the hand, the prehensive action or prehensive pattern, phylogenetic consistencies appear. The lorisoids reach for any object, whether branch or food, by spreading their digits widely apart, touching the object with the distal part of the palm, then closing their fingers around it. Lemuroids, in contrast, reach with the finger ends more-or-less parallel and touch with their fingers first. Each phylogenetic line has a single motor pattern, which is conserved through all the variants of feeding and locomotion (Bishop, 1962, 1964).

Both New World and Old World monkeys have gone beyond this stage, to differentiate "precision grip" from "power grip" (Napier, 1960). They have not only a motor pattern for locomotion but some separate control of the index finger and thumb, which are used for fine manipulation of bits of food or grooming tiny particles from each other's fur. In the New World monkeys, the digits lie, and flex, in parallel. Their common precision grip is a sideways "scissors" action, of thumb against index finger or index

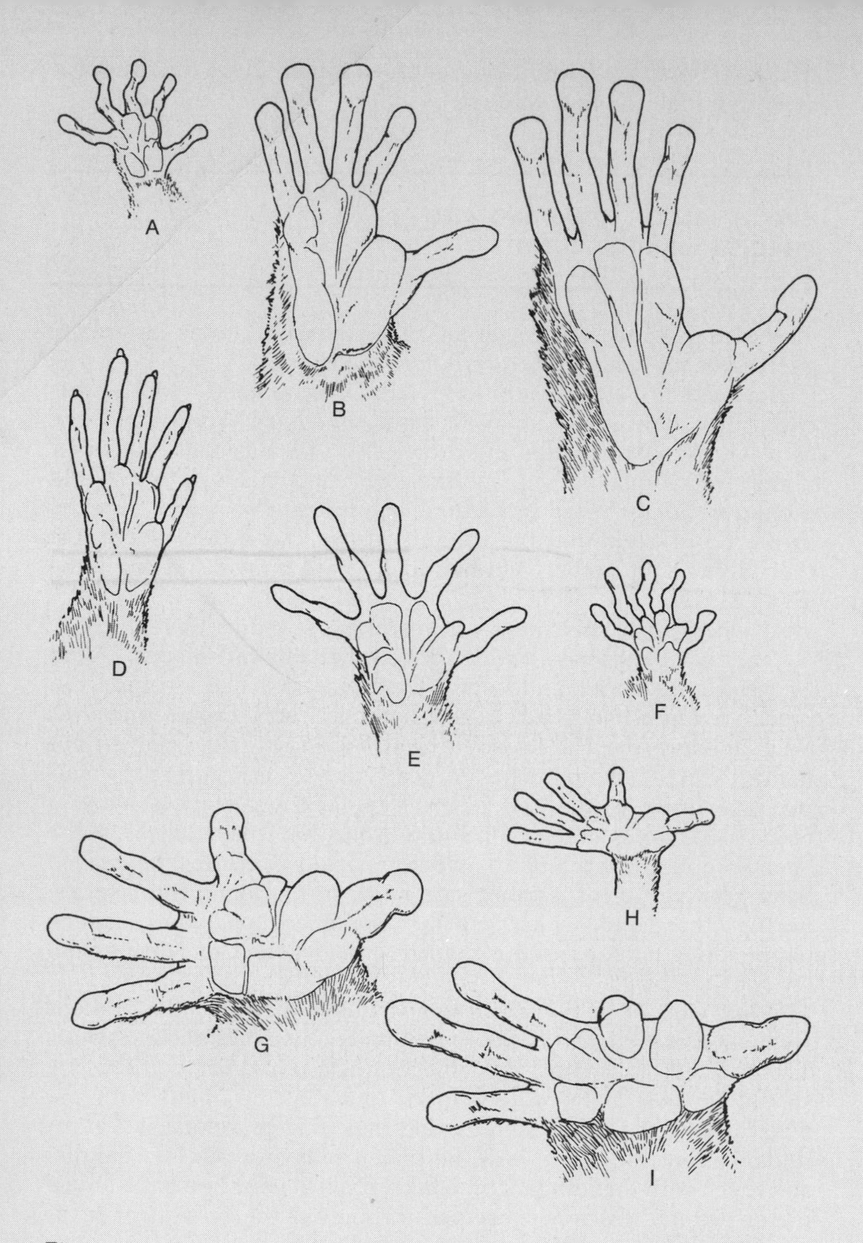

Figure 24 (*A*, mouse lemur; *B*, brown lemur; *C*, sifaka; *D*, hapalemur; *E*, thick-tailed bushbaby; *F*, Senegal bushbaby; *G*, slow loris; *H*, slender loris; *I*, potto). Among the lorisiformes, the bushbabies with splayed hands are vertical clingers and leapers, whereas the two lorises and the potto are slow, cautious quadrupeds with forceps-type hands. However, among the lemuriformes the sifaka, the one real leaper, is little different from the more quadrupedal brown lemur, and the quadrupedal mouse lemur resembles a bushbaby. Here, size differences seem as important as locomotor type. (After A. Bishop, 1962.)

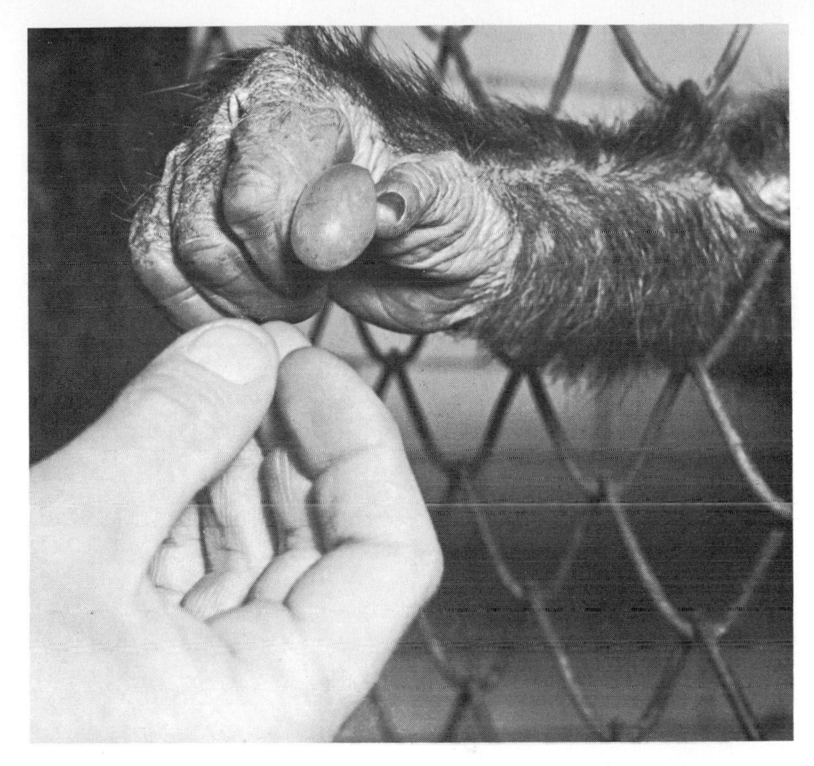

Figure 25 The chimpanzee's precision grip differs from ours but is capable of fine manipulation. (From J. R. Napier and P. H. Napier, 1967. By permission.)

finger against third finger. Old World monkeys, on the other hand, bring the thumb end against some part of the index finger. They may even partially oppose the finger tips of thumb and index finger.

There seems to be some correlation with ecology among the monkeys. The ground-living macaque–baboon group is more dextrous, with more highly differentiated precision grip, than the guenon species. In general, the larger forms, which give the impression of more variable or "intelligent" general behavior, are also those with more highly marked precision grip; fine control of the hand increases as one ascends the phylogenetic scale. This is true in both New World and Old World monkeys, even though the actual precision grip used differs in the two lines.

The apes have very marked precision grips, in which the thumb is partially rotated and pressed to the side or tip of the index finger (Napier, 1961). Here again, as one mounts the phylogenetic scale, dexterity increases. The human hand is the culmination of this tendency, selectively adapted to the control of fine tools.

SUMMARY

Primates range from tropical jungle to grassy plains, with species particularly adapted to swamp forest, forest edge, temperate woodland, and cliffs. Within high forest they are vertically stratified, from uppermost treetops to ground. This contrasts with the flexibility of most primate species, which can also adapt if necessary to a wide range of conditions. Major locomotor types are (1) vertical clingers and leapers, (2) quadrupeds, (3) "semibrachiating" or totipotent types, (4) brachiators, and (5) knuckle walkers. The categories refer to predominant locomotion or often to the fast-traveling locomotion. While feeding or playing, almost any primate is able to move in any fashion.

Food

Most primates are omnivorous. They eat fruit, leaves, insects, and even, when they can get it, meat. In captivity, most adapt to a diet of monkey chow, cereals fortified with vitamins and ground bone and offal, supplemented by anything from peanuts to chocolate ice cream.

As with locomotor behavior, this variability is the most striking factor. Of course, some species are more adaptable than others. The leaf-eating colobus monkeys are practically confined to the upper canopy of high forest, whereas, in contrast, savanna baboons range from the Sahara to the Cape in all but the densest forest or utterly treeless plain. However, it seems clear that many species may live in a wide range of habitat, taking advantage of a wide range of food, at least during good years.

In "bad seasons" of extreme drought, or cold, or failure of a staple food crop, the competition between primate species must intensify. Thus, many field studies of such long-lived and versatile animals must present a very partial picture. Little differentiation of food

TABLE 6 FOOD HABITS

	Fruits	Leaves	Insects	Notes
PROSIMIANS				
Lorisiformes				
Lorisidae				
slender loris	+		+	
slow loris	+		+	
potto	+		+	Birds
golden potto	+		+	
bushbaby				
thicktailed	+		+	
senegal	+		+	
needle-clawed			+	Resin
Demidoffs'			++	
Tarsiiformes				
tarsier	+		+	
Lemuriformes				
Lemuridae				
mouse lemur	+		+	
lepilemur	+	+		
hapalemur	+	+		Bamboo
lemur	+			
Indriidae				
indri	+	+		
sifaka	+	+		
avahi	+	+		
Daubentoniidae				
aye-aye	+		+	
CEBOIDEA				
Callitrichidae				
all?	+		+	
Cebidae				
night monkey	+		+	
titi	+		+	
howler	+	+		
spider	+			
cebus	+		+	
squirrel	+		+	
woolly	+		+	
CERCOPITHECOIDEA				
Cercopithecinae				
macaque	+			
mangabey	+			
baboon	+	+	+	Grass, occasionally meat
gelada	+	+	+	Grass, bulbs
guenon	+		+	Vervets eat eggs and chicks, Lowe's guenons eat flowers
talapoin	+		+	
patas	+	+	+	Grass, lizards
Colobinae				
langur	+	+		
colobus	+	+		
HOMINOIDEA				
Hylobatidae				
gibbon	+			
Pongidae				
orangutan	+			
gorilla	+	+		
chimpanzee	+		+	Occasionally meat
Hominidae				
man	+	+	+	Frequently meat

+ is a rough measure of significant reliance on a category of food, from anatomical evidence as well as field observation.

may be apparent between coexisting species unless the observer happens upon a period when the differences become crucial.

Table 6 gives a rough idea of the balance in the diet of many primates. The major categories are leaf eating, fruit eating, and insect eating. From intestinal anatomy, stomach contents, and captive specimens, it is fairly easy to determine the general biases of a species toward these three types of food.

It is also clear that specialized foliage-eating types have evolved in all four lines—lemurs, New World monkeys, Old World monkeys, and apes—whereas insect and fruit eating are widespread through the order.

FRUIT AND LEAVES: QUANTITATIVE STUDIES

Most field studies give some idea of the balance between leaf, fruit, and insect or meat eating. However, methods of recording differ, and it is difficult in any case to compare primates in different forests. One outstanding survey, by Hladik and Hladik (1969), gives quantitative comparison of the feeding habits of primates of Barro Colorado Island, in Panama.

Figure 26 summarizes their results. All five primate species live mainly on fruit, with the howler, spider, and night monkeys turning secondarily to leaves, whereas the cebus monkey and the tamarin instead catch live prey. However, within these gross categories the emphasis differs for each species. All prefer ripe, watery fruit, but the howler also eats quantities of immature fruit, whereas the others prefer fatty fruits, seeds, and seedcoats. Only the howler manages many mature leaves, but all eat some new leaves, flowers, or buds: new leaves are particularly high in protein. All eat some insects, but the cebus monkey and the tamarin are active hunters of larger insect prey. The Hladiks' further study shows that the leaf eaters catch few insects, the fruit eaters more—leaf protein and animal protein can substitute for each other, but fruit alone would have too little protein (M. Hladik, personal communication). Table 6 makes the same point from general survey of species.

The Hladiks reach three important conclusions. First, the biomass of the primates (4 kilograms per hectare for the howlers, 1 kilogram per hectare for spiders, 0.5 kilogram per hectare for the cebus) is quite comparable with that of terrestrial animals such as the deer, which is a grazing form like the howler, or the black bear, which is omnivorous like the cebus.

Second, there is an enormous amount of "wasted" fruit and leaves. It is a common observation that primates drop more than half their food; in Panama still more is left on the tree or ripens and falls to squash on the forest floor. Peccaries and coatis and fruit-eating birds and fruit bats feast as well, but still much is left.

The Hladiks feel that the howlers, at least, are not food limited on Barro Colorado.

The third conclusion is that the primates greatly influence the vegetation: primarily by distributing seeds through their own guts and planting them far away, complete with a pat of fertilizer. Many of the forest trees are adapted to this mode of distribution, with tough, heavy seeds. Some species even germinate better after pas-

Figure 26 Diet of monkeys (*A*, howler; *B*, spider; *C*, cebus; *D*, night; *E*, tamarin) on Barro Colorado Island, Panama. The shaded rectangles indicate the totals of three gross categories: leaves, fruit, and prey. The striped rectangles break down the totals into finer categories. No two species have similar dietary patterns. (After A. Hladik and C. M. Hladik, 1969.)

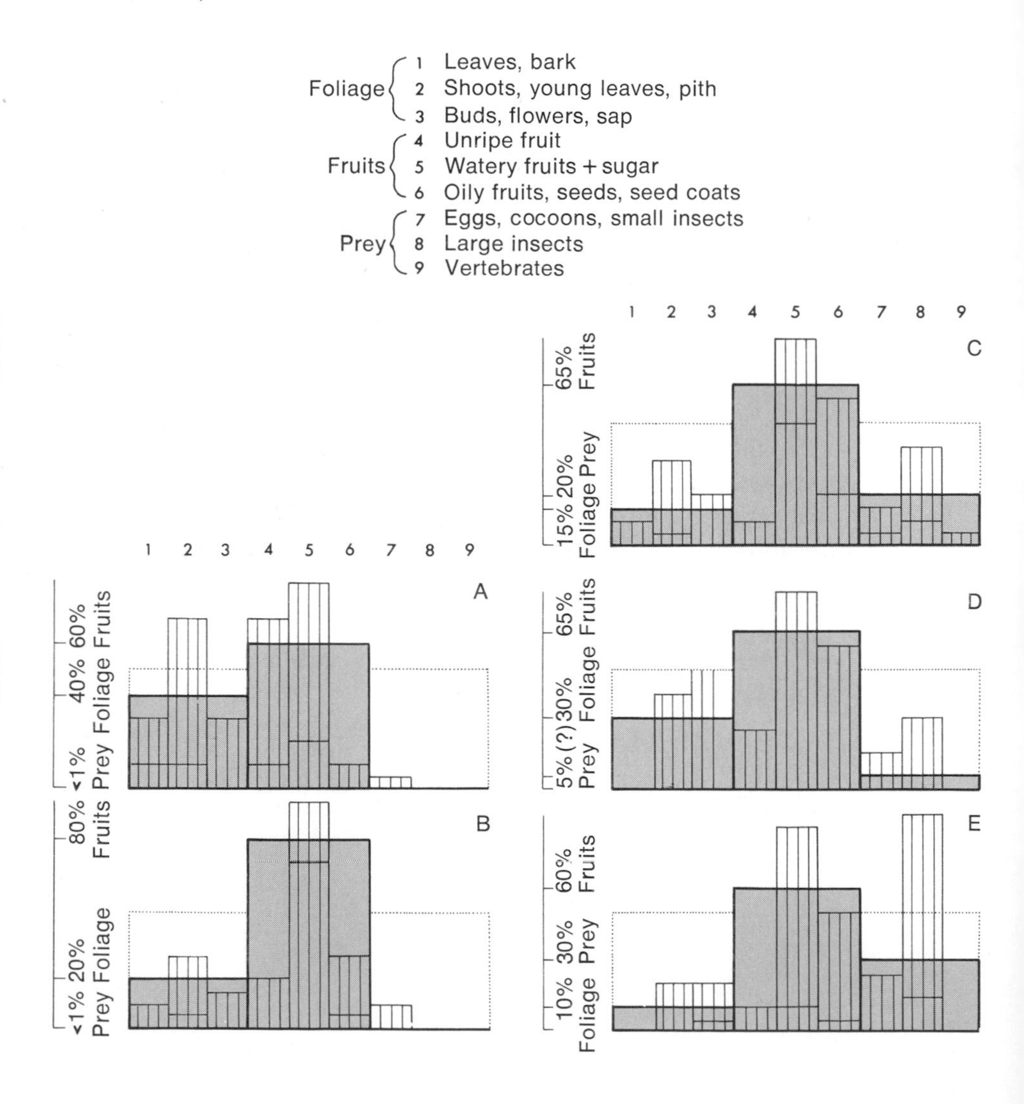

Figure 27 The howler monkey's diet includes a large proportion of mature leaves. (Courtesy of C. M. Hladik.)

sage through a monkey. In another setting, the vervets of Lolui Island in Lake Victoria are similarly spreading their forest. The grassy island is dotted with thickets, each centered on a termite hill (the vervets' favorite sitting place among grass) and each thicket conveniently composed of the monkeys' favorite food plants (Jackson and Gartlan, 1965).

Other studies of stomach contents give similar pictures of ecological separation. However, this method depends as much on which foods leave hard parts in the stomach as on the relative intake and cannot be quantitatively compared with the available food supply.

The Hladiks are currently working in Ceylon and say that the ecological specializations of the purplefaced langur, hanuman langur, and toque macaque resemble in many ways the ecological divergences of Panamanian monkeys (Hladik and Hladik, 1969). Thus, the general divisions of Table 6 may soon be more firmly based.

FRUIT AND LEAVES: FEEDING METHODS

The bulk of primate diet comes from plants. There is a spectrum of adaptation from species that eat chiefly fruit to those that browse largely on leaves to the terrestrial forms that can, if necessary, subsist mainly on grass. The leaf eaters—the colobines, the indriids, the howlers, and the gorilla—have specialized digestive tracts, with enlarged or lengthened intestines to cope with their leafy diet. Bulk eaters, from howler monkey to gorilla, have huge, broad molars that allow them to chew up such food. There are behavioral as well as anatomical adaptations to the various diets: skill in husking fruits with hands, or, more often, tongue and teeth, and use of the hands by baboons to wipe soil off a grass root or by gorillas to wipe stings off a nettle. Baboons graze with their hands, picking grass to bring to the mouth.

Spider monkeys give one fascinating performance: they attack the fruits of *Tocoyena pittieri,* which hang from a stout stem and are protected by a thick green skin. The spider monkey bites through the skin of a fruit, but, finding the pulp green and bitter, leaves it alone. One or two days later, the troop passes by the same way. Opening the fruit has accelerated its ripening; it is full of a sort of sweet jam, which the spider appreciatively scrapes out to the last drop—spitting out the seeds round about. Hladik points out that one does not need to invoke foresight in the monkey's performance, but the result favors both monkey and tree over natural, slow ripening with the fruit lost, intact, on the ground.

Another aspect to the staple food, besides its qualitative nature, is its distribution in time and space. Tropical forest is often pictured as a uniform, lush habitat for any vegetarian. This is not necessarily true. Fruits may ripen at any season—even individual trees of a species may ripen at their own time—and the cycle may be not yearly but 2 yearly or even about $1\frac{1}{2}$ yearly. Fruit-eating monkeys find sporadic bonanzas of fruit, where the animals congregate, that are interspersed by spaces or by periods of time when food must be sought much more widely. Even leaf eaters in a jungle do not browse at random. New leaves and buds offer far more protein and sugar for their bulk than tough old leaves; some species, such as the red colobus concentrate their feeding on those trees of a forest that are just coming into leaf (Clutton-Brock, personal communication). If the animals live outside tropical rainforest, they

Figure 28 The toque macaque is primarily a fruit eater, but most omnivores eat some leaves. (Courtesy of C. M. Hladik.)

usually contend with seasonal change or a much sparser food supply, or both. Extreme seasonality, or temperate zone life, imposes limits much like those of arid zone life, or that may overlap as in the case of the gelada. Yamada (1966) has studied the Japanese macaques that are the most northerly primates in the world. Troops that live above the snow line form smaller troops than more southern populations in Japan. They have the remarkable physiological adaptation that, during the end of summer and early fall, lactation nearly or totally stops. Babies of the previous spring forage beside their mothers and both lay down fat stores for the winter. Then the blizzards begin; almost no food is left except bark, which only the adults can strip with their full-grown incisors. At this point, the mothers resume lactating, sheltering and feeding their children until the buds swell with coming spring, when the year-old juvenile is finally weaned.

Figure 29 Spider monkey feeding.
(Courtesy of C. M. Hladik.)

SEED EATING

Clifford Jolly (1970) has proposed that a "small-object feeding complex" played a crucial part in the early differentiation of the hominid line. In a number of respects, *Ramapithecus,* the earliest fossil hominid, resembles living gelada baboons. The gelada feeds sitting down, shuffling along on its bottom, picking up grass blades, rhizomes, seeds, and insects with thumb and index finger. Its incisors are small, and, in the large fossil geladas, canines are also small. Its molar teeth are relatively large and are given shearing and grinding strength by the vertical arrangement of chewing muscles in a shortened face. (See Pilbeam, 1972, or C. Jolly, 1970, for anatomy.)

This "small-object feeding" seems to be separable into two aspects: the dental adaptations, and the adaptations for feeding while sitting down on the ground. It is very plausible that at least the dental adaptations parallel those of *Ramapithecus,* and account for our ancestors' initial divergence from the rest of the primates. Small front teeth and large molars could thus have evolved in an ordinary, small-brained primate long before it invented tools to replace the incisors for cutting or invented weapons to replace the canines when threatened.

The geladas' molars differ in shape from the hominids': geladas chiefly shear grass blades, while our ancestors chewed with a grinding action that seems more appropriate for small, hard seeds. Clifford Jolly points out that grass-seed eating could account not only for facial and tooth proportions but also for terrestriality, and for the fact that *Ramapithecus* fossils are found in deposits that were forest fringe—perhaps seasonally flooded, treeless areas within forests like the "dambos" of present-day central Africa.

This sets the stage for the evolution of tool using and hunting in Australopithecines and early *Homo,* while the robust Australopithecines, with their huge grinding molars, became the ultimate in primate seed eaters. It might even be the origin of our own fondness for starch—most modern hunters and gatherers collect cereal grains and nuts, not just seal blubber, and almost all agricultural peoples depend on a starchy staple, not just cow blood and milk.

The second group of relevant gelada characteristics are those that relate to sitting on the ground. The gelada feeds with an erect trunk, so the base of its skull is shaped to balance on top of the vertical spinal column. It has long arms and its index finger is shortened to give a good thumb-index precision grip when culling small objects. The female has signals on her breast as well as on her bottom that advertise her sexual condition. (See Figure 93, Chapter 11.) Both sexes, uniquely among Old World monkeys, have fatty sitting pads on their buttocks.

It is true that all these characteristics are shared with the later hominidae. However, it seems to me that most of these traits would fit with truncal erectness either in trees or on the ground. The precision grip is useful for any small objects. *Ramapithecus* might have fed in part on the small, hard seeds of leguminous trees, as well as on grass seeds. One chimpanzee population that ranges into open, dry, woodland depends on such tree seeds during the dry season (Suzuki, 1969). Vervets, when they feed on the bushes and low trees of a thicket edge, often stand on the ground on their hind feet and reach up to pull down food (M. Rose, personal communication). When *Ramapithecus* limb bones are found, it may prove to have been much more flexible in locomotion than the geladas, while still, importantly, a small-object feeder. The most unequivocal evidence that early hominids fed, like the gelada, while sitting down is that the gelada's buttocks are padded like modern man's—too much theory to rest on a couple of species' fat bottoms.

INSECT EATING

Insects make up a part of the diet of almost every primate. Of the primates that have been studied in the wild, only the lemur and sifaka seem to actually ignore insect food. Lorisoids, tarsier, small lemuroids, and, in the New World, the night monkey and squirrel monkey obtain quite a large proportion of their diet from insects.

Higher primates have, as well, a fundamental nutritional need for such food. Not only do they require a fair share of protein, which implies some meat eating, but they cannot manufacture their own vitamin B_{12}, which is obtainable otherwise only from foods of animal origin. Many zoo and captive primates have been found to suffer from vitamin B_{12} deficiency, which causes the nerves to degenerate, first peripherally and then in the brain itself. This results from the mistaken notion of their keepers that "primates are vegetarian" (Oxnard, 1967).

The smaller, primitive primates catch insects by pouncing on them, using hand, not mouth. More advanced primates also pick up insects with the hand, using, presumably, the precision grip. Baboons may slap at stinging forms such as scorpions, beating them to immobility before eating them (Marais, 1969; Bolwig, 1959; Hall, 1962a).

The whitefaced cebus monkey, which is cleverest of all the New World primates at manipulating tools in the laboratory, spends a

Figure 30 Slender loris eating an insect. (Courtesy of C. M. Hladik.)

Figure 31 The aye-aye has an elongated third finger with which it probes for larvae in trees. (Courtesy of J.-J. Petter.)

large part of its foraging time handling and breaking dead sticks, picking through the wood for insects (see Figure 32, page 66) (Thorington, 1967).

Finally, Jane van Lawick-Goodall's (1963) chimpanzees use tools, stripped twigs or grass blades, to poke into termite hills. The termites bite the intruding stick; the chimpanzees withdraw the stick and termites to lick off with their rubbery lower lips. This termite fishing has been found in another widely separated population of open-woodland chimpanzees and in forest-living West African chimpanzees, although not in other geographically intermediate populations (Suzuki, 1966; Jones and Sabater Pi, 1969).

Thus, catching the small-sized but highly valuable insect food may be linked throughout the primate line with the evolution of manual dexterity and manipulative skill. (See Chapter 16.)

MEAT EATING, HUNTING, COOPERATION

Most primates happen on and eat an occasional lizard or fledgling bird. The "insectivorous" prosimians are usually eager to pounce on such food, and captive tarsiers kill and eat mice. However, in all primates except man, eating vertebrate food seems to be a nearly fortuitous affair. Only baboons and chimpanzees regularly eat meat; only chimpanzees have been seen to hunt for, rather than stumble on, live prey.

Figure 32 Cebus pulling the wings from an insect. (Courtesy of C. M. Hladik.)

In contrast, in the hominid line, hunting has been one of the major factors in evolution. Speculation runs (e.g., Washburn and Lancaster, 1968) that hunting leads to cooperation between hunters, to food sharing, to division of labor between the sexes. More esoterically, hunting may have been crucial in the development of communication, thus language, and of techniques, thus tools and weapons. Food sharing between hunting men and gathering women implies some means of carrying food and a rendezvous or rudimentary "home." "Home," in turn, may have meant a wholly new approach to the helpless human infant and the even more cumbersome human 3-year-old—the men at least could leave the children at home.

Some of this superstructure of speculation has been based on the weekend hunters' delight in bagging a buck and the delight of nearly everyone but the Brahmin in attacking a juicy steak. But as far as the fossil record goes, man has been killing since *Australopithecus* and began cooperating to slaughter the mastodon at least as early as *Homo erectus*. It is instructive to compare our own evolved

Figure 33 Many primates eat some meat. The tarsier is a habitual predator. (San Diego Zoo Photo by Ron Garrison.)

hunting biology with the rare and exceptional hunting of the chimpanzee.

Jane van Lawick-Goodall has described such a hunt in detail:

> A group of chimps rested in the shade of a tall tree. In its branches, a juvenile baboon fed alone, separated by some 200 yards from the rest of his troop. Presently Huxley [a mature male] plodded up from the stream toward the peaceful chimpanzee group. About 10 feet from the fig tree he stopped, facing its trunk. To us he seemed unaware even of the existence of the small baboon above. Nonetheless as though he had in fact given a signal, the other chimps stood up. Two of the males moved to the base of the fig tree; three others stationed themselves under two nearby trees, the branches of which formed an escape route for the baboon. And then, very slowly, with infinite caution, Figan, the youngest of the males present (he was about eight at the time), began to creep toward his quarry . . . . (van Lawick-Goodall, 1967b)

This particular hunt ended in screams and frustration as the baboon troop arrived on the scene. After successful hunts, or after stumbling on newborn bushbuck in the grass, the males settle down to gorge on their prey. Apparently, they may recognize some rights of ownership; more dominant animals do not simply snatch meat from the killer but sit with outstretched hand and protruding, imploring lower lip. At intervals the meat eaters strip off pieces to give to other males or, more rarely, to begging females and children.

On the other hand, Kawabe (1966) saw a hunt in which one male and several females flung themselves in a group after a red colobus monkey and then snatched its body from each other for an hour. Kawabe feels there was no true "native cooperation" or voluntary sharing in this instance. However, he saw in it the *prerequisites* for cooperation—several hunters converged from different angles, then passed the meat around without actual fights and without a totalitarian dominance structure ensuring that the leading animal kept all.

In many ways, this is like the postulated behavior of early man. First, hunting is often a chimp *male* occupation. Second, it is an activity where wild chimpanzees show the rudiments of *cooperation.* Third, it ends, alone of all feeding reported, in the *sharing* of food, either by permitted snatching or by actual stripping off of a bit to give away. Chimpanzee hunting differs from human ways in that there is no great degree of foresight—the apes do not seek out or drive their prey but simply take advantage of animals that happen to be in vulnerable positions, nor do the apes use tools (although they throw stones or flail with sticks in threat, and it would seem a small step to using sticks and stones to kill). However, so much of chimpanzee behavior is like ours that it lends strong support to the view of our own evolution into "man the hunter."

SUMMARY

Primates eat fruit, leaves, insects, and meat. Vegetable food is the staple for most species. Leaf eaters can be distinguished by the anatomy of the digestive system. The hominids' initial divergence from other primates may have begun with seed eating. Quantitative studies are beginning to analyze utilization of vegetable food in relation to its availability. Insect eating is associated with long bouts of attention and with precise manipulation in many primate species, culminating in the use of tools by wild chimpanzees. Meat eating is rare in any primate. However, chimpanzees have the rudiments of cooperative hunting and share meat, as probably did early man.

Predation

PREDATOR PRESSURE

Very few people have actually seen a primate caught by a predator. Cynthia Booth recalls collecting a mother colobus monkey who fell, leaving her baby attached to a tree. A monkey eagle promptly swooped down to collect the baby. Snakes such as boa constrictors and pythons may catch some monkeys, and leopards probably eat baboons. Brain (1970) makes a good case that an early hominid child (*Paranthropus*) was killed by a leopard, then cached by the leopard in Swartkraans cave!

The degree of predator pressure seems relatively small: few individuals have disappeared in the course of any field study, and most of those were juveniles. Large-scale population fluctuations, such as in the Barro Colorado howler monkeys, are more plausibly attributed to epidemic or drought (Carpenter, 1965).

Rowell (1969) has studied a baboon population mainly of known individuals over a period of 5 years. The only other primates that have been followed so long as individuals are the Japanese macaques, which have no wild predators, and van Lawick-Goodall's chimpanzees, which may be somewhat immune to predation. Lion, leopard, and hyena were frequent in Rowell's study area, but all the deaths of adults in her troops could be attributed to old age. Two bodies were found—an aged male, and a young male that seemed to have died of ear infection. A dying female, her whole hindquarters a single sore, and an old male, "alone and apparently delirious," were also seen. Of course, predators might have dispatched the dying animals. There was considerable perinatal mortality, but most juveniles, once past infancy, matured to adulthood. Again, this suggests that disease, or other factors affecting perinatal mortality, was the principal regulator of population, not predation.

Although raptors and carnivores remain a threat to the primates, the most important predators are other primates. Chimpanzees catch and kill red colobus monkeys or young baboons. Baboons kill and eat vervets. Even though meat eating is rare in primates, it may still be significant from the standpoint of the primate being eaten!

Oddly, the victim species consort with their primate predators, showing no fear: vervets with baboons, baboons with chimpanzees. It may be, simply, that the predators are rarely in a hunting mood, which would be recognized by the victims—just as zebra do not flee the satiated lion.

In any case, primate hunting is uncommon and probably takes on major evolutionary importance only when we consider our own ancestors. Quite aside from the depredations of modern man—from the extinction of the giant lemurs to the burning over of habitats to the insatiable appetite of the drug firms—even as hominids evolved they must have had an immense effect on their coevals. And, as Rowell (1969) says, man's methods of hunting and the selection pressures he exerted probably differed from those of the carnivores.

Martin and Wright (1967) propose that Acheulean man with his hand axes was responsible for widespread late Pleistocene extinction in Africa among large mammals, particularly suids and bovids. One known primate genus that became extinct at that time was *Simopithecus,* a baboon. Earlier, during the Villafranchian and middle Pleistocene, the giant baboons *Parapapio* and *Dinopithecus* and the giant *Cercopithecoides* became extinct. It seems possible that *Australopithecus* began by eliminating these primate relatives, perhaps in part by direct competition rather than by hunting per se.

ALARM CALLS

Lemurs and sifakas give different calls for aerial and ground menaces. A flying hawk (or airplane) elicits roars and screams: the primates take cover low in the trees. On the other hand, ground carnivores and people are greeted with yapping or the "sifaka" hiccup that gives the sifaka its name. Although at the first yap the animals leap up off the ground, they then approach and "mob" their enemies as small birds mob a cat—thus indicating their relative safety (Jolly, 1966a).

Squirrel monkeys as well make different noises for hawks and ground predators, their terror indicated by the pretty names of "chirp" and "peep" (Baldwin, 1968). Vervets give not only air-raid and ground alarms but also a "snake chutter" specifically for snakes (Struhsaker, 1967c).

Moynihan (personal communication) says that many New World monkeys mix the different sorts of cry in their alarm chorus, showing clearly that the sounds represent different degrees of alarm rather than semantically designating classes of objects. Among the lemurs as well, animals may give the hawk scream when seized or if the observer approaches too close. However, the lemurs usually avoid mixed choruses by entraining each other's yap-yap-yap in perfect synchrony. Thus, the differentiation need not indicate complex mentality in vervet, lemur, or the many birds that give two types of alarm call. The calls at least *function* semantically, with the troops in no doubt whether to flee upward or downward.

DEFENSE AGAINST PREDATORS

Chance and Clifford Jolly (1970) have developed a major theory of social structure, based on, initially, the reactions of defense or flight by adult primates. (This will be discussed at more length in Chapter 10.) They draw a sharp dichotomy between the species where the male distracts a predator, such as by a bouncing display as in the patas, and the species where the males actually defend the group. In the first case the females scatter and flee, ignoring the male, whereas in the second the females and subordinates look to their leaders in moments of stress. Chance and Jolly choose only terrestrial species for their examples: savanna baboons far from trees, savanna chimpanzees, and the patas. Of course, Australopithecines were terrestrial as well. However, Chance and Jolly themselves emphasize that the hanuman langur is an intermediate case and that forest baboons or forest chimpanzees may flee ignominiously with little or no structure of attention. And three male patas, their example of a diversionary animal, have been seen to chase down a jackal, which eventually released the infant patas it had caught (Struhsaker, 1969). On the whole, the majority of primates seem to provide such intermediate cases, where the males may threaten or attack, but only in the right circumstances, and the females have a choice of either watching the males or *sauve-qui-peut.*

The males of nearly every social primate play a special role in challenging predators, particularly if an infant is threatened. This is true of arboreal howlers (Carpenter, 1964), forest guenons, savanna vervets (Struhsaker, 1967a, 1969), langurs (Sugiyama, 1964), chimpanzees, gibbons, and gorillas. The male usually limits himself to barks and abortive charges, but defense seems to be a male role throughout at least the monkeys and apes. Furthermore, it may be concentrated among the dominant males, as in macaque troops (Bernstein, 1966a), or even be the clearest sign of dominance, as in the cebus monkey (Bernstein, 1966b).

Baboon males may even harass a lion, a dangerous procedure. When a savanna-living baboon troop encounters a big cat, it may retreat in battle formation, females and juveniles first, the big males with their formidable canines last, interposed between the troop and the danger. This is not a universal pattern. Rowells' forest-edge baboons simply ran away to the safety of trees, each at his own speed, which meant strongest males first and females with infants lumbering at the rear. However, it is plausible that the strength and long canine teeth of the baboon males have been selected in part as predator deterrents.

The chimpanzee and gorilla are large enough for even more efficient counterattack. Gorillas are too slow to run in any case. A big male, to judge by his reaction to people, advances with the magnificent "chest-beating" display. If outraged out of his normally pacific temper, he can also efficiently rend and bite a human being—but Schaller (1963) attributes the disappearance of some gorilla males to leopard attack.

The only time chimpanzees have been seen with a wild leopard, they ignored the beast and casually departed. However, Kortlandt (1967) has placed a stuffed leopard, with staring glass eyes and mounted on a movable trolley, in the path of wild chimpanzees and filmed the chimpanzees as they advanced, bristling and screaming—and flailing with sticks or awkwardly throwing the sticks. The stuffed leopard, unlike any real animal in possession of its senses, did not retreat, and held still for heavy clubbing squarely on its back (see Chapter 16).

The most exciting question is how many populations of chimpanzees might show such reactions. Forest populations seem more likely to retreat to the trees than to attack. Kortlandt has tested zoo chimpanzees that were caught in either forest or open woodland. He believes the open-country chimpanzees are more likely to use stick or stone in threat and thus that weapons originated with the demands of life on the ground. His evidence is necessarily flimsy from zoo tests, if only because a chimpanzee that is offered

Figure 34 (opposite) A chimpanzee attacks a stuffed leopard using a stick as a club. The maximum hitting speed, calculated from the films, was 50 to 60 miles per hour, or quite enough to break a real leopard's back. The leopard can just be seen to the right in the grass. (Courtesy of J. van Orshoven, R. Pfeijffers, and J. C. J. van Zon, Sixth Netherlands Chimpanzee Expedition by the University of Amsterdam.)

Figure 35 (this page) The chimpanzees as a group drag off the "carcass" of the stuffed leopard, whose head has come off. (J. van Orshoven, R. Pfeijffers, and J. C. J. van Zon, Sixth Netherlands Chimpanzee Expedition by the University of Amsterdam.)

contact and experience with objects is so quick to learn. For instance, Jane van Lawick-Goodall's chimpanzees have progressed from the near random waving of branches in excitement through brandishing and banging her empty kerosene tins to accurately heaving stones at visiting psychoanalysts. The chimps have it in them clearly, but it may be almost as difficult to say for a chimp as for a human being what behavior is "natural."

SUMMARY

Predator pressure on adults seems surprisingly light. Primates, particularly protohominids, may have always been the major predators on other primates. Predator defense includes flight, mobbing, distraction display by males, mock charging by males, and rarely real attack. Most primates flee under most circumstances, but there is wide variation even within species or troops. Males of most social species will charge under some conditions, particularly if an infant is threatened.

Interspecific Relations

COMPETITION

One of the chief theories of modern ecology is that species cannot live in too close competition in a stable situation. What is meant by "too close"? Usually, this is circularly, or tautologically, defined. If one studies an "undisturbed" habitat containing species that have evolved over centuries in relation and adjustment to each other, then the various species that exist there are assumed to have partitioned the environment, and its resources, among themselves. If, however, an introduced or expanding species is ousting another, the competition between these two is said to be "too close."

There are a number of ways for one species to displace another. One may simply increase in numbers of individuals while the other decreases to extinction. Or the second species may adjust behaviorally—be literally driven away from the geographic area or be driven to marginal habitats or less preferred foods. However, if only one species can live on the less preferred foods, it already supposes some difference between the species. Natural selection in the region of competition may emphasize the differences—the process of "character divergence."

Thus, the "distance" between species may be measured by any one of several parameters. Hutchinson refers to the life space of an animal as a multidimensional niche. The niche can be measured in physical space, in food preference, in substrate preference—in any factor by which the animal relates to its environment. A problem for mathematical ecology is then to quantify these relations: to relate, in turn, some measure niche size to the species composition of the community.

One aspect of these relations that is particularly significant for primates is the question of behavioral variability. Most living things have some degree of adaptability to different ecological conditions—starting from the osmoregulation in protozoans through to the differing social organizations of primates. However, there is little observational proof that some dimension of variable behavior may be small under conditions of close interspecific competition and larger without. Island-living birds provide one example. For instance, nesting on the mainland they may restrict their nest sites to a few types of vegetation, whereas in the West Indies, with fewer bird species, they are far more catholic in vegetation choice (Klopfer, 1967). Thus, the actual range of behavior shown by an individual may be restricted by the presence of other species.

A further question is how the variability of behavior in one niche dimension may restrict variability in others. MacArthur and Levins (1964) discuss "specialist" and "jack-of-all-trade" species. If two species are very similar in body size, habitat, and so forth, and thus are likely to come into close competition, they may "specialize" in one dimension of their niche—for instance, by preferring different foods. Thus, they can overlap widely in habitat without driving one to extinction. However, if they are jack-of-all-trades in food, their ranges of diet having wide overlap, then they must specialize somewhere else, such as physically dividing the habitat by living in different geographic areas. The spatial separation may be no greater than from top to middle of a tree, or from larger branches to smaller ones, but the distance must be maintained in some dimension.

One final aspect of behavioral variability and niche size is the temporal one. All competition theory is based on competition for scarce resources. If food and space and other resources are abundant, two species could virtually overlap without competition. Heavy predation or disease is one way to achieve this effect, both of which keep the numbers of each species well below the carrying capacity of the environment. Another way to find this apparent effect is to study the populations only in a good season, or a good year, when there is enough for all. The limiting factors might not be operating at this particular time although the behavior of the animals might well give clues to the limits.

NICHE DIFFERENTIATION IN PRIMATES

In parts of the African rainforest, fourteen different species of primates coexist. However, the accurate assessment of primate ecological differences is only just beginning. And, as observational conditions are so difficult in rainforest, this is perhaps not the place to start.

First, primates may be separated by gross habitat choice, as discussed in Chapter 2, which involves preference for a whole range of parameters. For instance, blue monkeys, *Cercopithecus mitis*, overlap in range with their cousin the vervet, *C. aethiops*. However, the blues clearly prefer true forest, whereas the vervets range from forest edge to forest clumps to tree savanna (Gartlan and Brain, 1968). In forest edge and savanna, vervets overlap with baboons, but the baboons, larger, better defended, and more prone to eat grass, can range farther away from the trees. Finally, in the open plains, patas monkeys run through the grass, although their habitat overlaps again with those of vervet and baboon (Hall, 1965).

Crook and Aldrich-Blake (1968) analyzed in more detail the separation of two generically different Ethiopian baboons, the gelada and the olive. They found that in the areas of overlap between the two each retained its characteristic food supply. The geladas ate grass and bulbs and remained on the ground, foraging for 70 per cent of the day, even in the same woodland where olive baboons climbed, picked fruit, and obtained enough food in much less time. The geladas, as well, retained their characteristic one-male units, whereas the olives showed a very loosely bound multimale structure, somewhat like that reported by Rowell (1966a) for Ugandan forest-based olive baboons.

Jones and Sabater Pi (1969) compared two species of mangabey, the graycheeked and the whitecollared, in a quite different area—the high forest of Rio Muñi. The graycheeked mangabey prefers high, closed canopy forest. It eats a very specialized diet, is wholly arboreal, and flees when frightened across the canopy. The whitecollared mangabey prefers swamp forest and gallery forest and even invades cultivated fields. It eats a much more varied diet and is partly terrestrial, fleeing when alarmed along the ground.

Bernstein (1967a) discussed the far more complex case of a Malayan forest with two species of macaque, two of langurs, and gibbons (Figure 36). The pigtailed macaques were mostly terrestrial, but even they were primarily arboreal animals. Gibbons spent more time than the others in medium levels of trees, and pigtails were more spread out vertically in the trees, but the other three were

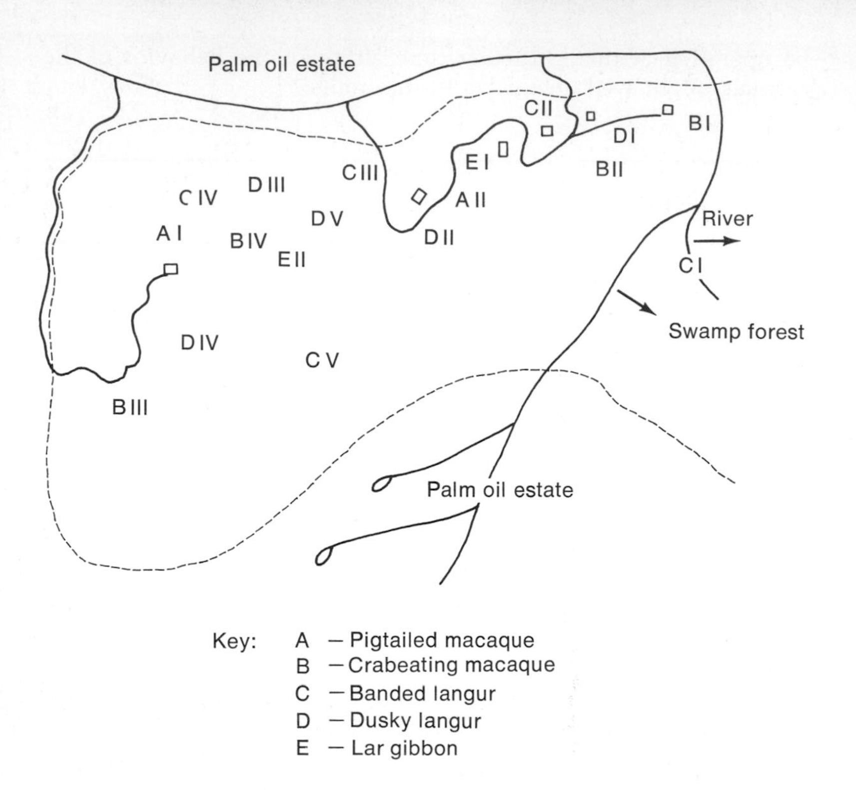

Figure 36 Primate species distribution in a Malayan forest. The primate species in any forest form a mosaic. Each keeps some distance from neighboring troops of its own kind but overlaps other species with apparent indifference. (After I. S. Bernstein, 1967a.)

all treetop animals. The langurs, although leaf eaters, ate a considerable proportion of fruit, whereas the fruit eaters ate leaves as well. They obviously differed in locomotor patterns: langurs are relatively inactive but leaping, gibbons brachiate, and macaques are "straight" quadrupeds. Frequently, different species traveled and fed together,which will be discussed below. In short, although all five species had obvious anatomical and behavioral differences, it was difficult to discern ecological differentiation, at least by qualitative study at a single site.

ACTIVE ANTAGONISM

Usually, when primates of different species are in the same area, they ignore each other. Mixed groups may feed together and cross through each other, detouring perhaps to different branches, but with scarcely a glance in the others' direction. Competition between

Figure 37 Adult male savanna baboon eating a vervet guenon. (From S. A. Altmann and J. Altmann, 1970. By permission of the publishers, and S. A. Altmann, holder of the copyright.)

species is almost never shown by overt behavior. Jolly's account of ringtailed lemurs "teasing" sifakas is almost the only reported harassment of one species by another, and even that was rare.

Primates occasionally prey on each other. (See Chapter 4.) Baboons catch and eat vervets; chimpanzees eat red colobus and baboons.

ACTIVE FLOCKING

Primate species may also actively join each other, however. In Bernstein's (1967a) Malayan jungles, among West African *Cercopithecus,* on Barro Colorado, primates of different species may move and forage together for a length of time. As well as troops joining for an hour or more, individuals may attach themselves to troops of another species. This is understandable if the individual is a solitary released far from his own habitat, such as the brown lemur that became a member of a ringtailed lemur troop. It is stranger when a primate *chooses* another species, such as the vervet (of unknown provenance) that Rowell saw moving with and grooming the members of a baboon troop, although vervets also lived in the area. Later, this animal joined another baboon troop, where he was accepted as well, in spite of the fact that baboons occasionally eat vervets. The companionship may only be partial—the male gibbon of Bernstein's study area spent a part of his time with the banded langurs, although he returned as well to his mate and child.

Moyniham speculates on the selective advantage of "mixed-species flocks" in tropical birds, and his conclusions also apply to primates. Such a flock offers many of the advantages of single-species groups: for defense against predators and because a food supply found by any one individual becomes available to all. However, if the various species eat the same food, it must come in large enough packets, or high enough concentration, for many individuals to feed together. Another alternative, with a mixed-species flock, is that each species prefers a slightly different type or location of food. Then the various animals may feed adjacently, mutually secure from predation, but not in "too close" competition. This may well be true of the guenon species that habitually flock together, because the moustached guenon, for instance, eats more leaves than its congeners. It may also be that only one species derives most of the benefit. Gautier (1969) has analyzed the relations of spot-

Figure 38 A young savanna baboon plays with a young vervet guenon. (From S. A. Altmann and J. Altmann, 1970. By permission of the publishers, and S. A. Altmann, holder of the copyright.)

TABLE 7 INTERSPECIFIC ASSOCIATIONS IN GABON

	De Brazza's guenon	Black-and-white colobus	Talapoin	Whitecheeked mangabey	Agile mangabey	Mona guenon	Moustached guenon	Spotnosed guenon
De Brazza's guenon								
Black-and-white colobus					+			+
Talapoin						+	+	+
Whitecheeked mangabey					+	+	+	+
Agile mangabey		+		+		+	+	+
Mona guenon			+	+	+		+	+
Moustached guenon			+	+	+	+		+
Spotnosed guenon		+	+	+	+	+	+	

+ indicates that the monkey species were seen together. De Brazza's guenon, although present in the area, never associated with other species. The spotnose, at the other extreme, associated with everything but the De Brazza. Not all mixed groups include only two species; up to five species were seen together.

After Gautier and Gautier-Hion (1969).

nosed and moustached guenons. The spotnose is larger, noisier, and more evident to hunters: in a mixed band, the spotnose male is the most likely to be killed. A Gabonais proverb runs "the little spotnose should take advice from the little moustache monkey."

The flocking, as Gautier (1969) clearly shows, is an active process, with certain species more likely to join than others (Table 7). Moustache monkeys following a talapoin band may be drawn outside their normal range. The grouping of spotnose and moustache is so frequent that often the "loud call" of the spotnose male serves as interband spacing call for both groups, whereas the moustache male gives his call later or not at all. This may depend on a simple threshold difference: the loud call is given in alarm or to any loud noise, and the spotnose may be more easily alarmed (Struhsaker, personal communication). However, the spotnose call still functions for both groups together.

Gautier found that in four forest areas about half his sightings of monkeys were of mixed bands, and the bands ran to as many as five species together, three guenons and two mangabeys (Table 7). However, aberrant individuals that join the wrong species simply indicate how the strong primate tendency to sociability can combine with the flexibility of primate learning to produce almost any sort of social behavior.

SUMMARY

Many primate species are clearly differentiated spatially and in food supply. However, their long life span and potential variability of behavior mean that it is often difficult to observe species competition directly. Many species may feed near each other, but usually animals ignore each other. There is some predation and, among forest monkeys, interspecific flocking.

Why Be Social?

No mammal can live a totally solitary life. At least mating and the first stages of raising the milky young require two or more animals to adjust their behavior to each other. From this minimum any further degree of contact is possible. For instance, many apparently "solitary" mammals know their habitual neighbors and challenge a stranger to the area more fiercely than a known conspecific. Lepilemurs live "alone," each to his nest hole—but in tiny overlapping home ranges separated by wide patches of similar forest that no lepilemur inhabits (Petter, 1962). Mammals may form feeding aggregations, or breeding herds, or multigeneration nursery groups of dam with her adult daughters. The males may wander off, alone except to mate, or may form bachelor groups of males only, or keep harems-like stallions. Male and female may cooperate to bring up the young: a pair of foxes with their cubs of the season, a pair of beavers with 2 years' offspring. Finally, there is the grouping typical of a few carnivores and many primates in which an infant of either sex is likely to remain for life in the troop of its

TABLE 8 GENERAL ECOLOGICAL CORRELATES OF SOLITARY OR GROUP LIFE

	Favors solitary life	Favors group living
Food dispersion	In small packets	In large packets or continuous
Food catching	Found by individual, searching	Vegetable food at stable sites *or* Found by following others *or*
	Caught by stealth	Caught by cooperative hunting
Predator defense	Hiding	Inaccessible sites *or* Mutual defense

After Eisenberg (1966) and Crook (1965).

birth. Here, only a few males leave the troop to become solitaries: many remain, as adolescents and adults, to become integral members of the social unit that includes their own mother, brothers, daughters.

What are the evolutionary advantages of a relatively solitary existence, or one in daily proximity with a group of conspecifics? Crook (1965) has recently reviewed the evidence from birds, and Eisenberg (1966) that from mammals. Their two studies independently came to very similar conclusions. Even though a high proportion of the field descriptions are flimsily based, the enormous amount of data, from two different vertebrate classes, makes a convincing picture (Table 8) within which to place the primate details.

FOOD SUPPLY

The first, all-important variable is the distribution of food and the means of its procurement. Crook and Eisenberg agree that for species whose food is clumped in small, separate packets, which require individual skill to find or catch, the individuals are likely to be solitary. This is often expressed as the maintenance of a year-round feeding territory. In birds, the definition must be enlarged to include the nesting pair, when the pair and their young occupy one territory during the breeding season. Typical of this group are specialized insect eaters among both birds and mammals, as well as small carnivores among the mammals and raptorial birds. All the solitary primates are highly insectivorous, except for leaf-eating lepilemur and frugivorous orangutans.

If, on the other hand, food is either uniform or abundant in very large patches relative to the animal, this permits or promotes sociable feeding. Examples of uniform dispersion are the rolling grasslands with their herds of range game, whether Russian saiga antelope, American bison, or the wildebeeste of the Serengeti, or else the plankton schools of the sea grazed by the blue whales. Examples of large-scale clumps of food are fruiting trees, where congregate flocks of frugivorous birds or monkeys or fruit bats. The birds that feed in flocks, either seasonally or year-round, tend to be fruit eaters or unspecialized insect-eaters; among the primates omnivores or vegetarians also live in social units.

Two specialized forms of social behavior are related to food supply. The first is lek or arena behavior, in which a male stakes out a territory or display site, then mates with as many females as he can attract. Subsequently, the females go off to bear and raise their young. Lek behavior evolves largely under the pressures of intense sexual selection. However, Crook points out that it depends on a food supply that is relatively abundant, at least seasonally. The male ruffed grouse or bull Pribiloff seal does not eat during the mating season—he must live, and strut, and fight, on an energy reserve of stored fat. The Uganda kob's stamping ground is shorn of grass to a few inches above ground—high unnibbled hay beyond his reach marks the edge of his territory. The female similarly must support her young alone, which is common in mammals but impossible for many birds. Lek behavior or intense seasonal polygamy is a common pattern in mammals, especially the artiodactyls, but is not found at all among primates. Food may be a crucial constraint here—or may not—in any case, the pattern is interesting for its absence.

The other pattern is that of cooperation, or at least continued association of a family group. This is the most common one among primates. Crook, in studying birds, concludes that such a pattern is likely to evolve when an erratic, or highly fragmented, food supply favors mutual hunting, storage, and sharing of food among family members, as in the magpies of the Australian desert. Eisenberg cites pack-hunting carnivorous mammals: cape hunting dog, lion, killer whale. Here, the primates do not fit the system. Except for man, and in the very rare meat eating of chimpanzees, primates neither hoard food nor share it, except in the sense of allowing others to feed nearby. Even mother monkeys do not give up their food to their infants. Much of primate behavior can only be understood in the daily relationship of the social group, but the advantages seem more related to shared experience than to shared nourishment.

PREDATION

A second variable in determining whether an animal can be social is predation. There are roughly four ways of coping with predators: hiding, being inaccessible, running away, and self-defense.

On the whole, cryptic animals tend to be solitary—it is easier to hide one than many. This applies as well to birds with cryptic nests. Many birds whose food supply permits flocking out of the breeding season turn to defending an exclusive territory around their hidden nest. Among many orders of mammals, nocturnal forms are more likely to be solitary than their diurnal relatives, and those that live in thick cover more than those of the open spaces. As with the size of food supply, cover is a relative quantity—thick grass is a forest to hide the shrew, but it is open space for the giraffe.

The primate line is readily divided between nocturnal and diurnal. Nocturnal forms are solitary feeders, except perhaps forked and woolly lemurs. Diurnal forms are permanently social, except perhaps orangutans. The exceptions either seem to form fairly loose groupings or else are too little known for much comment, or both. As between forest and savanna forms, the savanna troops may be larger (see below) but *all* are social.

A second way of evading predators is by inaccessibility. With birds, again, the nest site is crucial. Weaverbird trees with scores of pendant nests, seabird cliffs with thousands of pairs on the dizzy ledges, are communities of the hard-to-reach. The food supply and dispersion are adequate in the first place to permit such congregations, and then the protected sites provide enormous advantage. However, Crook points out how different the behavior is here from that of a built-up family unit. Typically, the aggregated birds fiercely defend their territory from intruders—not a feeding territory, but a square foot of cliff ledge around the gull nest, or the individual entrance hole in a weaverbird common apartment house.

Seal islands, coney cliffs, and bat caves are the mammalian equivalent. Whatever the other behavioral attributes promoting gregariousness, safety plays a major role.

To some extent, primates might be thought safe in the trees—but many predators, such as the ubiquitous birds of prey, are quite at home there. Furthermore, many other tree-living vegetarians, such as the squirrels, are solitary, not social. Thus, inaccessibility probably has little to do with the tightly knit primate group.

Another sort of protection is through mutual defense. This may be fairly simple—more eyes and ears are more likely to spot a predator, an alarm call by one animal may save any number of the group. The group aids as well by distraction: the cheetah who swerves from one gazelle to another loses both. Thus, social life helps those who run away.

Society also aids in active defense. The males of many primate species approach and threaten predators. If an infant has fallen to the ground, it may be the troop's dominant male who retrieves it from the menace of watching humans. Male plains baboon defense against lion or leopard is particularly striking, but infant retrieval by males is seen in species as diverse as the langurs of Malaysia, howlers of Panama, and West African chimpanzees (Bernstein, 1968a; Carpenter, 1934 in 1964; Nissen, 1931).

Joint defense is a unifying mechanism in birds and other mammals as well. It is particularly clear in ungulates, which flee as a herd or which may even close ranks with horns and forefeet outward like the circle of beleaguered musk oxen. Thus, the primates are orthodox group-livers in their predator defense as well as their food dispersal.

EVOLUTION OF SOCIAL DEPENDENCE

Finally, in spite of all generalizations, it is clear that particular orders, as well as particular species, show their own idiosyncratic means of adaptation to social life and derive particular advantages from it. One example is the whales and porpoises, which support wounded comrades at the surface to breathe or their newborn young in the critical first moments of life, (or, for that matter, other objects of the right size and shape).

Primate young do not have critical first moments so much as critical first months or years. The support of at least their mothers, for a comparatively long period, is necessary for any young primate to reach maturity—and the mother, in turn, seems to need the support and protection of her group. We will discuss this at much greater length in the sections on mother and infant behavior and on the ontogeny of learning. However, it must be clear even now, although the "ecological" factors of food supply and predator defense may have originally favored primate social groupings, that once formed, these primitive groupings took their own line of evolution. As the social group permitted ever-prolonged dependence, so the social dependence of infants and even adults determined the particular, primate, nature of society.

SUMMARY

Food supply dispersed in small packets favors solitary feeding; food supply in large packets or uniformly dispersed allows social grouping. Thus, many insectivorous birds and mammals, including primates, are solitary, whereas fruit- and leaf-eating primates are social. Predator evasion by hiding is easier if alone: nocturnal primates, like many other nocturnal mammals, tend to be solitary, and those in thick forest tend to live in smaller groups than those in the open. Inaccessible sites favor large aggregations, although not necessarily with social bonds between the units: this is true of cliff-nesting birds and cliff-sleeping baboons. If the animals neither hide nor are inaccessible, a social group provides warning or defense. Besides the major variables of food and predation, animals evolve particular dependences on social life. Social learning and long-dependent youth are typical of primates.

Group Range, Size, and Structure

Chapters 1 through 6 have portrayed the habitat of modern primates: the differences and relations among species and the general ecological setting of solitary or social life. Chapter 7 sums up the social structure within species: attempting to deal coherently with the interrelated factors of group size, home range, and exclusive rights to parts of the home range.

PRIMATE GROUP SIZE AND ECOLOGICAL GRADES

Comparing the ecology of all birds and mammals can show why it may be that primates tend to live in social groups rather than alone. It does not explain the vast range of social groupings. Some primates live in tightly knit troops, some in fluid "neighborhoods."

Text continues on page 102.

TABLE 9 GROUP SIZE

Observer	Species	Group size, mean	Group size, range	No. groups counted	Notes
	I PROSIMIANS: LORISIFORMES				
Hill	Slender loris	1			
Elliot	Slow loris	1			
Jewell	Golden potto	1		25	
Jewell	Potto	1		4	Nigeria
Walker		1			Uganda
Haddow	Senegal bushbaby	2	1–4	25	Uganda
Sauer			2–9		SW Africa
Haddow	Thicktailed bushbaby		1–9		Uganda, Kenya
Jolly		3		1	Zambia
Jewell	Allen's bushbaby		1–4	6	
Jewell	Needleclawed bushbaby	1		19	
Jewell	Demidoff's bushbaby		1–2	59	Night
Charles Dominique					Noyau with internal harem structure
	II PROSIMIANS: LEMURIFORMES				
Jolly	Ringtailed lemur	16	12–24	3	
Petter	Variegated lemur	3	2–4	4	
Petter	Black lemur	10	6–12	10	Day } Same site, NE Madagascar
Jolly		9	7–11	5	Day } Same site, NE Madagascar
Petter		22		1	Night } Same site, NE Madagascar

Jolly		6	6	2	SW Madagascar
Petter	Mongoz lemur	7	6–8	2	
Petter	Redbellied lemur	5	4, 5	2	
Jolly	Hapalemur	5	4, 5	2	
Petter	Lepilemur	1			Harems of overlapping territories
Petter	Dwarf lemur	1			
Martin	Mouse lemur	2	1–2	8	Male nests
		4	1–15	30	Female nests
		8		1	Bisexual nests
Jolly	Forked lemur	2		1	
Petter	Indri	3	3–4	4	
Jolly		3		1	
Petter	Woolly lemur	3	3	2	
Jolly		2		1	
Jolly	White sifaka	5	2–8	12	
Petter	Aye-aye	1			
	III ANTHROPOIDEA: CEBOIDEA				
Thorington	Redhanded tamarin	4	2–6	6	
Thorington		2	2	2	
Hladik	Geoffroy's tamarin		6–8		
Moynihan	Night monkey		1–2		
Mason	Dusky titi		6		Forest patches
		3	2–4	9	Continuous forest

Cross sectional; i.e., when troops changed size in the course of a study, the single census with most troops was taken. If same area is revisited after a period of 3 or more years, both censuses are given.

Where possible, only data from single sites are included in any one entry.

Excludes provisionized troops: Cayo Santiago rhesus, Monkey Jungle squirrel monkeys, and most Japanese macaques.

Among prosimians and chimpanzees, solitaries are included in the total count. Among Anthropoidea, groups only are included; extratroop solitaries are not counted. This is clearly artificial for hanuman langurs, where males may be solitary or join male groups.

TABLE 9 GROUP SIZE (continued)

Observer	Species	Group size, mean	Group size, range	No. groups counted	Notes
Carpenter	Mantled howler	17	2–45	23	Panama 1932
Carpenter		17		28	Panama 1933
Carpenter		18		15	Panama 1935
Collias		8		30	Panama 1951
Carpenter		19		44	Panama 1959
Chivers		13	11–18	14	Panama 1967
Pope	Black howler	7	4–14	17	Argentina
Oppenheimer	Whitethroated cebus	10	8–15	9	
Thorington	Blackcapped cebus	6	5, 7	2	
Thorington	Squirrel monkey		5–8		Day
Thorington		18		1	Night
Carpenter	Blackhanded spider monkey	10		17	Day
Carpenter		33		1	Night
Eisenberg			3–6	4+	Mangrove
Eisenberg			20		
	IV ANTHROPOIDEA: CERCOPITHECOIDEA: Cercopithecinae				
Simonds	Bonnet macaque	35	6–58	4	
Rahaman			10–50		
Bernstein	Pigtailed macaque	39	30, 47	2	

Bernstein	Crabeating macaque	30	14–70	4	
Furuya		30		1	
Southwick	Rhesus macaque	15		230	Roadside
Southwick		19		26	Canal bank
Southwick		11		34	Railroad
Southwick		17		50	Village
Southwick		22		39	Town
Neville		18	11, 25	2	Town
Southwick		42		15	Temple
Southwick		50		5	Forest
Neville		37	20, 54	2	Wet Forest
		16		1	Pine Forest
		58	38, 77	2	Submontane forest
Takeshita	Japanese macaque	66		"all"	Unprovisionized
Suzuki		35	12–70	4	Snowy areas
Izawa		13		2	
Deag	Barbary macaque	18	12–25	6	Cedar forest
Chalmers	Graycheeked mangabey	19	16, 25+	2	
Jones		9–11		1	
Struhsaker			10–12	2	
Struhsaker	Whitecollared mangabey		3–18+	3	
Jones			11–23		
Hall	Chacma baboon	27	8–65	20	SW Africa
Hall		31	15–58	15	S Africa
Hall		48	12–109	18	Rhodesia
Washburn	Yellow baboon	80	12–85	15	Amboseli, Kenya, savanna
DeVore	Olive baboon	41	12–87	9	1959 Nairobi, savanna
DeVore		42	27–76	8	1963 Nairobi, savanna
Rowell		35	30–45	3	1963 Uganda, Queen Elizabeth Park, gallery forest
Rowell		56	29–74	3	1968 Uganda, Queen Elizabeth Park, gallery forest

TABLE 9 GROUP SIZE (continued)

Observer	Species	Group size, mean	Group size, range	No. groups counted	Notes
Crook		17	2–49	1	Ethiopia, cliff forest
Kummer	Hamadryas baboon	5	2–13	8	One-male units
Kummer		54		2	Sleeping aggregations, various sites
Kummer		83		6	
Kummer		82		1	
Kummer		110		1	
Kummer		354		5	
Struhsaker	Drill	24	9–55	12	
Crook	Gelada baboon	9	5–35	30	Ethiopia, Semyen (One-male groups)
Crook		12		11	Ethiopia, Debra Libanos (One-male groups)
Crook		156	30–400	24	Ethiopia, Semyen, wet (Herds)
Crook		90	25–300	35	Ethiopia, Semyen, dry (Herds)
Crook		85	40–200	11	Ethiopia, Debra Libanos (Herds)
Struhsaker	Vervet guenon	24	7–53	10	Amboseli, Kenya
Gartlan		11	6–21	46	Lolui, Uganda
Gartlan		18	13–25	3	Chobi, Botswana
Gartlan		11	4–23	10	Murchison, Uganda
Wingfield			7–51	9	Kariba, Rhodesia
Struhsaker	Moustached guenon	4	2–5	3	
Gautier		9	5–14		
Struhsaker	Preuss' guenon	4	2–7	15	

Aldrich Blake	Blue guenon	13	12–17		
Struhsaker	Mona guenon	9	3–13	6	
Bourlière	Lowe's guenon	9	11, 12	1	1964 same troup
Bourlière		6	3–15	1	1969 same troup
Struhsaker	Crowned guenon	13	9–19	7	
Struhsaker		15	11–19	3	
Gautier	De Brazza's guenon	4	3, 5	2	
Struhsaker	Spotnosed guenon	10	7–17	13	
Struhsaker		9	5–13	8	
Gautier		18	15–20	3	
Struhsaker	Redeared guenon		4–29+	4	
Gautier-Hion	Talapoin	60		1	1966
		115		1	1968
Hall	Patas monkey	18	5–25	8	
		4		1	Male group
	V ANTHROPOIDEA: CERCOPITHECOIDEA: Colobinae				
Bernstein	Banded langur	15	10–20	5	
Poirier	Nilgiri langur	9	3–25	14	Bisexual
Poirier		14	2, 3	2	Male group
Tanaka			10–25	5	Bisexual
Bernstein	Silvered langur (lutong)	30	20–51	6	
Furuya		22		1	
Bernstein	Dusky langur	13	9–17	5	
Jay	Hanuman langur	19	10–28	3	Forest, N India (Bisexual group)
Jay		24		6	Scrub, N India (Bisexual group)
Sugiyama		29	12–44	16	(Bisexual group)
Sugiyama		14	9–35	28	Forest, S India (Bisexual group)
Sugiyama		17	9–24	10	Scrub, S India (Bisexual group)
Ripley		25	12–42	4	Forest, Ceylon (Bisexual group)

TABLE 9 GROUP SIZE (continued)

Observer	Species	Group size, mean	Group size, range	No. groups counted	Notes
Jay		4	2–10	10	Scrub, N India (Male group)
Sugiyama		9	5, 14	2	
Sugiyama		12	2–32	6	S India (Male group)
Kern	Proboscis monkey	20		8	
Booth	Black-and-white king colobus	6		1	
Struhsaker		6	2–8	5	
Schenkel	Black-and-white Abyssinian colobus	10	6–15	4	
Ullrich		13		1	
Struhsaker		5	2, 8	2	
Marler		8	2–12		Uganda, Budongo
Marler		6	3–9		Uganda, Queen Elizabeth Park
Booth	Olive colobus	10–15	5–20		
	VI ANTHROPOIDEA: HOMINOIDEA				
Carpenter	Lar gibbon	4	2–6	21	
Ellefson		3	2–6	28	
Bernstein		3	2, 4	2	
Carpenter	Agile gibbon		2–6	6	
Ellefson		3	2–4	8	

Carpenter	Siamang		2–6	8–10	
Ellefson		4	4	2	
Struhsaker	Chimpanzee	4	2–10	10	Cameroun forest } Subgroups
Reynolds		2–6		215	Budongo forest } Subgroups
Sugiyama		4	1–40	280	Traveling } Budongo forest Uganda } Subgroups
Sugiyama		5	1–30	234	Feeding } Budongo forest Uganda } Subgroups
Itani		32	23–43	3	Tanzania woodland } Large traveling group
Suzuki		35	23–48	5	Tanzania woodland } Large traveling group
Van Lawick-Goodall		60–80			Tanzania woodland } Community
Reynolds		70–80			Budongo forest } Community
Nishida		29			Tanzania woodland } Community
Sugiyama		50+			Budongo forest } Community
Kortlandt		70–80			Congo forest } Community
Schaller	Mountain gorilla	15	5–27	11	
		8	3–18	6	
Fossey		13	5–19	9	

TABLE 10 TROOP STRUCTURE AND ECOLOGY

	Solitary	1♂ + 1♀	1♂ + ♀♀	♂♂ + ♀♀ Mean 4–30	♂♂ + ♀♀ Mean 31–150
NOCTURNAL					
Grade A	Slender loris				
	Slow loris				
	Golden potto				
	Potto				
	Demidoff's bushbaby ⟷		⟶ Demidoff's bushbaby[a,d]		
	Needleclawed bushbaby				
	Mouse lemur ⟷		⟶ Mouse lemur[a,d]		
	Dwarf lemur				
	Lepilemur ⟷		⟶ Lepilemur[a,d]		
	Aye-aye				
	Night monkey ⟷	⟶ Night monkey			
DIURNAL, ARBOREAL					
Grade B Leaf eating			Langur, 5 spp ⟷	⟶ Nilgiri langur[b]	
				Sifaka	
				Howler, 2 spp	
			Black colobus ⟷	⟶ Black colobus	Red colobus
				Proboscis monkey	
Grade C Omnivorous		Marmosets	Guenon, 7 spp	Brown lemur	
		Dusky titi ⟷		⟶ Dusky titi[b]	
		Gibbon, 2 spp	Cebus monkey ⟷	⟶ Cebus monkey (2 spp)[b,c]	
		Siamang		Geoffroy's tamarin	

		Squirrel ←	→ Squirrel[b]
		Spider ←	→ Spider[a]
		Graycheeked mangabey	Talapoin
PARTLY TERRESTRIAL			
Grade D	Hanuman langur ←	→ Hanuman langur[b]	
Leaf eating	Mountain gorilla ←	→ Mountain gorilla[b]	
Grade E		Ringtailed lemur	Drill
Omnivorous[e]	'Hoest's guenon	Vervet	
		Macaque, 6 spp ←	→ Macaque, 5 spp[b,c]
		White-collared mangabey	Savanna baboon, 4 spp[c]
Grade F	Hamadryas baboon ←		→ Hamadryas[a]
Arid country	Gelada baboon ←		→ Gelada[a]
	Patas ←		→ Patas[b]

[a]Group splits and rejoins, commonly foraging in small groups and sleeping in large groups.
[b]Two grouping tendencies in different troops or populations of one species.
[c]Exchange of adult males between groups has been observed.
[d]Noyau of semisolitary individuals.
[e]Chimpanzee groupings too fluid to include.

Some live in a monogamous family of two adults, some in a band of two hundred.

Table 9 (page 92) shows the average size of grouping of primate species, as currently available from the literature. It also shows the number of groups counted of each species, as a reminder of how very patchy are the data!

In Table 10 (page 100), group size and structures are arranged by some ecological factors: nocturnal versus diurnal, arboreal or partly terrestrial, omnivore or largely leaf eating. This is a modification of the "grade" system proposed by Crook and Gartlan (1966).

The grades are an attempt to classify primates by those ecological factors that are relevant to social structure. This is a heuristic device, a search for general similarities rather than a hard-and-fast set of classes. Like Napier's locomotor categories, it is an attempt to divide a continuum, although recognizing that any one species may have a wide variety of social groupings or survive under a wide variety of ecological conditions.

Crook and Gartlan use multiple social and ecological descriptions of their grades. Here I have begun with ecological criteria and added the group structure on another dimension, as shown in Table 10. Table 10, in thus spreading out the classification over two dimensions, should indicate as well how rough the correlation is. Because I have taken different criteria, I call these grades A through F rather than Crook and Gartlan's I through V.

The grades will be discussed individually below. However, two major points must be made here: First, more than half of the species known form stable multimale troops, a grouping structure very uncommon in other mammals, and furthermore such troops have developed independently among lemurs, New World and Old World monkeys, and apes. Second, there is a general progression from upper left to lower right across Table 10; that is, very roughly, there is a tendency to larger group size from ecological grade A to grade F.

HOME RANGE AND TERRITORY

Some definitions are in order here. First, *home range* is the area normally occupied by an animal throughout its adult life. This excludes long juvenile wanderings, when many mammals emigrate from their birth place to new feeding grounds. It usually also excludes long migration routes—the two ends can be qualified as "summer home range" or "winter home range" or the whole specified as "annual home range."

Home range tends to be shown as an area on a map, evenly crosshatched within the farthest limits of the animals' movement. Of course, this is misleading. Animals, like humans, have known familiar paths from bed to supermarket to local bar—or sleeping

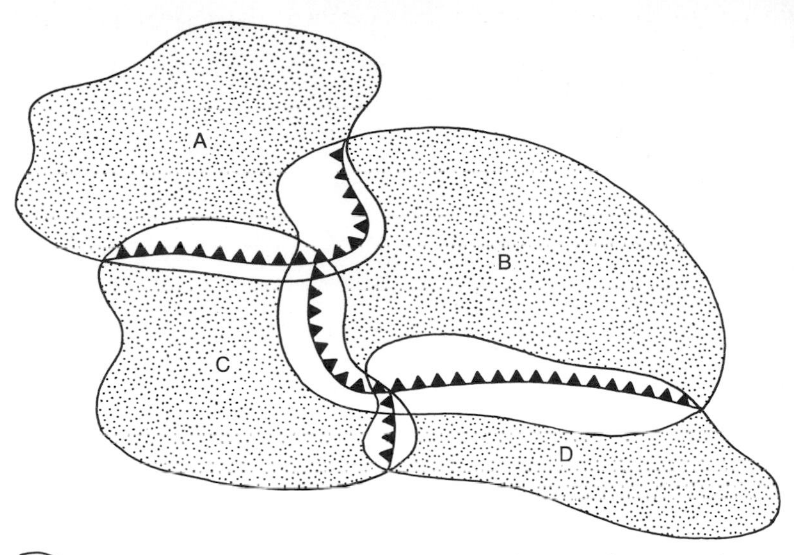

Figure 39 An idealized map of home range and territory. (After F. Bourlière, 1964.)

tree to feeding tree to waterhole. The actual pattern of use is complicated and easiest to define in large, diurnal species, which can be watched, semicontinuously, as one studies primates. Nocturnal, timid animals, which can only be trapped and retrapped, or tagged with radioisotopes or little radio transmitters, are considerably harder to trace.

Territory, on the other hand, was defined by Burt as *defended area.* Nearly all vertebrates have limited home ranges; far fewer can be seen to defend actively a portion of the range, excluding conspecifics. Pitelka (1949), observing sandpipers that seemed to respect each other's areas without overt defense by the owner, suggested that *exclusive use* be another definition of territory. Although the ecological result is much the same, that one animal has exclusive right to an area of ground, in practice this is still another definition. *Defended territory* is the whole region where an animal successfully wins battles and drives away its neighbors; *exclusive territory* is the area that the neighbors never enter or enter only on a brief foray, perhaps chasing the owners, but do not stop to feed. As Figure 39 shows, the areas of home range, defended territory, and exclusive territory are all different.

Still another concept is *core area,* first used by Kaufmann in his study of Panamanian coatis. This means, mainly, the area where the animal habitually sleeps, feeds, and so on. As such, it is a very

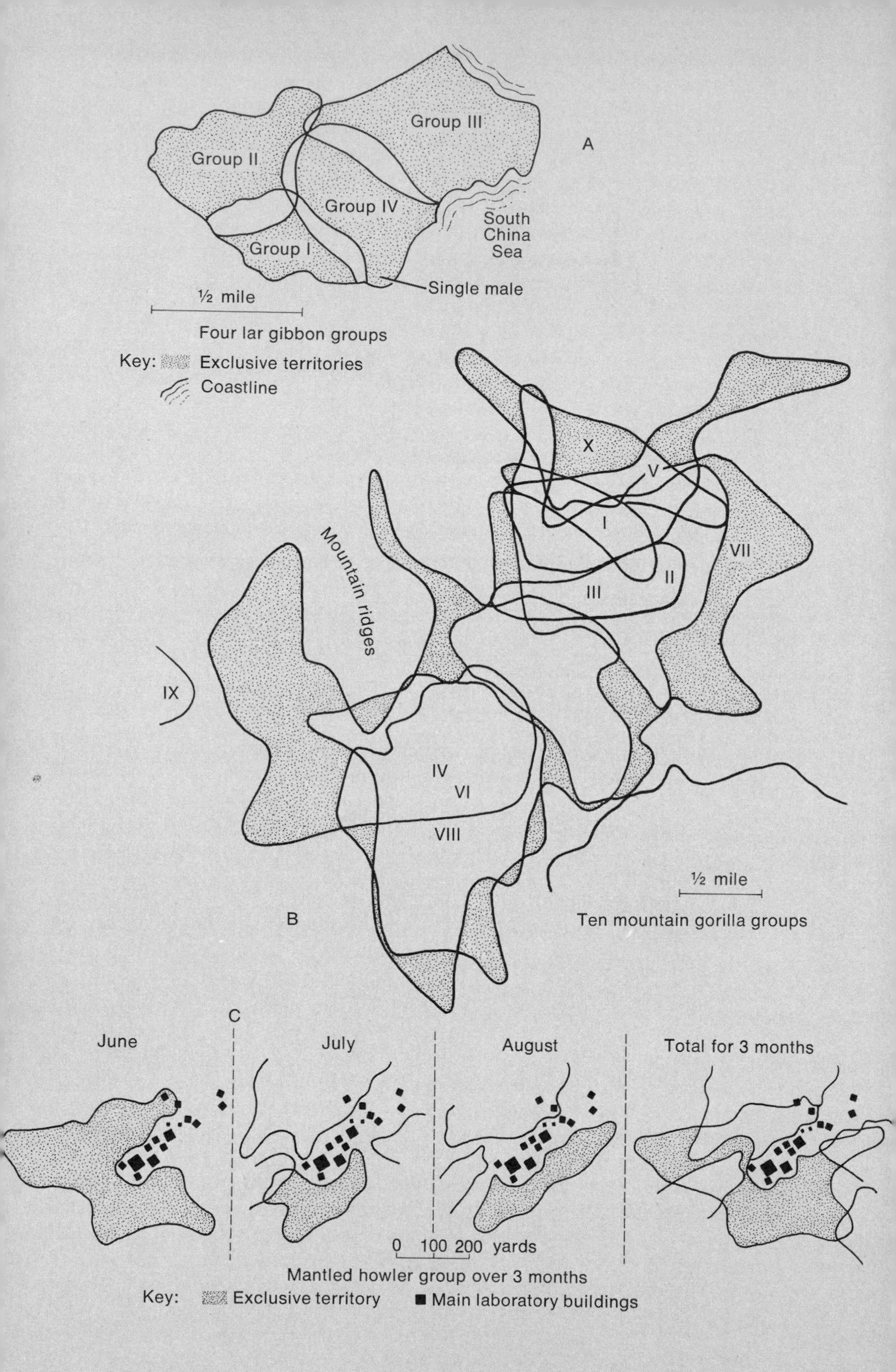
Group III
A
Group II
Group IV
South
China
Sea
Group I
Single male
½ mile
Four lar gibbon groups
Key: Exclusive territories
Coastline
X
V
I
Mountain ridges
VII
II
III
IX
IV
VI
VIII
½ mile
B
Ten mountain gorilla groups
C
June
July
August
Total for 3 months
0 100 200 yards
Mantled howler group over 3 months
Key: Exclusive territory
Main laboratory buildings

Figure 40 (opposite) Patterns of intergroup spacing: gibbons, gorillas, and howlers. *A:* Gibbons maintain stable, defended territories with fixed boundaries and small zones of overlap. *B:* At the other extreme, gorillas share nearly all their home range. Group males may join, avoid, or threaten each other on meeting, but this has no relation to a geographic territory. *C:* Howlers have a third pattern. Over 3 months, groups shifted home range. At any time, groups avoided each other by means of dawn chorus howling, but the 3-month ranges largely overlapped. (After J. O. Ellefson, 1968; G. B. Schaller, 1963; D. J. Chivers, 1969.)

useful concept—knowing the core area tells one much more about an animal's habits than just knowing the outer limit of the home range. However, it happened that in Kaufmann's coatis troops did not enter the core area of their neighbors, and he thus tacked on to his original definition of "intensive use" the definition of "exclusive use"—essentially Pitelka's "exclusive territory."

In this book I shall use the terms "home range," "defended territory," "exclusive territory," and, finally, "core area" in the sense of intensively used area. When referring to other sources, one must remember that "territory" and "core area" each have two current definitions and to check which the author is using.

How do solitary animals divide the available space in the forest? Isolated fights may temporarily separate animals or establish one individual's priority to food, water, or females. However, the majority of vertebrates stay within a known home range and establish a more permanent set of relations with the few individually recognized neighbors. Neighbors' home ranges may overlap extensively, with a linear dominance hierarchy in which the subordinate animal gives way to his superior wherever they happen to meet. (See Chapter 10 for measures of dominance.) This is apparently the case in American woodchucks. "Dominance" or "hierarchy" may, on the other hand, depend on spatial location. The classic case is Steller's jay, where the relative priority of individuals' winter feeding depends how far the feeding table is from the center of each animal's range—birds nearest their own summer nest site take precedence over those from further away. In some species, this spatially dependent dominance becomes so exclusive that the environment is divided into a mosaic of home ranges that hardly overlap at all. One classic case here is a primate, the gibbon, adjacent groups of which may share only 10 per cent of the home range of either (Figure 40). (See Marler and Hamilton, 1966, for fuller treatment.)

Going the other way, when does one stop considering dominance hierarchies between individuals as a form of spatial division and start treating them as the internal structure of a group? Perhaps rats, house mice, and rabbits show the sort of intermediate structures that are most difficult to classify neatly. Here, the members

TABLE 11 HOME RANGE AND TERRITORY (in km²)

Species	Home range	Home range per animal	Territory[a]	Territory per animal	Territory per home range (%)
Grade A: Nocturnal					
Lepilemur	0.002	0.0003			
Grade B: Arboreal leaf-eaters					
White sifaka	0.02	0.005	0.01	0.003	55
Howler, 1933	0.67	0.03	0.64	0.02	95
1951	0.18	0.01	0.16	0.01	90
1959	0.18	0.01	0.14	0.01	80
1967[b]	0.12	0.01			40
Nilgiri langur, Poirier	0.6–2.6	0.07–0.29			
Tanaka	0.11	0.08			
Lutong langur	0.2	0.07			100
Black-and-white colobus	0.10	0.01			100
Grade C: Arboreal omnivores					
Black lemur, forest	0.06				
scrub	0.4				
Titi	0.004	0.001			80
Cebus			0.86	0.06	
Gibbon, Carpenter	.45	.11			
Ellefson	1.02	.34			85
Graycheeked mangabey	0.13	0.08			
Talapoin	4	0.04			100
Lowe's guenon	0.03	0.002			100

[a] Almost always exclusive territory, for one to ten troops.
[b] Three months' range, other howler data 1 month to 5 months.

of one nest or warren are definitely a single group, each ranked with respect to each of the others and each ready to defend the nest against intruders. However, they forage more or less individually and overlap at food sources extensively with members of other nests. Again, a far-flung dominance hierarchy orders the individuals, but this apparently shades from one nesting group to the next. Indeed, Norway rats may form closed "clans" that do not tolerate a total stranger, even in the feeding ground, but this sort of multiple organization has to be spelled out, not just slotted into a single definition.

Species	Home range	Home range per animal	Territory[a]	Territory per animal	Territory per home range (%)
Grade D: Semiterrestrial leaf-eaters					
Hanuman langur, S India	0.17	0.01	0.09	0.006	55
N India, forest	0.3–6.5				
scrub	3.9–7.8				
Gorilla	1.6	0.84			→0
Grade E: Semiterrestrial omnivores					
Ringtailed lemur	0.06	0.003			
Bonnet macaque	5.2	0.09			
Rhesus, town	0.05	0.002			
moist deciduous forest	1.0	0.05			
pine forest	3.1	0.2			
Savanna baboon, Uganda gallery forest	4.6	0.12			
Nairobi	23	0.59			
Amboseli	39	0.56			
Vervet, Amboseli	0.44	0.02	0.39	0.01	90
Patas	52	1.73			

On the whole, primates are simpler to categorize. In most species, tightly knit groups tend to sleep, move, and feed together throughout the day. Thus, the group can be treated as an individual—it has its home range and territory, and the core area can be defined by tracing the movements of the body of the troop.

Tables 11, 12, and 13 summarize some of the available estimates of primate home range, territory size, and population density. Probably, many of these estimates are noncomparable, and some are near guesses, but they again give a picture of differences of size and overlap among different populations.

TABLE 12 POPULATION DENSITY ESTIMATES

Species	Animals per km^2
Grade A: Nocturnal	
Lepilemur	3000[a]
Grade B: Arboreal leaf-eaters	
White sifaka	244[a]
Howler, 1933	31[b]
1951	15[b]
1959	52[b]
1967(est.)	57–64[b]
Banded langur	98[b]
Dusky langur	86[b]
Nilgiri langur	107[a]
Lutong (langur)	150[b]
Black-and-white colobus	83[a]
Grade C: Arboreal omnivores	
Dusky titi	412[b]
Whitethroated cebus	17[a]
Whitecheeked mangabey	75[a]
Spotnosed guenon	58[b]
Black-and-white colobus	83[a]
Lowe's guenon	495[a]
Talapoin	29[a]
Gibbon, Bernam River	8[b]
Trengganau	4[b]
Gombak River	3[b]
Tanjong Triang	5[b]
Grade D: Semiterrestrial leaf-eaters	
Hanuman langur	
Ceylon, wet forest	56[b]
dry forest	66[b]
S India, forest	83–131[b]
scrub	16[b]
N India, forest	6[b]
scrub	3[b]
Gorilla, Virunga volcanoes	1.1[a]
Kayonza forest, Uganda	0.6[b]
Grade E: Semiterrestrial omnivores	
Ringtailed lemur	312[a]
Pigtailed macaques, forest	102[b]
Crabeating macaque, forest	168[b]
Rhesus macaque, bhabar forest	148[b]
moist deciduous forest	192[b]
chir-pine forest	137[b]
Savanna baboon, S Africa	3[b]
Amboseli	4[a]
Nairobi	9[b]
Uganda forest	11[a]
Vervet (guenon), Amboseli	70[a]
Amboseli optimal habitat	386[a]
Lolui	87[b]
Chimpanzee, savanna	1[b]
forest	7[b]
Grade F: Arid-country forms	
Hamadryas baboon	2[b]
Patas	0.035–0.6[b]

[a]Population estimated by measuring the ranges of a few adjacent troops, then multiplying, assuming similar vegetation to continue. Usually gives maximum figures, as observers choose rich areas, with highly concentrated populations, for their study sites.

[b]Population estimated by measuring an area, then censusing number of troops or individuals within it. This method gives lower estimates, both because some troops may be missed and because a certain amount of suboptimal or unoccupied area is usually included.

TABLE 13 POPULATION DENSITY ESTIMATES, SUMMARY

0–1 animals per km^2	Patas monkey
	Gorilla, Kayonza forest, Virunga
	Chimpanzee, savanna woodland
2–10 animals per km^2	Hamadryas baboon
	Savanna baboon, in tree savanna
	Gibbon
	Hanuman langur, N India, forest and scrub
	Chimpanzee, Budongo forest
11–100 animals per km^2	Savanna baboon, in forest
	Hanuman langur, S India, scrub
	Hanuman langur, Ceylon forest
	Whitefronted cebus
	Howler
	Talapoin
	Spotnosed guenon
	Vervet guenon
	Graycheeked mangabey
	Dusky langur
	Banded langur
	Black-and-white colobus
101–200 animals per km^2	Hanuman langur, S India forest
	Nilgiri langur
	Lutong langur
	Rhesus macaque, all forest sites
	Pigtailed macaque
	Crabeating macaque
201–500 animals per km^2	Sifaka
	Ringtailed lemur
	Titi
	Lowe's guenon

TABLE 14 INTERGROUP BEHAVIOR

Species	Long-distance intergroup calls	Close-range ritualized "battles"	Biting	Close-range avoidance	Amicable mixing, juvenile play	Exchange of adults
Grade B: Arboreal leaf-eaters						
White sifaka	−	+	−	−	−	
Indri	+					
Howler	+	+	−	−	−	
Purplefaced langur	+	+	+			
Nilgiri langur	+	+	−	−	−	+
Lutong (langur)	−	+	−	−	+	
Black-and-white colobus	+	+	−	−	−	
Grade C: Arboreal omnivores						
Dusky titi	+	+	−	−	+	
Cebus	−	+	−	−	−	+
Blue guenon	+	+	+			
Spotnosed guenon	+	+	+			
Lar gibbon	+	+	+	−	+	
Grade D: Semiterrestrial leaf-eaters						
Hanuman langur, Ceylon	+	+	+	−	−	
S India	+	+	+	−	−	
N India	+	−	−	+	+	
Gorilla	−	−	−	+	+	+
Grade E: Semiterrestrial omnivores						
Ringtailed lemur		−	−	+	+	
Macaque spp.	−	−	+	+	+	+
Savanna baboon	−	−	−	+	+	+
Vervet	−	+	+	+	+	+
Chimpanzee	+	−	−	−	+	+
Grade F: Arid-country forms						
Hamadryas baboon	−	−	−	−	+	−
Gelada	−	−	−		+	

+ present.
− absent.
Blank: data not available.

Table 14 summarizes reports of intergroup behavior, which ranges from physical combat and biting through apparently unremarked exchange of group members. This will be discussed under each grade.

ACTIVITY, INTENSITY OF USE, AND ENERGY BUDGETS

As important as the size of the home range is its quality: the intensity of its use and the amount of energy the animal can derive from it. The other side of the same calculation is the amount of energy the animal expends: thus, the energy budget of the individual.

Although everyone recognizes the importance of this aspect and nearly all field workers attempt some assessment of the temporal activity of their animals, there seems to have been only one quantitative attempt so far to measure the energy budget of a primate.

C. Smith has studied the howler monkeys on Barro Colorado Island, recording the animals' activity in 10-second blocks, as well as the food they eat and the remains they excrete, with the caloric value of both. Most field workers claim to identify only 20 to 50 per cent of the food plants of "their species," with little attempt to estimate quantity, let alone caloric value of the foods eaten, which gives a clearer idea of Smith's ambition. When his results are published and combined with the Hladiks' analysis of availability and food value of howler food plants, there may be a real estimate of one primate's relation to its food supply.

Unfortunately, the cruder estimates of activity are totally noncomparable with each other. Table 15 gives estimates of howler

TABLE 15 ACTIVITY OF PANAMA HOWLER MONKEYS, MEASURED BY FOUR DIFFERENT SYSTEMS

Activity	(%) Time of Day			
	Altmann	Bernstein	Chivers	Richard
Rest	51.5 (rest-play)	16.4	59.5	79.45
Feed	24.5	13.3	21.5	9.97
Move	23.9	67.3	17.0	9.17
Interact		3.0		0.35
Vocalize				0.29
Urinate and defecate				0.01

From Richard (1970, personal communication).

TABLE 16 DAY RANGES

Species	km
Grade B: Arboreal leaf-eaters	
White sifaka	0.3,
Howler	0.3
Lutong (langur)	0.2–0.5
Grade C: Arboreal omnivores	
Dusky titi	0.01,[a] 0.6[b]
Grade D: Semiterrestrial leaf-eaters	
Hanuman langur, S India	0.4
N India	1.6
Gorilla	0.4–0.7
Grade E: Semiterrestrial omnivores	
Ringtailed lemur	0.5–0.6
Vervet, Amboseli tree savanna	1.2
Rhesus, town	0.8
bhabar forest	1.3
tropical, moist deciduous forest	1.4
pine forest	2.6
Savanna baboon, Uganda gallery forest	2.4
Nairobi	4.8
Cape	4.8–6.4
Grade F: Arid-country forms	
Hamadryas baboon	13.4
Gelada baboon	6.4
Patas monkey	2.5, 0.7–11.8

[a] Total distance.
[b] Path length.

monkey activity from four different studies. Each author defined his own categories in what seemed reasonable terms and equally reasonably measured the activities of one individual, the troop as a whole, or the majority of the troop. *Within* each study, the results may be highly meaningful, as when Chivers showed the influence of weather on activity. However, inasmuch as these studies dealt with the same species, in the same place, and very likely with some of the same individual animals, and yet estimates of "resting" vary from 16 to 79 per cent, it seems hopeless to extrapolate further afield.

The one measure of activity that does seem worth comparing over a number of species is "daily range," the average distance traveled by a troop during one day. As Mason (1968b) points out, it is not often clear whether this means distance as the crow flies or path length of individual animals. More usually, it is probably a smoothed path length: the movement of the body of the troop, without allowing for individual detours and backtracks.

Table 16 gives a number of primate daily ranges. Even allowing for the differences in type of measurement and for uncertainties in estimating, the differences are huge. Further, they are consistent over grades: least in grade B; and by far the largest in grade F.

Finally come the core areas, or most intensively used portions of the range. These may be assessed by eye as the densest part of a map of superimposed day ranges. Mason actually measured the amount of time titi monkeys spent in the various areas of their range (Figure 41, page 114). Surely, more quantitative work comparable with Mason's will be done, but at the moment little is known of range use and core areas.

GRADE A: NOCTURNAL PRIMATES

Grade A primates are the nocturnal forms. In diet most are insectivorous. The lepilemur is an exception, being wholly leaf eating.

Even in this first, fairly homogeneous grade, there are exceptions in diet and qualifications in social structure. All the same, it is fair to say that the nocturnal, insectivorous primates are in general the "solitary" ones. The whole pattern of behavior is probably causally related, as we saw in the general pattern outlined for all birds and mammals, with smallpacket food and hiding from predators.

However, grade A is fascinating in that it gives clues to the origins of primate social structure. Although these animals are "solitary" in the sense that they feed alone for most of the night, further analysis shows highly differentiated relations between neighbors.

The underlying pattern, from studies of Demidoff's bushbabies, pottos, mouse lemurs, and lepilemurs, seems to be that the territory of a male overlaps the territories of one or more females. This contrasts, for instance, with those small rodents that defend territories against an intruder of either sex. This *overlapping* of known individuals, if it occurred in the primate ancestors, could have made a starting point for adult association in social groups (Charles-Dominique, personal communication).

The lepilemurs have this system in pure form. They defend their territories with frank shouting matches conducted between same-sex neighbors (Charles-Dominique and M. Hladik, personal communication). Mouse lemur females are more sociable, sleeping rolled up together in groups, and males may also sleep in nests with each other (Martin, personal communication). Pottos seem to have simi-

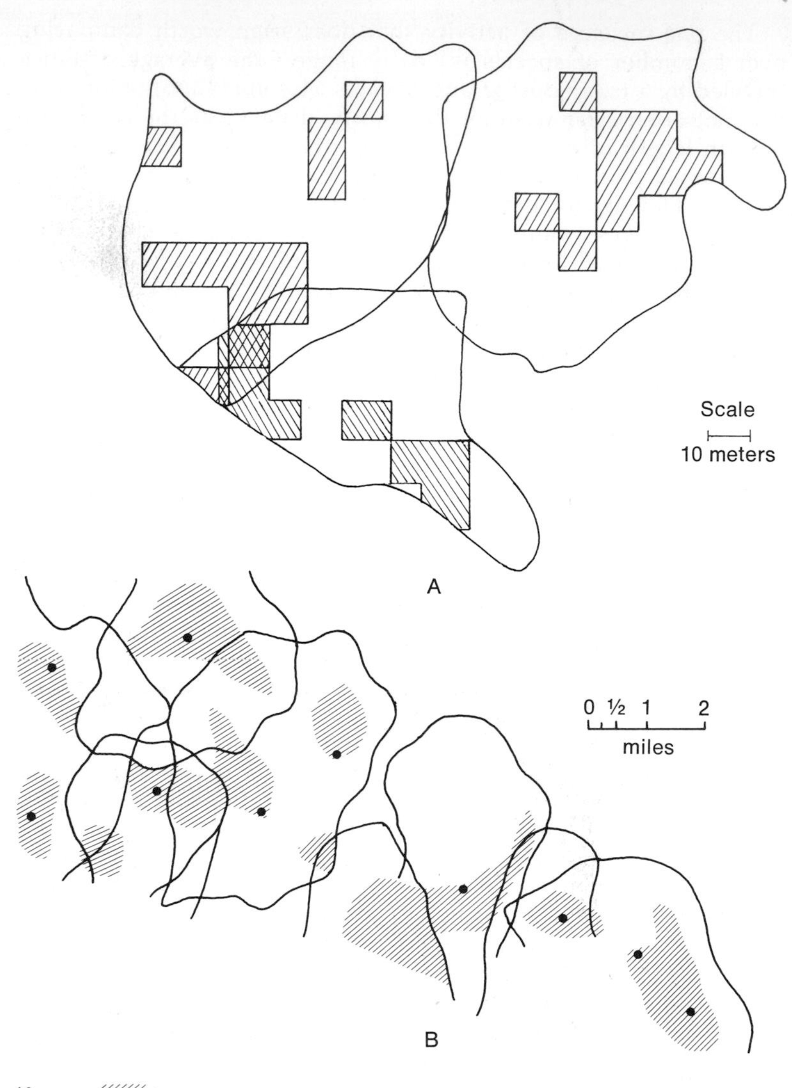

lar spatial relations, although most of their social contacts are mediated at long intervals through their all-too-pungent scent left behind on branches (Charles-Dominique, personal communication).

The nocturnal form known in most detail is Demidoff's galago, or bushbaby, from the work of Charles-Dominique. The tiny bushbabies live in a highly structured neighborhood: a group in a single corner of the forest, whose individuals have individual ranges. Males sleep alone or with females in contact groups in liana bundles. Females often sleep in groups in leaf nests that they construct. There are four categories of males. "A" central males have a mean weight of 80 grams. They have large ranges within the female aggregation and many social contacts with the females. A harem

Figure 41 (opposite) Patterns of home range use: titis and savanna baboons. *A:* Titi monkey pairs live in minute defended territories, with vocal "battles" at the boundaries. *B:* Savanna baboon troops range widely, overlap in much of their range, but generally avoid other troops. Thus baboons spend a majority of time in the central areas of their range, whereas titis may concentrate on a disputed boundary. Savanna baboon ranges are of very uneven richness, but troops may center on particular sleeping trees, which thus become a focus of a "core area," and other troops avoid these trees, preserving the spacing. The sleeping trees and areas of lusher grass remain relatively constant through the seasons. Titis can sleep anywhere in tropical forest but probably shift areas of intensive use as individual feeding trees come into fruit. Thus the pattern of use of home range reflects the whole biology of the species. (After W. A. Mason, 1968b; I. DeVore and K. R. L. Hall, 1965.)

system seems indicated, with only certain females meeting each male. "B" central males also range within the aggregation, but weigh only 60 grams, have smaller ranges, and have no contact with females. Peripheral males range around the edge of the noyau, with social contact only with each other, whereas vagabond males make occasional visits. Charles-Dominique has followed individual males' rise to "A" status, with weight gain, harem, and all.

Thus, these nocturnal forms are like other nocturnal, insectivorous mammals in usually feeding alone and escaping predators alone, but they not only (like most other mammals) have a pattern of social relations but these relations are quite probably ancestral to the diurnal primate associations of males with females.

Figure 42 The mouse lemur generally moves and feeds alone and hides in holes in trees where it may also build nests. Although apparently solitary, mouse lemurs have a social system based on overlapping ranges. (Courtesy of R. D. Martin.)

GRADE B: DIURNAL, ARBOREAL LEAF-EATERS

Crook and Gartlans' grade II includes small-group forms, defined principally on social structure rather than diet. I have classed as grade B "diurnal, arboreal leaf-eaters." Again, one cannot be hard and fast. The howler eats more fruit than leaves on Barro Colorado, and so does the white sifaka in southern Malagasy forest. Still, all of these show anatomical specializations for leaf eating—sacculated stomachs and long or very large intestines capable of coping with great bulk. Crook and Gartlans' grade II takes in, as well, the gibbon and the titi. Both of these frugivorous animals live as mated pairs with their subadult young. Both share many behavioral patterns with the leaf eaters. Red colobus are an exception in the opposite direction: They specialize in eating shoots or new leaves, and live in large troops with large home range (Clutton-Brock, personal communication).

The typical grade B forms, plus gibbon and titi, tend to form small families, or troops, as borne out by Table 10, and to have very little aggressive or threat behavior within the troop. Males and females show little anatomical dimorphism—males are neither behaviorally nor visually adapted to impress their near and dear, and never try to "throw their weight about." However, males often give different calls, or have different scent glands, from their mates—the long-distance signals.

In contrast to peaceful family life, grade B forms have highly ritualized spacing mechanisms, some used when troops meet and some in the mornings at long range before the animals make their first movement of the day (Table 14). Howlers and colobus make remarkably similar bellows, langurs whoop, the titi and indri and gibbon sing. When one troop begins a chorus, others echo from mile to mile. Primatologists use the morning chorus to find other troops: in two cases it has been shown that the primates do too. Chivers (1969) demonstrated quantitatively that after the dawn chorus howlers tend to move away along a vector from the two nearest troops, unless adjacent troops are within only 150 to 300 yards, when they forage toward each other, to meet and roar later in the morning. Gibbons, more argumentative according to Ellefson (1968), sleep in the center of their territories, then forage outward to the boundaries. They frequently head for the nearest neighbor heard during the dawn chorus of "great calls." Then, at the boundary, males chase and challenge each other in acrobatic leaps for 1 or 2 hours, often swinging to dead branches, cracking them off, and swinging on as the branch plummets down. Rarely, one male may catch and bite another—perhaps twenty-five times in a lifetime of territorial display every other morning. Meanwhile, the female swings about too, or supports her mate with more "great calls"—but she and the juveniles wander off to feed long before the males finish their tournament. The males, in turn, forage on average for

Figure 43 The wild howler monkey howls both in a dawn chorus that preserves group spacing and on occasions when two troops meet. The howler monkey may also howl when threatened by an observer. (Courtesy of C. M. Hladik.)

$1\frac{1}{2}$ hours longer than the females in the evening, perhaps making up for the extra energy they expend and for the head start the females have in feeding.

Although these loud calls in most species occur both as long-distance choruses and in short-range confrontations, the black-and-white colobus only roar spontaneously or when echoing distant troops. If two troops actually meet, the males shake branches and leap crashing through the trees, but do not roar (Marler, 1969c).

Chivers makes a sharp distinction between the spacing of howlers and that of gibbons. Figure 40 shows ranges, exclusive territories, and overlap of the groups of the two species. The gibbons maintained year-round, sharply defined territories, with only 10 to 15 per cent of the area shared, whereas the howlers' ranges shifted from month to month. Chivers argues that the howlers were defending something more like individual space, which moved with the group and was maintained principally by retreating from others' proximity. This may prove true of other forest monkeys as well, although not the colobus, which may remain faithful to one sleeping tree for 5 years (Marler, 1969c). Therefore, even with apparently similar spacing mechanisms, the actual nature or even presence of territories may vary widely.

This pattern of ritualized, territorial defense has been seized upon by popularizers to "explain" aggressive behavior of every primate,

Figure 44 The male howler monkey, like many other primates, has enlarged vocal sacs that give resonance to his call. (San Diego Zoo Photo.)

Figure 45 (above) An arboreal primate, the siamang. This is how troops of arboreal primates usually look to the ground-based observer, which in part explains our lack of data on such species. The small troop size may be typical. (Courtesy of D. J. Chivers.)

Figure 46 The siamang in close-up. (Courtesy of D. J. Chivers.)

most especially man. However, it seems most highly developed in these small-group forms and to go with such a peaceful life in the family that observers rarely see one animal taking priority for anything or rarely even spot low intensity threats that might assert such priority. Furthermore, an observer new to the species often mistakes territorial "battles" themselves for some intergroup social act.

Ellefson has speculated that the whole system may be related to the relative food availability and energy expenditure. Primates with food of low nutritive content, such as mature leaves, or locomotion with high energy expenditure, such as leaping or brachiating, tend to have small maximum individual ranges. This is borne out by the small day ranges of grade B (Table 15). Thus they live in small habitually inactive troops and defend their range to the full against conspecifics—eventually dividing the forest into a spatial mosaic and evolving dramatic, if not melodramatic, means of affirming their ownership.

GRADE C: DIURNAL, ARBOREAL OMNIVORES

Grade C primates are what most people picture as "typical" monkeys—the organgrinder cebus, or the African guenons, bounding along through the trees in a chattering band, squashily munching a tropical fruit and dropping it half eaten on the passer-by's head. In fact, such monkeys are the least well known to science. People who want to watch for a year or two choose either the inactive forms of grade B, which one can at least stay with in a tropical jungle, or else the open-savanna forms, visible a mile away from the top of a Land-Rover.

Blue monkeys (a forest guenon) keep appearing over 2 hours' watching in one place—the observer must decide whether he has asymptotically approached seeing all the individuals of the group. To quantify the social relations of age–sex classes of forest mangabeys, one must first quantify the probability of seeing each age–sex class through openings in the foliage. The difficulty of knowing just what is a troop, and which individuals compose it, means there is almost no data on home range size or utilization to compare with the grade B monkeys inhabiting the same forest (Aldrich-Blake, 1970; Chalmers, 1968a).

On the whole, it seems likely that there is a higher frequency of threat or dominance interactions within grade C of monkey species. There are also no obvious dawn choruses, although the guenons have a loud call given at moments of excitement, particularly when they see another troop, and mangabeys make calls that could be used for spacing. However, Aldrich-Blake (1970) and Struhsaker (1969) report real intraspecific group combat, with biting, between troops of blue guenons and of spotnosed guenons.

One striking difference is that at least some of these species have a certain fluidity of group size. Three troops of black lemurs foraged separately in coherent bands through the day, but joined together to sleep in the same tree (Petter, 1962). Old World talapoins and their ecological New World counterpart, the squirrel monkey, forage in small subgroups, but reunite in a troop of fifty to a hundred to sleep (Gautier-Hion, 1970). In the New World, the spider monkeys wander off far from their groups—the males especially may spend little time among the bands of females and juveniles (Eisenberg and Kuehn, 1966). This convergent evolution of troop structure, although probably not universal among grade C monkeys, suggests at least the view that these active frugivores are under different pressures toward grouping than the small-group animals of grade B. Aldrich-Blake (1970) believes this fluidity relates to the erratic fruiting cycles of forest trees. When a large fig tree provides a bonanza of fruit, the troop congregates together—otherwise they do better in small feeding units or even alone.

GRADE D: SEMITERRESTRIAL LEAF-EATERS

Only one species of leaf-eating monkey has adapted itself to partly terrestrial life and thus freed itself to colonize the forest fringe. This is the hanuman langur, or sacred monkey of India. Hanuman langurs have the most variable social structure yet reported for primates. Under high population pressures, they seem to form one-male harems and bachelor bands. At intervals a band may take over a harem and after fighting leave the harem with a new master, all other males being driven off, or perhaps split the harem into two parts, each with its own master. If, however, a harem is not invaded for 5 years or more, the aging master tolerates his own grown sons, and a small multimale troop results. With still longer peace, the troop may grow to fifty members with five adult males, such as the one Phyllis Jay studied in North India. When such a troop grows socially unwieldy, it is quite conceivable (although not yet observed) that it should split by a kind of amoebic fission, several males and several females joining each daughter unit.

This flexibility of social structure may, as Jay points out, be correlated with the hanuman langur's ecological adaptability. Certainly, forest langurs have been seen to form only small harems, which defend territory like other grade B primates—never the large multimale troops that seem more like those of the following grade E (Sugiyama 1964, 1965a, 1965b; Jay 1965; Yoshiba, 1967).

Mountain gorillas fall in grade D simply on the grounds of logic—they are terrestrial leaf- and stem-eaters. They can, in fact, be compared with other leaf eaters because they live in small groups, have small daily range, and, for their weight, have small home ranges. Each group is led by one silverbacked male, but many

Figure 47 A semiterrestrial leaf eater, the hanuman langur. (Courtesy of S. Ripley.)

groups have more than one male. They do not defend geographic territories, but widely overlap home ranges. When two groups meet, males may glower and chest-beat or the groups may mingle and groom or males may even shift groups.

The sedentary small-group proclivities of the gorilla recall other leaf eaters, but the thoroughly individual treatment of individual neighbors resembles only the chimpanzee—and man.

GRADE E: SEMITERRESTRIAL OMNIVORES

Monkeys that have adapted to life on the ground are particularly interesting to man, the most terrestrial of primates. On general grounds, one might expect larger groups to feed on widely spread grass than can feed on a clump of fruit in one forest tree. One might also expect larger groups to be less vulnerable to the ubiquitous savanna predators. On the whole, it is true that terrestrial primates make larger troops than arboreal species.

Crook and Gartlan's grade IV includes the savanna baboons and macaques and the vervet guenons that have invaded the forest edge and tree savanna. Grade E, here, also includes the species that come to the forest floor but do not venture out of the forest: black mangabeys, mandrills, crabeating and pigtailed macaques, as well as forest-living troops of the species that can also range onto the savanna.

Here, generalizations must be on much shakier ground, for no New World monkeys are terrestrial, and the terrestrial lemurs of Madagascar became extinct a few hundred years ago, killed off by man. The ringtailed lemur is included, as a woodland-terrestrial species, although it spends only 10 per cent of its time on the ground. But the problem arises of what levels can be validly compared—baboons, mandrills, and macaques are very closely related, and are also related to the mangabeys. Most similarities between macaque and baboon or between forest and plains species can be attributed as readily to phylogeny as to ecology.

Hence, it is more profitable to compare populations on the microlevel and to look for differences. Vervets in Amboseli Park, Kenya, formed significantly larger troops than their conspecifics on Lolui Island, in Lake Victoria. Lolui is the lusher habitat and has no predators. Similarly, three troops of baboons whose ranges included rich gallery forest in Uganda were smaller, with significantly smaller home ranges, than baboon troops in the sparse and dangerous open-savanna environment. They also exchanged members frequently, particularly males, and even subadult females (Rowell, 1966a, 1969). Lindburg (1967) noted that among some rhesus monkeys as many as 30 per cent of the adult males changed group during the breeding season.

Although these differences are in the same direction as the differences between savanna and wholly arboreal forest monkeys, the forest-living species related to savanna forms do not lend much support. Struhsaker's troop counts of forest guenons seem much like vervets of the savanna, in small troops. In the forest, the guenon tendency may be for one male rather than several. The drills and mandrills, forest-living terrestrial baboons, form multimale large troops like the baboons of the savanna. Thus, it is clear that phylogeny may be a very important factor, as well as habitat (Struhsaker, 1969).

Vervet males in Lolui (the forest habitat) do give a recognizable call on seeing other groups and defend clear-cut, minute territories, even scent marking with their jaws (Gartlan and Brain, 1968). In the savanna, vervets line up, with aggressive spats *within* the troop, at home range or territorial boundaries. In the savanna, they may physically fight, or mingle and groom—in both habitats, males occasionally change troops. Thus, vervets, like forest guenons, have strong intergroup antagonism, which probably, in both places, is territorial defense. In more forested habitat this is expressed by long-distance calls, whereas in the savanna it is expressed by visual avoidance or confrontation.

The troops of grade E monkeys of the baboon–macaque line space themselves out, each in its own home range. However, they do not have the ritualized long-distance spacing mechanisms or

Figure 48 The ringtailed lemur, a semiterrestrial omnivore. (Courtesy of C. H. F. Rowell. From A. Jolly, 1966a.)

Figure 49 Howls of the ringtailed lemur serve as both a spacing mechanism between troops and a contact call within troops. (Courtesy of C. H. F. Rowell. From A. Jolly, 1966a.)

the formal territorial tournaments of the grade B leaf-eaters. Instead, they avoid each other visually, usually with little overt sign. Macaque males may climb trees and violently bounce up and down on a branch, but, at least in Japanese macaques, it seems to vary from troop to troop whether branch shaking is an *inter*group or *intra*group communication (Carpenter and Nishimura, 1969).

Southwick's account of temple-living rhesus monkeys is illuminating, for it shows what happens when the usual open-country avoidance mechanisms break down. At times the troops he watched surprised each other coming around the corner of a Hindu temple complex. Caught at close range, they fought, sometimes with bloody wounds.

Again, such behavior has been extrapolated to man. Perhaps our own savanna-living predecessors had little ritualized or formal territorial defense behavior. Then, if circumstance forced groups into sudden contact, they might have fought rather than retreated with hostile courtesies. This is more plausible than arguing from the forest monkeys—but still nearly all savanna-living primates

Figure 50 The chimpanzee's "pant-hoot" is a long-distance call that may bring bands together or announce their arrival rather than space them. (Courtesy of Zoological Society of London.)

space themselves out without physical conflict. It seems as likely that we could have evolved alternate spacing mechanisms while we evolved the capacity to build Hindu temples!

Finally, among the semiterrestrial forms, there is the chimpanzee. Chimpanzees wander through forest and tree savanna, joining and splitting, friends pant-hooting to each other across the valleys, hurrying to rejoin for a time, then off visiting elsewhere. Jane van Lawick-Goodall concluded that the only basic unit of chimpanzee society is the mother and her infant. However, some types of groupings occur more than others. The mother and her family, all her children and even adolescents, often travel together. Females with children may join together or bands form of males. An estrous female is likely to have several males in attendance (see Figure 51).

Nishida (1968) concludes that the companionability of the males is one of the major binding forces: not only do they travel with other animals, but their greater excitability leads them to interact much more frequently with their companions. His "familiarity index" may partly reflect relative boldness of the animals, which might be more likely to come to his feeding site in male groups or mixed groups than alone, but it may also reflect a real bond between chimpanzee males.

However, on an even larger scale, the chimpanzees of an area seem to form discrete groups, or *regional populations,* of about forty to eighty animals. Nishida, by provisioning, estimated that his

Figure 51 Chimpanzee parties (*A*, traveling; *B*, feeding) in the Budongo Forest, Uganda. The regional population was about 56 animals, of which 18 were males. Subgroups ranged from single individuals to the majority of the community. The chimpanzees split up more while traveling and congregated to feed. Females did not travel alone as often as males, even if one adds in mother–young pairs, but females and mother–young pairs fed alone as often as single males. Males were far more likely to form single-sexed "clubs" than females, both while feeding and while traveling. (After Y. Sugiyama, 1968.)

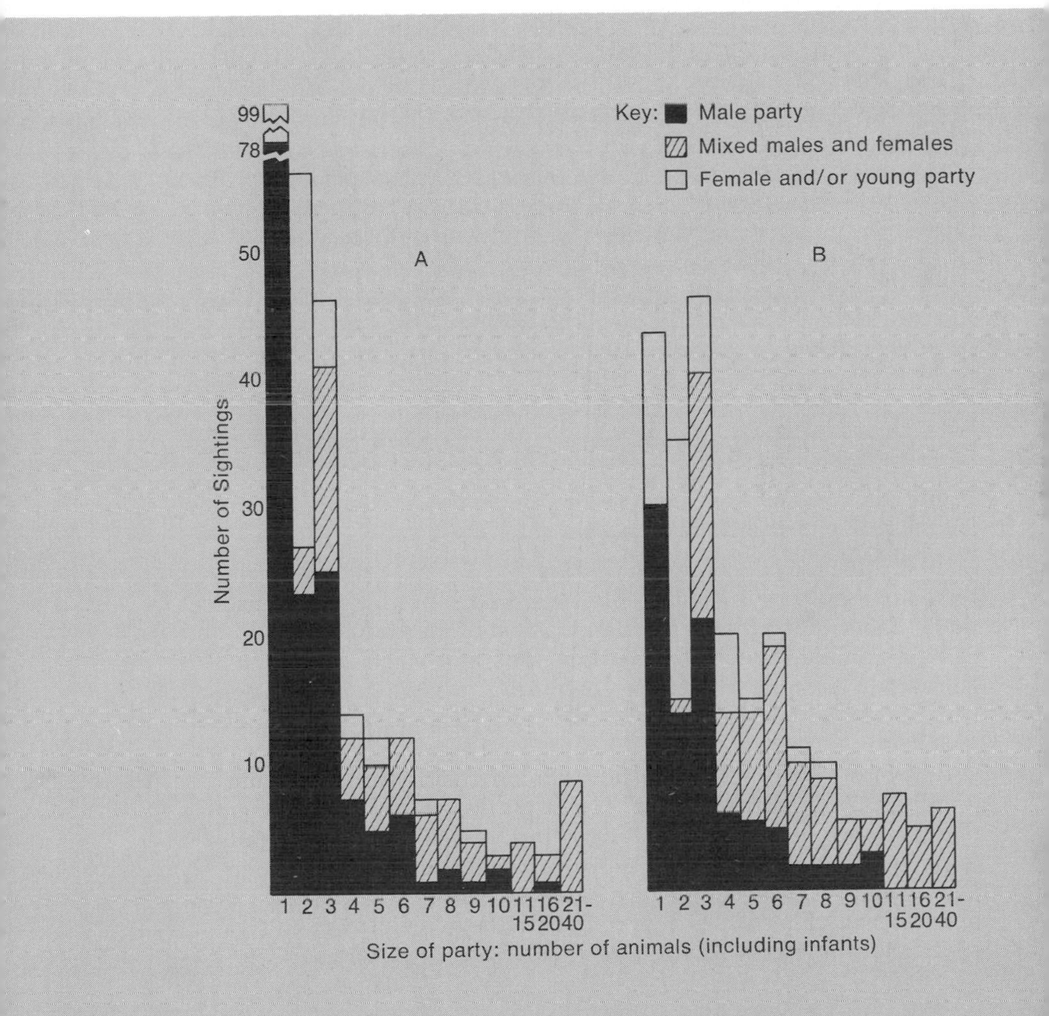

Figure 52 A chimpanzee group in the Gombe Stream Reserve, Tanzania. (Courtesy of H. van Lawick.)

regional population included only 29 animals, but others estimate more (Table 9). With each population, most of the individuals know each other, and the whole thing functions as a single community. At least in savanna, the entire community may migrate between two ranges as food supplies change with the seasons (Nishida, 1968).

Reynolds (1968) points out how similar this is to human communities, and particularly to communities of hunter-gatherers (DeVore and Lee, 1968). Hunting tribes as well split and rejoin, in part in relation to the food supply. Humans as well have groupings of adult males, although in humans the males cooperate to hunt or "work." Hunting tribes frequently form regional groupings, of the forty to eighty size of the chimpanzee populations.

Human males and females have quite different relations: chimpanzees mate promiscuously and do not recognize paternity. However, as Reynolds writes, "the essential characteristic which makes human society as complex as it is—the playing by the individual of different roles in different groups at different times, and the recognition of a nexus of relationships with other individuals over time and space—this characteristic is present in chimpanzees and to some extent gorillas, and was, it is suggested, present in the common ancestor of apes and man."

GRADE F: ARID-COUNTRY FORMS

Three species of primates live in very sparse, dry environments, with little or no access to trees. These are the "sacred" hamadryas baboon, a close relative of the common savanna baboon; the gelada, which is only distantly related to other baboons; and the patas or red hussar monkey, which is a close relative of the vervet and forest guenons. These three have presumably adapted independently to arid-country life. All three have arrived at a harem structure, which led Crook (1966) to argue that *reduced* size of the foraging unit and reduced competition for food between the females and nonbreeding males (by exiling bachelor groups to marginal areas) would be advantageous under very harsh conditions.

The argument is weakened as more recent study shows that the guenons live in one-male harems even in high forest, and if anything in smaller troops than the open-savanna patas. Patas, if not spatially territorial, are antagonistic like forest guenons, the adult male chasing away other groups when he sees them. The patas harem system may then be phylogenetically conservative, not a recent open-country adaptation.

However, the geladas, which Crook himself studied, strongly support the idea. During the dry season they forage as small units; in the lush wet season the units coalesce into feeding herds of hundreds of baboons.

Geladas and hamadryas have, superficially, the same organization. During the day, the harem units forage each in their own direction. At night, hundreds of animals unite on the "sleeping cliffs"—the thousand-foot Rift Valley precipices of Ethiopia. However, Crook's study of geladas and Kummer's (1968) analysis of hamadryas reveal differences of formation. Hamadryas males, even as subadults, may adopt juvenile females as the rudiments of a harem or may attach themselves to a much older male as a two-male team. At times, many units join to challenge others, indistinguishable in a band, temporarily, from the multimale troops of savanna baboons. Geladas, on the other hand, have no such social links between harem males, and subadults form all-male groups on the periphery of the herd, isolated socially from the harems. It is thus quite likely that the two species have converged on the same pattern

Figure 53 Primates of arid country, which form small one-male units that can forage separately but that also unite into large sleeping groups. These hamadryas baboons are digging in the sand for water. (From H. Kummer, 1968.)

Figure 54 Holes dug by hamadryas baboons searching for water. (From H. Kummer, 1968.)

at different times or from different origins—hamadryas very plausibly from a large, multimale troop structure like that of savanna baboons, geladas from sources unknown.

Different hamadryas bands at times will not share a sleeping cliff, but within the hamadryas or gelada herd, there seems no territorial defense at all. Male intolerance of each other seems entirely centered on defense of the females—if you will, intragroup aggression raised to the point that drives other males right out of the group—but very nearly independent of geography.

If Clifford Jolly (1970) is right that the earliest hominids were seed-eaters, with an adaptive complex similar to gelada baboons, it is possible that they, too, lived in small harems, which could join at will into larger bands. Crook argues that here there is a clear parallel with human pair-bonding. If small foraging units are advantageous in harsh conditions and if predators make it unsafe for females and young to travel alone, then a useful system binds males to females in small units and makes them feel they "belong" to each other. The sleeping cliffs, like seabird cliffs, are safe retreats, so that it would be possible for basically antagonistic units to compress their claims down to a few feet of sleeping ledge. However, if the different units can forage together when the rains come, they will be able to exploit *both* rich and sparse environments effectively with widespread herd tolerance but small-family loyalty.

SUMMARY

Primates can be divided into ecological grades with different habitats. Group size and structure, home range size, and type of spatial separation correlate very roughly with ecological grade.

A. Nocturnal primates are mainly solitary or live in overlapping individual ranges, the range of a male overlapping the ranges of one or more females. They probably locate and/or space out from each other in part by scent marking.

B. Arboreal mature-leaf-eaters tend to live in small groups or one-male harems. They are sedentary, with short day ranges and small home ranges. They have highly ritualized spacing mechanisms, usually vocal. The spacing mechanisms usually seem to be defense of a fixed geographic territory almost as large as their home range, but in howler monkeys they may simply separate groups in rather fluid home ranges. Gibbon and titi monkey, although omnivores, belong behaviorally to this group. Red colobus, which specialize in new leaves, form large groups in large ranges.

C. Arboreal omnivores again have one-male or small groups, except the talapoin and squirrel monkeys, which may group a hundred animals together. Little is known of their home range, but they move more actively than leaf-eating monkeys and have fewer long-distance spacing mechanisms. Cebus and guenons have intergroup calls and intergroup battles with chasing and biting. Old

World and New World arboreal omnivores, and black lemurs, may form more scattered groups, either with separately foraging subgroups or mixing of members.

D. Semiterrestrial leaf-eaters include only the hanuman langur and gorilla. They resemble other leaf eaters in having small groups, sedentary habits, and small ranges but are otherwise idiosyncratic.

E. Semiterrestial omnivores include forest and savanna forms, mainly Old World monkeys, except the chimpanzee. Ground-living monkeys form larger groups than do the arboreal monkeys, with much larger ranges, and commonly show intergroup avoidance rather than defense. Differences within species support the same argument. Chimpanzees flexibly join small or large groups of any composition, within regional populations of about fifty animals.

F. Arid-country forms live in one-male units. Patas monkeys have adapted the forest guenon one-male group, and territorial intolerance, to savanna life. Hamadryas and gelada baboons forage in small one-male units or large groups and sleep in large groups on cliffs.

Conclusions for man

The social structures that seem most relevant to early hominids are those of the chimpanzee and hamadryas or gelada baboons, which combine flexibility in small foraging group size with the possibility of uniting into large regional bands or communities (forty to eighty animals). Chimpanzees have a far-flung nexus of personal relations; geladas and hamadryas have marital jealousy, if not marital love.

Neither great apes nor the macaque–baboon line actively defend territory or have long-range spacing mechanisms. (Macaque groups fight when their individual space is threatened.) However, the guenon line, in forest or savanna, does defend territory. Thus, the spatial separations in savanna seem to depend as much on phylogeny as ecology. Therefore, although the home range of the hominids must have depended on their diet, the exclusivity of their home range must be largely deduced from modern man.

II / SOCIETY

Learning and Instinct

DEFINITIONS

"Learning" and "instinct" are loaded words. They carry overtones of predestination against free will, racism against egalitarianism, vitalism against mechanism—although it is not always clear which vice or virtue will be attributed to which. Biologists and psychologists have argued bitterly over the existence and meaning of learning and instinct.

At least, one must admit that in some real sense primates learn more than other mammals. This book largely deals with the emergence of primate intelligence—not only the capacity to learn, but to organize learned information. We must therefore consider some meanings of learning and instinct before seeing how primate social behavior and primate intelligence are both learned and innate.

Figure 55 The homunculus. Drawing of a spermatozoon with a preformed human in its head. (After Patten, 1958, from Hartsoeker, *Essay de Dioptrique*, Paris, 1694.)

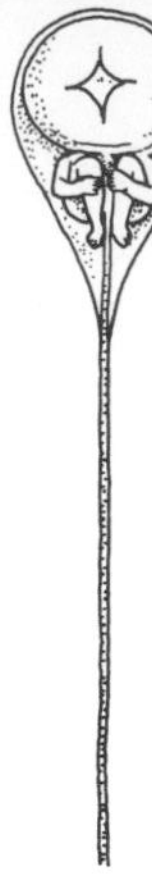

It may help to go back to a much older controversy, which science has settled (or at least outgrown). In the eighteenth century "preformation" battled "epigenesis." Preformationists believed that human shape was immutable. They saw in the sperm a minute homunculus already in his ordained pattern, ready to inflate into adulthood, for how else could human shape arise? "Their ardour for their cause was not dampened even by the absurdity . . . of the encasement concept—the implication that each miniature must in turn enclose a miniature of the next generation" (Patten, 1958), so that all succeeding generations of humanity must have been preformed one inside the other in Adam's testicles.

This is the anatomical equivalent to the naïve, extremist view of instinct—a view that is not held by any modern biologist, although it has been set up occasionally by environmentalists as a straw man to attack. The opposite naïveté, that man is born with his mind a blank slate, on which the environment writes and *wholly* determines his subsequent behavior, has never penetrated biology. What might be the anatomical equivalent? That the germ plasm is neutral, developing according to its embryological environment? That a sea-urchin egg placed in the appropriate womb would grow into a man or a kangaroo, or a human ovum dropped into high tide might produce a sea urchin?

Kaspar Friedrick Wolff, in 1759, set forth his conception of *epigenesis*—development by differentiation, in which new shapes are organized out of those that exist already, but need not resemble them. This became the foundation of modern embryology. We take it for granted that genetic information is coded in the nucleus of the fertilized egg. At each stage—the fertilized egg, the dividing egg, the embryo with primitive cell layers, the later embryo sprouting limb buds—the parts of the embryo are formed by both heredity and environment. Which one determines that the limb bud shall cleave into fingers rather than toes? Both, for if the buds are grafted on other parts of the body at an early stage, organs will grow appropriate to the part of the body where they are transplanted, that is, appropriate to their environment. At a slightly later stage, the pattern of each cell lineage is fixed, so that a transplanted forelimb becomes a forelimb, even though it sticks out from the abdomen. Or is this a fair statement? Perhaps one should say that a forelimb bud left in its proper place learns from its environment to become a forelimb, and, transplanted too late, cannot give up the forelimb habit.

In embryology, it seems that the inherited codes set the most general pattern first—the cephalocaudal axis and division into neural tissue, muscle-bone tissue, and visceral tissue. Then progressively finer structures differentiate—rudiments of each organ—and at last the details within each organ differentiate. At each stage there is enormous redundancy of control, so that minor differences in growth do not upset the functional patterns. It is hardly fair to trace the coiling of each kidney tubule back directly to the action of genes in the egg—the tubules coil within the general pattern set by their "environment," the kidney.

The important question, then, is "How much latitude for variation has a given organ at any stage in life?" At the earliest stages the cells are not even fixed by organ, and later on by organ but not by detail of organ. Throughout life they retain some responsiveness—muscles strengthen with exercise, viscera hypertrophy under demands for more adrenalin or increased urine flow. The digestive system lengthens under a high vegetable diet, shortens under a meat diet (Hladik, personal communication).

Clearly, then, "inherited" or "environmentally determined" are *relative* terms. They indicate the *degree of variability* that related organs, animals, behavior patterns will show in different environments. If all the members of a species, or of an inbred strain, show a single characteristic in spite of very different environmental treatment the characteristic is relatively innate. If, however, there is great variability under different treatments, one can say that the trait is relatively more determined by environment.

Marler and Hamilton (1966) put it: "When a geneticist speaks of an inherited trait he refers not to a characteristic of one individual but to the difference between two individuals or groups of individuals, or populations .... The method of exploring the relative contribution of these factors to variation in the population is to hold either genotype or environment constant, and observe the effect of systematically varying the other in experimental populations .... At no point is the inference drawn that a particular trait in a given individual is inherited; rather a certain difference between the traits of the two individuals is shown to be inherited."

Thus, there are three fundamental points to defining "environmental" or "innate" control:

1. *Anatomical and behavioral traits are both learned and innate:* biological organisms interact with their environment at every level, at every moment of time.
2. Learning and instinct must be considered as unfolding "epigenetically" from stage to stage. An adult animal may urine-mark its territory, with a complex behavior sequence in some sense innate, yet this is a final flourish in the use of the excretory and nervous systems that are themselves a product of genetic control and environmental fields within and surrounding the embryo. Thus, *to speak of learned or innate control, one must specify the level of detail and the stage of development concerned.*
3. An individual does not just "have" innate traits. Rather, an "innate" trait appears the same in several genetically similar individuals reared in different environments, or it differs in several individuals of different genetic stocks raised in identi-

cal environments. *The term "innate" is relative.* There are always ways to change the environment enough to modify even highly innate behavior. The relative innateness of a trait thus *depends on the range of environmental conditions sufficient and necessary* for the behavior to appear.

DIFFICULTIES IN RIGOROUS MEASUREMENT

Two common procedures in studying learned and innate behavior are *deprivation experiments* and *teaching experiments.*

Deprivation experiments remove apparently relevant factors from the growing animal's environment. If the animal then responds like its normal conspecifics on first presentation of a stimulus, one can say that the response is relatively "innate." For instance, male stickleback fish have red bellies when courting. Males that have never seen a red object or another fish will respond when they first see a crude, redbellied fish model. They attack it as they would attack a rival male, so both their perceptual recognition and their attacking motor patterns are "innate"—at least with respect to fish shapes and red things.

There are many methodological difficulties with the deprivation experiments, which Lorenz (1965) lists at the end of *Evolution and modification of behavior.*

First, only positive results count. If the fish does *not* attack the model rival, the experimenter may have simply used an inadequate experimental technique or general bad rearing that blocked other, more widespread systems than the particular system one was trying to test.

Second, the experimenter must be thoroughly familiar with the animal's normal behavior. This allows him to recognize disjointed components of larger behavior patterns. It also helps avoid general bad rearing.

Third, if a deprivation experiment is testing sensory recognition, it needs as many different animals as there are sensory cues to test. Animals are commonly biased toward learning biologically important information very rapidly, so if one tests a particular animal a second time, it may really respond to what it learned on the first test. On the motor side, however, the animal may show in a single test that it "knows" a whole series of action patterns.

Fourth, the test must offer an adequate set of stimuli to release the behavior. It is no use examining innate nest-building patterns in rats unless the rats have a familiar sheltered area to build in. Even wild-reared, experienced mother rats will not nest if you dump them into a strange, bare cage.

Fifth, the experimental and control animals must have genotypes as close as possible. Comparisons across species are likely to be nonsense.

Skinner, talking about the *teaching experiment,* again stresses difficulties of technique—the need for controlling and recording the exact sequence of stimuli and reinforcements. He shapes learning in the rat or pigeon in his Skinner box by rewarding successive approximations to the response desired, then trains by a controlled schedule of rewards. The results of even this highly simplified system can seem complex. When a pigeon responds to several intermittently flashing lights with an occasional series of pecks, interrupted by the random delivery of a pellet of grain, an intelligent lay observer might well be baffled by what was going on. Only the cumulative record of schedule, response, reward would illuminate the pigeon's (or the experimenter's) performance. How much more complicated, then, is human learning, with no Skinner box to cut off irrelevant input and no wires leading to a set of pen recorders that note exactly what was done to us and what we have done in reply.

It is paradoxical that all Lorenz' technical warnings concern keeping the environment rich enough for the experimental animal to behave normally. Lorenz' ideal is microdeprivation—to remove only the relevant experience being tested, leaving the animal normal in all other respects. Skinner, in contrast, prefers to deprive the animal of every experience except the particular item being taught—Skinner's "teaching experiments" involve far more deprivation than Lorenz' "deprivation experiments." This is leading perhaps into the metapsychology of scientific theories rather than the psychology of animals!

One example may illustrate the complexity of methodological problems. How would one determine whether a baby's smile is innate? A baby gives full social smiling, with eye-to-eye contact, sometime after 6 weeks of age. On the motor side, then, one must allow no practice in smiling for at least 6 weeks. It would not be enough to feed the baby intravenously to avoid windy smiles, for babies also smile at changes in the environment, including human voices. Much better to reversibly paralyze the facial nerve. Then, when the paralysis is lifted, if the baby smiles, the pattern is innate. However, if the baby does not smile, one is faced with Lorenz' first caution: negative results do not count. Perhaps the nerve was simply damaged; perhaps the child has learned that attempts to smile do not work (i.e., bring no response from adults); perhaps one has a more subtle, generalized effect of bad rearing—a child subjected to such an experiment might not feel like smiling.

On the sensory side, the child should be deprived not only of seeing smiles, but of seeing faces, which seem to be a cue for full social smiling. Reversible blindness for 6 weeks would seem to be the answer here—with the same queries if the child, afterward, would not smile. The alternative, of never seeing a human being, might imply no cuddling and no stimulation, which is certainly bad rearing for a small baby.

This is the sort of experiment that would give conclusive answers—perhaps it suggests how brutal is much research on species for which we have less sympathy than human babies. It also shows how "bad rearing," which shocks us sentimentally, may also destroy the conclusions scientifically.

Of course, there are ways to approach such certainty. Blind babies not only smile at voices, but turn their eyes toward the voice—"eye-to-eye contact" independent of sensory feedback. Men of all races and cultures smile in the same way, which suggests that the smile is relatively innate. However, it may be that all normal humans learn to smile in early infancy, reinforced by their mothers' delight in the first windy grins, just as all normal mallard ducks learn in the first hours of life that a duck, not Konrad Lorenz, is their mother (Eibl-Eibesfeldt, 1968).

CHARACTERISTICS OF "LEARNED" AND "INNATE" BEHAVIOR

Although it is only by experiment that one can *prove* a behavioral item depends, or does not depend, on a particular range of previous experience, it is much easier in practice to recognize behavior that is *probably* at the innate or learned end of the spectrum.

Highly "innate" behavior is usually

1. Widespread or universal throughout the species.
2. Stereotyped in pattern on the motor side.
3. Responsive to highly simplified models, containing only a few cues of the total normal situation on the perceptual side.

If the behavioral item is a social recognition or response, both the motor act and the perceptual cues may be "exaggerated" or "ritualized." That is, there may be selection on both sender and receiver for an unambiguous message, a situation strikingly different from the usual background—thus, bright colors or repetitive, showy courtship dances. (Ritualization will be discussed in the next chapter, on communication.)

In contrast, largely "learned" behavior is characterized by

1. Variability among individuals of a species.
2. Variability in motor pattern.
3. Variability in types and possible multiplicity or complexity of perceptual cues.

Primates depend on learning more than do any other mammals—their "specialty" as an order is complex and variable behavior. On the other hand, ethological theory has largely concerned the more fixed responses of fish and birds. (But see Ewer, 1968, for discussion of innate behavior patterns in mammals.) Ethology has much to say about primate communication—the expression of the emotions. It says something about emotion itself, in that it assumes that there is a biological basis for and selective processes at work on sexual behavior, threat behavior, and so forth. However, the social relations in a primate troop are largely learned—some "inevitably" learned from any mother of one's own species, some uniquely learned from the particular individuals that surround each primate child.

A large part of the fascination in studying primates is to see how an order of animals has evolved such dependence on learning.

SUMMARY

Any behavioral trait is *both* learned and innate. The relative importance of learning or instinct depends on the range of environmental conditions sufficient and necessary for the trait to appear. If it appears in animals reared under a wide range of conditions, including deprivation of apparently relevant experiences, the trait is relatively innate; if it needs a particular, very narrow range of prior conditions, it is relatively learned. Experimental proof is technically difficult. However, relatively innate traits are often (1) widespread throughout a species, (2) stereotyped in motor pattern, and (3) responsive to highly simplified perceptual models. Relatively learned traits tend to be variable (1) among individuals, (2) in motor pattern, and (3) in sensory cues.

9 Communication

We rarely tell a person "I like you," and hardly ever "You bore me." We rarely need to say it—a deep look in the eyes or a glance away, a step or a shift of the shoulders is enough. Saying the phrase would suddenly raise the situation to a different level of intensity. At still higher intensity of love or anger, speech becomes again inadequate: we physically caress or hit each other (Argyle, 1967).

In fact, most personal communication is mediated nonverbally. Although we value love sonnets and love letters, courtship can do without them. In fact, the content of conversation may be quite irrelevant to the relationship between the speakers: they mean only "Please pay attention to me for I am noticing you," which is what van Hooff (1967) calls "grooming talk." Speech itself will be discussed in Chapter 18. The evolution of nonverbal communication is the subject of the following pages.

Marler (1965) has written the best general account of primate communication; see his article for fuller descriptions, especially of signals in their context.

SIGNAL, MOTIVATION, MEANING, AND FUNCTION

An act of communication has four aspects, which can be called *signal, motivation, meaning,* and *function* (Tinbergen, 1951; Hinde, 1966b; Smith, 1968).

The *signal* is the form of the act: the squawk or stare or stink itself. The signal can be photographed or tape-recorded or gas-chromatographed. One may have difficulty in choosing the size of unit to treat as a single signal—what is a whole and what merely a component—and the observer's estimate of meaning will determine the size of his units. However, the signal can, in principle, be described in terms of form alone.

Motivation refers to the feelings of the animal sending out the signal. We ascribe such feelings according to unequivocal acts that sometimes occur with the message. If the animal has been known to shriek and run away, or to growl and bite, we may call the shriek fearful and the growl aggressive. Furthermore, one can extrapolate from a shriek to a squeal, or from a growl to a low growl, and say that quite probably signals of common form have similar motivations. Thus, the squeal may indicate some degree of fear, the low growl a degree of aggression. One can also extrapolate to some extent between closely related species. If a related species growls but never bites, quite possibly the growl originated in aggressive situations, although it may or may not still indicate aggressive feelings. Although internal states (or feelings) are presumed to cause the signals, in practice the only empirical data are the statistical correlations between a given display and the likelihood of unequivocal attack or fleeing. One can also measure relation to physiological state: the feeling of hunger can be equated to hours of deprivation of food or to blood sugar level. This is clearly easier for hunger than for such feelings as dislike or love.

There is considerable controversy at the moment over the size of useful categories of motivation. Traditionally, the three big categories for social signals are fear, aggression, and sex. However, these three axes correlate only very loosely with the uses of many signals (Tinbergen, 1951; Hinde, 1966b). Alternatively, one can pick motivations that correspond to every usage of what seem to be unit signals (Andrew, 1963a). These motivations turn out to be very general, such as tendency to locomotion. Factor analysis can contribute here, but at least some of the difference seems to depend as well on the size of component chosen as the signal.

Meaning of a message one determines from the reactions of the other animal. This depends on the total context. Thus, a direct stare may often mean a threat, but the threatened animal will respond to the stare with a whole range of behavior, based on its assessment of the sender's eyebrows, ears, nose, stance, age, sex, behavior in the previous minutes, lifetime history, and spatial position, as well as whether the receiver has hay fever that puts him in a foul temper anyhow.

Finally, *function* is the evolutionary advantage of giving a particular signal with an associated range of meanings.

Many of our common descriptions of communication imply all four aspects together. For instance, "alarm bark" carries connotations of the sender's alarm, the receiver's alarm, and the evolutionary function of warning the troop, as well as some indication of the signal forms. The difficulty is that the four are rarely in one-to-one relation. For instance, lemurs scream (*signal*) when seized, or when they see a flying hawk, or when another lemur screams: the *motivation* may be high-intensity shock, sudden terror. However, the *meaning,* is much more precise: "take cover." The *function,* finally, is as an air-raid alarm, specifically saving close kin from attack by birds of prey, which may preserve the caller's genes, even if he himself becomes a better target. Similarly, langur males whoop in many situations, apparently *motivated* by sudden surprise and excitement, including the approach of a rival group. In this case, the whoop *functions* to space neighbors and to preserve sufficient food for the harem females and young. The *meaning,* though, as it reaches the other group's male, is not the functional "Overgrazing threatens our environment," but "Get the hell out of here."

EVOLUTION OF DISPLAYS

Communicative behavior evolves through at least two steps (Tinbergen, 1951). Originally, a communicative item is a by-product, or a single aspect, of some otherwise useful behavior. Later, the behavior becomes "ritualized" if it is under selective pressure in its own right for more effective communication. Still later, some already ritualized behavior may be used in new social situations, with a concurrent shift of meaning.

The origins of displays must be sought in events that occur at moments of high emotion. However, they cannot interfere with other urgent needs of the situation, such as speedy locomotion. There are several groups of such auxiliary gestures, which provide the origins of most displays: autonomic responses, intention movements, and displacement activities.

Autonomic responses are produced by the sympathetic and parasympathetic nervous systems. Sympathetic discharge readies the organism for "fight or flight." It shunts blood from the skin and internal organs to the brain and muscles, in readiness for extreme physical exertion. Thus one may go white with fury, or its opposite, apoplectic pink, bristling haired or sweaty palmed. Darwin (1872) called this the "direct action of the nervous system."

A second common origin for displays is in intention movements. A slight start, a bobbing as though about to leap, may indicate the intention of movement. One of the most widespread mammalian and primate signs of dominance or of threat is erect, stiff-legged posture, often with staring at the adversary or subordinate. It is easy to see how this could have originated from the first movements of attack. These are what Darwin called "serviceable associated habits." Facial expressions made with vocalization, such as the O-shaped mouth with loud howling, might fall in the same class. One major set of movements is the "protective" responses, in which an animal draws back the mouth corners and shakes its head to dislodge noxious food or a bad smell. A whole battery of primate "fear grins" may be traced back to the protective responses. These are not so much the intention of movement as the movement itself, taken from a general context into a social one (Andrew, 1963b).

A third group of displays comes from displacement movements, apparently irrelevant activities that appear when an animal is caught in a situation of conflict. Thus a blackheaded gull, confronting a strange female, may neither fight nor court her, but break off from the beginning of either to preen itself or pull up a few blades of grass. The student facing an examination may drum his fingers on the table or twist his hair. These displacement gestures themselves can become the basis for communication to the blackheaded gull-ess or to the examiner.

Although "pure" intention movements, autonomic expressions, and so forth may communicate emotion, we do not call them *displays* until they have reached the second stage, that of ritualization (Huxley, 1914). Ritualization, in the biological sense, means that an item of behavior has been subject to selection that has increased its communicative value—in particular, that has made it less ambiguous, more easily interpreted.

Ritualized behavior can be recognized by just those properties that resemble human ritual. First, it is exaggerated. The original flushing becomes brighter, the slight bob to spring becomes flinging the head in a sharp jerk. Second, it is stereotyped, stylized. A gesture is less ambiguous if it is always performed in a single form, at a single level of intensity (Morris, 1957). Third, it may often be repeated. Repetition not only reinforces the message if it was not received the first time but also takes over the function of communicating intensity. In short, just as one would expect to recognize ritual if dropped into an unknown New Guinea tribe, so one would expect to recognize display in an unknown species of bird.

Finally, there is the question of the arbitrary nature of display. An item of behavior selected purely for communication need not necessarily have other constraints. Baboons raise their eyebrows in threat; men frown; it does not matter which if you know what species your enemies are. However, many displays retain some functional connection with the autonomic or intention movement of their origin, and so are not entirely arbitrary.

There may be other correlations with the rest of the repertoire.

An animal that is bigger is more likely to win a fight. It is thus no accident that bristling hair and erect posture, which make the animal look bigger, are common components of threat. The opposite is true, as well—if the animal makes itself small, by cowering and sleeking its hair, it may divert threat. Darwin, as well as Tinbergen and Lorenz, discovered that appeasement gestures are commonly the opposite of whatever, in a particular species, constitutes the threat. If the beaked or sharp-toothed face is threatening, a look away that hides the face may itself be ritualized to "head flagging" in appeasement.

There are, as well, environmental constraints on the form of displays. Many alarm calls, in birds and New World primates, are high thin whistles that are difficult for the predator to locate. Long-distance spacing calls of forest monkeys are often bellows—a low-pitched sound carries farther through the trees, than either a high-pitched sound or a visual signal (Marler, 1968).

Thus, in describing the evolution of any display, there are three things that might be ideally considered: its origin, its ritualization, and external constraints upon its form.

COMPONENTS, CONTEXTS, AND GRADATIONS: SIZE OF REPERTOIRE

At first sight, the units of communication seem naturally given. Most vocalizations have a beginning and an end; most facial expressions appear as transitory changes, with a "relaxed face" before and after. We assume that choosing the unit is largely a technical problem, of making sure what the senses of the animal record, and recording likewise.

The technical problem exists, of course. Bushbabies apparently hear ultrasonics; cebus monkeys may be red–green color-blind, and nobody knows what primates do or do not smell.

However, there is a still more important logical problem. Almost any unit that one chooses has subcomponents that vary somewhat independently, and in turn is itself a component of larger units, in which it will contribute to different meanings. In this sense, speculations about the size of the communicative repertoire have no meaning. A primate may integrate its lifetime experiences in the response to any given act!

What one really wants is some idea of how much information an animal can receive, remember, and process. If this were available, then one might work back to see how many relevant components could make up a single message—in practice, though, we have to work the other way.

As well as the problem of time span, there is a related problem, classifying the types of communicative displays.

Earlier ethologists were saved from complexity by the very rigidity and stereotypy of displays. Because there are strong selection pressures for making many messages unequivocal and because fish and bird displays are more stereotyped than those of primates, it seemed at first that complexity would not be a major problem. Thus, one could begin with a behavioral repertoire of reasonably distinct signals, analyze the situations in which each display occurred, and then reach conclusions about the underlying motivation.

The striking aspect of primate displays is that few are clear-cut: most grade into each other. As Rowell (1962) pointed out, the agonistic noises of rhesus monkeys form a continuum. Although one picks out certain modal barks and grunts that are given most frequently, there are intermediates between each of the main types. Marler (1969a) goes further to say that in wild chimpanzees *every* call is part of a continuous series.

Similarly, primate facial expressions are appalling to classify. Major attempts are those of van Hooff (1967), Grant (1969), and Blurton-Jones (in press). Van Hooff (1967) speaks of compound expressions, such as the "bared-teeth face," with specifications of what eyes and eyebrows do at the same time. Grant categorizes mouth and eyes separately; Blurton-Jones takes it down to what each lip is doing.

The size of components in a continuum is crucial, both for studies of motivation and for comparing species.

On motivation, let me paraphrase Blurton-Jones (in press), who takes the example of brow raising in children to illustrate some differences of theory. Children raise their eyebrows in conversation (especially with adults), when they are surprised, and when they are fleeing. One can classically interpret conversational and surprised brow-raising as indicating a slight tendency to flee, or else say that they are evolved greeting displays that have lost their original fleeing motivation. On the other hand, Andrew (1963a) looks for what is common to all the situations, and might in this case turn to Darwin's explanation that brow raising allows one to scan a wide visual environment. In this case, the Darwinian hypothesis is very attractive. However, if a larger unit had been taken—the wide-open mouth and raised eyebrows of the child running away—this would clearly be a "fear face."

In comparing species, the importance of using small components lies in the fact that what one chooses as modal or related groups of displays for a particular species are often intermediates for another species. For example, we would probably pick "crying" or "cry face" as one of our modal human expressions. Chimpanzees make cry faces, but as an intermediate transitional expression when they are changing from their "whimper face" to their "bared-teeth scream face." Thus, our modal "crying" is their transitional form, whereas their modal "whimper" we would more likely consider transitional in ourselves. The same applies to the vocalizations associated with the faces, although the noises must be measured and analyzed separately, not just assumed to correlate with particular facial expressions.

A second example is the smile. In Old World monkeys "smiles" or grimaces frequently grade into fearful screaming; in the chimpanzee they are related to bared-teeth screaming but also have a greeting and reassuring function, whereas in ourselves smiles more often grade into laughter or play faces. Thus, the same continuum would be grouped differently for man and monkey. Describing subcomponents in relation to overall context is crucial for what seems at first glance even such obvious groupings as smiling with laughter.

However, compound or modal expressions are extremely useful. If the observer has overcome his technical problems and managed to record a reasonably natural sample of behavior, modal expressions *could* tell him the communicative biology of the species: what it is important to communicate clearly. Modal expressions are those most commonly directed toward other members of the species. And the very intergradations and variability of primate expressions, as well, tell one that in groups of higher primates it is important to communicate the nuances of feeling with a certain subtlety.

EXPERIMENTAL AND MATHEMATICAL TREATMENT OF COMPONENTS AND CONTEXTS

An objective analysis of exactly what is communicated should include all the components of the signal at a moment of time, a history of signals immediately preceding that moment, an earlier history showing the whole relationship between the animals—and, having thus described the signal, an equally detailed account of the response and subsequent responses.

In practice, this means either experimental restriction of the signal to manageably small units or a statistical analysis of the "noisy" information of normal social situations. R. E. Miller *et al.* (1967) have used the experimental approach. Two restrained monkeys, equipped with a battery of physiological recorders, are linked by closed-circuit television that shows one a picture of the other's face. One monkey sees a stimulus indicating either shock or a food reward. The second monkey, watching the first one's facial expression, presses appropriate levers so that both avoid shock or both receive the reward. This would be ridiculous gadgetry if it merely made the trivial point that one monkey can tell whether another is frightened. It becomes interesting when the monkeys cannot tell. Isolated monkeys, reared for the first year of life without companions, neither respond to facial expressions nor "send" them so that normal monkeys can respond effectively.

Altmann (1962, 1965, 1968a,b) has gone furthest in statistical analysis of complex situations. He first made an extensive catalogue of communicatory acts in the rhesus monkey (1962). It is in this first stage that the subjective bias, or flair, of the observer is apparent—what is a unit act? Is "avoids staring at" a communication? (It is.) How do you subdivide play? Although most observers—and most rhesus—might arrive at roughly the same catalogues, clearly the subsequent mathematical treatment depends on this first intuitive list.

Later, Altmann ran a stochastic computer analysis (1965) showing that the unit acts occurred in sequences of different probabilities at least three units long. It is hardly surprising that a rhesus memory extends to two preceding actions! He also analyzed the troop as a whole (1968) to show the frequencies of interaction between animals of different age and sex. Such a large body of data, taken under fairly natural conditions, may be more effective than laboratory results in critically testing abstract behavioral hypotheses (1968).

However, what emerges from both Miller's and Altmann's results is that quantitative analysis of communication has the seeds of detailed explanation in the future but so far tells us less than does intelligent empathy.

OLFACTORY COMMUNICATION

Olfactory communication may be less important in primates than in many other mammals, as primates rely so heavily on visual and vocal signals. However, both prosimians and New World monkeys have permanent scent glands. Brown lemurs mark other group members, as well as branches, by rubbing with the anogenital region. Ringtailed lemurs have a stylized threat display, in which the male draws his ringed tail through the forearm glands, then shivers it over his head at his opponent like an outraged feather duster. Wild sifakas mark branches with throat glands or urine in the course of territorial conflict. Slow and slender lorises use brachial glands in defense and urine marking both as a territorial sign and in orientation. New World monkeys, such as spider and cebus and woolly monkeys, rub their chest glands on branches and sniff each other's chest glands. Both the lorisoid prosimians and the New World night monkey, squirrel monkey, and cebus mark by dribbling urine onto a cupped hand, then rubbing the hand on the foot of the same side, and finally scrubbing the foot on the branch. This urine-washing sequence is so similar in form and timing among all these animals that it may well be inherited from a common ancestor (Epple, 1967; Epple and Lorenz, 1967; Castell and Maurus, 1967; Schmidt and Seitz, 1967; Seitz, 1969).

Old World monkeys and Hominidae seem to use scent commu-

Figure 56 The Senegal bushbaby, like many other mammals, scent-marks with urine. The lorisoid prosimians and some New World monkeys have a specialized pattern of urinating on a hand, wiping a foot with it, and then walking on the branch. (Courtesy of T. Bekker.)

Figure 57 The sifaka urinates directly on a vertical trunk; its lifted tail serves as a visual signal to show that it is scent-marking. (A. Jolly.)

nication far less than New World monkeys and prosimians. However, male rhesus recognize estrus in the female chiefly by the vaginal scent (Michael and Keverne, 1968). In man, axillary hair may chiefly function for scent dispersal, as well as for physical lubrication (Goodhart, 1960)—so we, like the prosimians, may have a specialized scent structure. In man, as well, we know the occasional huge emotional impact of a half-forgotten smell—remarked on by Darwin, or the taste of a madeleine in linden tea that wafted Proust into seven volumes of recreated memory.

Although studies are in progress on primate scent-marking, its role in any one species has not been fully described. Captive sugar gliders (*Petaurus breviceps*, an arboreal, nocturnal marsupial that resembles a prosimian in looks and habit) communicate individual, sexual, group, and territorial identification through scent (Schultze-Westrum, 1965). There are at least nine separate chemical components in the urine and tarsal scent of blacktailed deer. The components seem to have an additive effect—which means that the same problems of displays, their components and their contexts, will arise with scent marking (Müller-Schwarze, 1969).

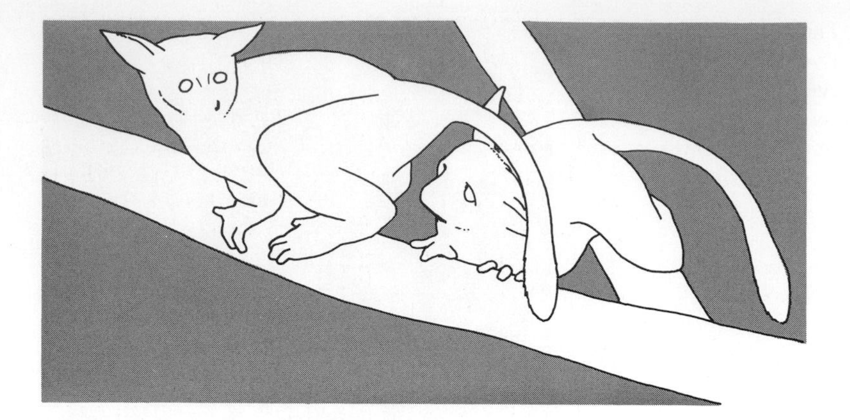

Figure 58 Olfactory communication in the Senegal bushbaby. Bushbabies, like most other mammals and many other primates, secrete a special odor from the vagina of the estrous female, which the male sniffs prior to mating. They also have specialized scent marks—in this case urine washing—that are used in many situations including courtship. (After G. A. Doyle, A. Pelletier, and T. Bekker, 1967.)

Figure 59 The ringtailed lemur has specialized arm glands with which it perfumes its tail. (From A. Jolly, 1966.)

TACTILE COMMUNICATION

Tactile communication plays a major part in primate life. Primates as an order are contact animals, in Hediger's (1950) term. Mothers carry the young for long periods on their bodies. Adults frequently sit or even sleep together in furry clumps. Above all, primates groom each other. Prosimians (except the tarsier) lick and scrape each other's fur with the toothcomb, a specialized structure composed of all the lower canines and incisors. Bishop (1962, 1964) suggests that in prosimian ancestors of higher primates grooming fur may have also played a role in the evolution of fine control of the hand. Monkeys and apes part the fur with their hands, removing fine particles with fingers or lips. One zoo chimpanzee even removed an object from another's eye while the second submitted for long minutes to the operation (Miles, 1963). Certainly, grooming helps to remove dirt and parasites, but it is much more than that—it is the social cement of primates from lemur to chimpanzee. Anthoney (1968) describes its ontogeny in the baboon from an infant's suckling the teat, to grasping and sucking fur, to the adult pattern. This accords well with the apparent emotional overtones of grooming and being groomed. As with all other gestures, though, there are differences even among related species: bonnet

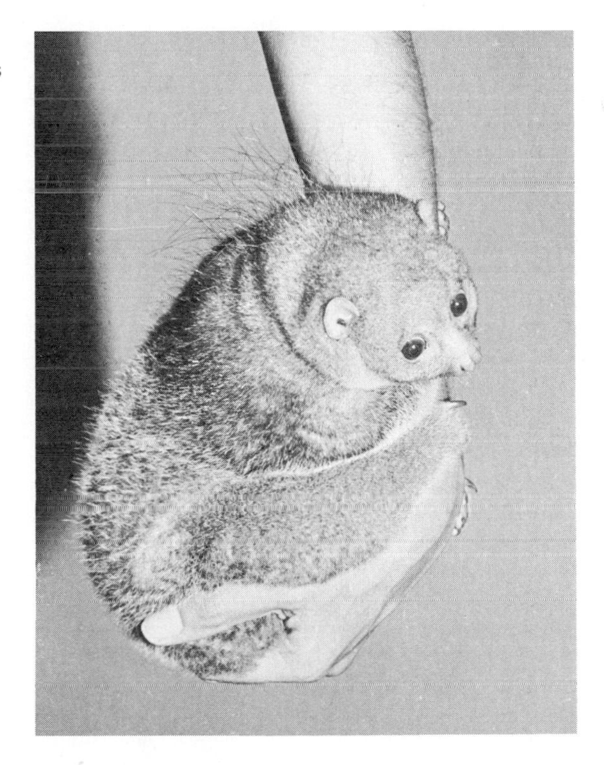

Figure 60 The potto has specialized tactile sensory hairs on the back of its neck. (Courtesy of A. Walker.)

Figure 61 (opposite) Titi monkeys entwine tails in tactile contact. (San Diego Zoo Photo by Ron Garrison.)

macaques sit in cuddlesome clumps, whereas pigtailed macaques maintain an arm's-length distance (Rosenblum *et al.*, 1966).

Moynihan (1967), surveying the New World monkeys, concludes that adult mutual grooming was probably originally a precopulatory pattern only, which it still is in some small, hole-nesting forms, and that it took on general social functions independently in the various lines—and even decreased in frequency in the howler and squirrel monkeys.

Finally, in addition to grooming itself, there is a huge repertoire of patting and nuzzling lumped as greeting behavior—as well as the agonistic contact of cuffs and bites and even kicks. Chimpanzees, particularly, pat each other's hands, faces, and groins, lay a hand on each other's back in reassurance, and kiss in affection.

VISUAL COMMUNICATION

Visual communication involves facial and ear expression, hair erection, and general posture and tail position. Visual communication "must include the specific characteristics of the senders' morphology. It may be partly for this reason that the dynamic elements of visual signals are often similar in many different primates" (Marler, 1965). Species, size, sex, and all of the individual characteristics such as dominance and kinship status accompany every smile or scowl, and thus need no repetition. Properly, visual signals include these long-term markers. As many primates, like birds, are visual animals and can see in color, groups of sympatric species may be distinguished by brilliant pelage or bizarre face masks, as well as by call or scent. The marmosets, lemurs, and guenons include some of the showiest of mammals.

A much shorter-term marker is the sexual swelling of females in estrus. Some prosimians, most macaques, baboons, mangabeys, talapoins, and the great apes develop highly swollen pink or red labia when in estrus. There is some doubt how much these actually function as a visual signal, as the behavior or scent of the female seems more important in arousing the male—but he can hardly be unaware of her blazing behind (Rowell, 1967b).

Bodily posture is one of the most consistent communicative gestures throughout mammals as a whole. Confident or threatening animals hold themselves straight, "look big," and walk with stiff-legged swagger. Submissive ones hunch over, crouch, lie down. Any marks of species or sex are thus displayed by the first, concealed by the second.

Text continues on page 162.

Figure 62 (above) Chimpanzee tense-mouth face. Posture and bristling hair reinforce the facial signal. (Courtesy of H. van Lawick.)

Figure 63 (at left) Human tense-mouth face. Heads of state are dominant males, often photographed making gestures of confident threat. (Courtesy of Wide World Photos.)

Figure 64 The Senegal bushbaby in a staring bared-teeth scream. This open-mouth defensive face persists throughout the primate line. (Courtesy of S. Bearder.)

Figure 65 Golden lion marmosets with open-mouth agonistic face. (Courtesy of Zoological Society of London.)

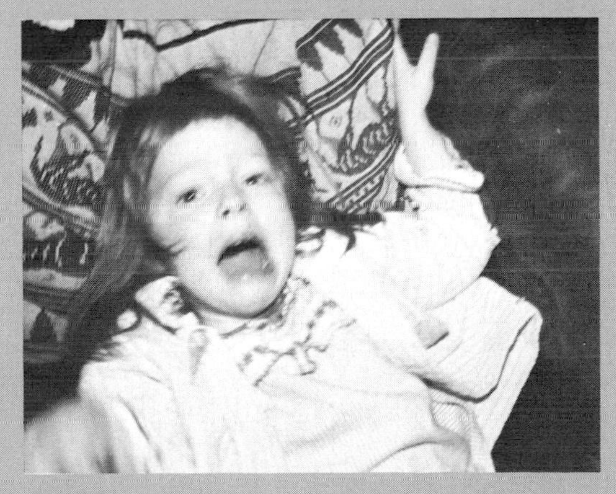

Figure 66 Child with open-mouth, screaming, defensive face, objecting to photograph. (A. Jolly.)

TABLE 17

Name	Face	Situation	Bushbaby	Lemur	Cebus	Spider	Baboon	Guenon	Chimpanzee	Man	Human name
Relaxed face			Yes	Yes	Yes	Yes	Yes	Yes	Yes	Yes	
Alert face	Eyes wide, lips may be parted	Novelty, etc.	Yes	Yes	Yes	Yes	Yes	Yes	Yes	Yes	
Tense-mouth face	Eyes wide, mouth narrow slit	Confident threat or attack	No	No	Yes, brows down	?	Yes, brows down	Yes, brows normal	Yes, brows frown	Yes, brows frown	Silent glare
Staring open-mouth face	Eyes wide, mouth open, lips cover teeth	Inhibited threat or mobbing predator	Yes, intention bite	Yes,	Yes, brows down	Yes	Brows up	Brows normal	Brows frown	Brows frown	Angry shout or scold
Staring bared-teeth scream face	Eyes wide, mouth corners drawn back, teeth and gums show	Terror, flight, temper tantrums	Yes	Yes	Yes	Yes	Brows up	Brows normal	Brows up	Brows up	Scream
Frowning bared-teeth scream face	Eyes narrow, brows down, mouth corners back, teeth show	Total submission, infant distress	No	No	?	?	Yes	Rare	Yes	Yes, eyes narrow	Intense crying

Silent bared-teeth face	Eyes stare or evade, brows relaxed or up, mouth corners back, teeth show	Social fear or submission, or friendly approach, or bad smell	Yes, with protective responses, not social	Yes	Yes	Yes, but also with attack	Yes	Yes	Yes, often greeting	Yes, eyes narrow	Polite smile
Bared-teeth gecker face	Same with rapid noise	Subordinate flee–approach conflict, infant discomfort	Yes, with defensive threat calls and infant clicks	Yes	Yes, with defensive threat calls and infant squeaks	?	Yes	Yes	Yes	Yes	Begging cry, nervous laugh
Lip-smacking face	Sucking jaw movements and tongue protrusion, eyes wide	Greeting, sex grooming	No	Rare	Yes	No	Yes, brows up	Rare	Rare	No	
Pout face	Eyes wide, mouth corners forward, "o-mouth"	With contact calls, and especially infant begging	No	Yes	?	Yes, brows up	Yes	Infant only?	Yes	Infant mainly	Pout, begging
Hoot face	Mouth corners far forward, "trumpet-mouth"	With long-distance calls	No	Yes	? (Marked in howling howler)		No	?	Yes	Rare	Howling
Relaxed open-mouth face	Eyes normal or narrow, mouth wide with corners up, brows normal	Play, especially rough-and-tumble	No	No	No	Yes	Yes	Yes	Yes, and with panting grunts	Yes, and with laughing, eyes narrow	Laughter, play

Classification from Van Hooff, with material from Andrew, Moynihan, Struhsaker, Van Lawick-Goodall, and Eisenberg.

Figure 67 Senegal bushbaby with staring open-mouth face in threat. The lips are pulled forward to cover the teeth. Compare with the defensive face of Figure 64. (Courtesy of T. Bekker.)

Figure 68 Ringtailed lemur in staring open-mouth threat. (Courtesy of J. Buettner-Janusch, from R. J. Andrew, 1963.)

Figure 69 The red uakari open-mouth threat. (San Diego Zoo Photo by Ron Garrison.)

Figure 70 Human open-mouth threat. (Courtesy of B. Campbell.)

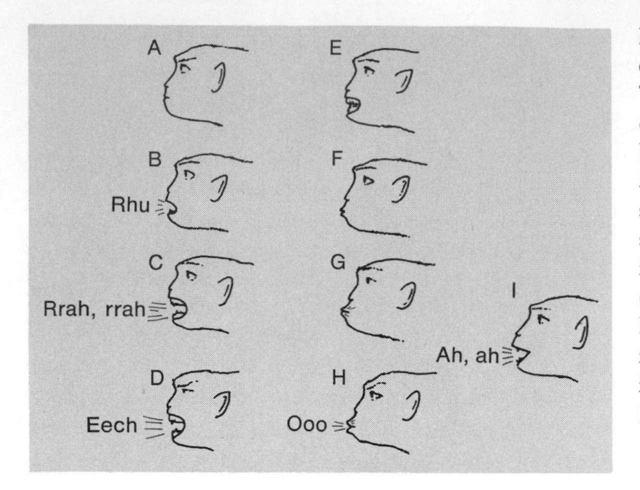

Figure 71 Compound facial expressions in a macaque. *A:* Tense-mouth face. *B:* Staring open-mouth face. *C:* Staring bared-teeth screaming face. *D:* Frowning bared-teeth screaming face. *E:* Bared-teeth silent (teeth-chattering) face. *F:* Lip-smacking (teeth-chattering) face. *G:* Protruded-lips face. *H:* Pout face. *I:* Relaxed open-mouth face. (After J. A. R. A. M. van Hooff, 1967.)

As the permanent markers changed with the evolution of each new species, the dynamic ones remained conservative. Table 17 shows some primate homologues of human facial expression. The homology is quite straightforward in that the same muscles are used in our different-shaped faces and in that the situations are recognizably similar for each face. However, the balance of expressions and the ones that commonly merge with each other are different in each species (Hinde and Rowell, 1962; Blurton-Jones, 1967, in press; Grant, 1969; Van Hooff, 1967, Andrew, 1963b).

One example worth examining in detail is the smile. Some insectivores draw back the corners of their mouths and shake their heads when they bite unpleasant food or smell a strong smell. Many human babies do the same if offered unwanted food; so do juvenile lemurs that bite a rotten tamarind pod. Andrew proposes that this primitive rejection or protective response, which originally served to dislodge food from the mouth, evolved into a fear grin of monkeys and apes. If there was an intermediate stage when the animal grimaced at the mere smell of a conspecific, more particularly a threatening, dominant conspecific, the response could then be ritualized into a visual signal of fear and submission. From there, its emotion could change from real fear to appeasing greeting—Old World and New World monkeys and apes all use the grin in both situations, at different intensities. When two animals meet, either or both may grin—but the subordinate grins more on the whole. There is a further refinement in both baboons and chimpanzees—the dominant animal may grin, or rather smile, "reassuringly" at a timid subordinate that fears to approach. Finally, we have the human smile, which certainly may still be given as a "nervous grin" to one's boss—but is more usually just greeting, warmth between people, promoting friendly contact. The human infant's active social smiling draws his mother almost irresistibly. There may still be strong ambiguity in the motivation of infants' smiles, but the effect is in every sense attractive (Ambrose, 1963).

The smile illustrates evolution of a single gesture from noncommunicative origin to ritualized display. It also illustrates how displays themselves can change in meaning. The various bared-teeth faces of the Old World monkeys frequently shade into each other, and all bear a fairly clear relation to fear. In man, however, the grin of real fear is rare. Blurton-Jones (in press) suggests that smiling and crying, both extremely important in our immobile infants, have taken over the possible faces with stretched-back lips, so that human fear now uses the facial components of monkey threat. With us, the bared-teeth expression of social greeting, or smile, is much more likely to grade into the high-intensity "play face" of laughter.

Similarly, the student of lemurs would group the pout and hoot faces together; in both the mouth corners round forward to produce "oooo" sounds of varying intensity, and the infant contact call matures into the adult long distance howl. In man and chimpanzee, we are more likely to think of pout face grading through a whimper face (or in man into crying).

Another example of such a change has been discussed by Wickler (1967). Many female mammals "present" their hind end to the male when soliciting mounting. Female primates of most or all nonhuman species do so as well. However, among Old World monkeys presenting may also be a gesture of submission—a subordinate of either sex may present to his superior before taking a piece of food, and the superior may perfunctorily mount or even thrust before allowing him to do so. Wickler discusses as well the role of the genitalia in visual communication—display of male genitalia may indicate

Figure 72 Primate faces with mouth corners pulled back are highly complex. They can be traced back to a "protective grin" in such animals as the ringtailed lemur. (J. Buettner-Janusch in R. J. Andrew, 1963.)

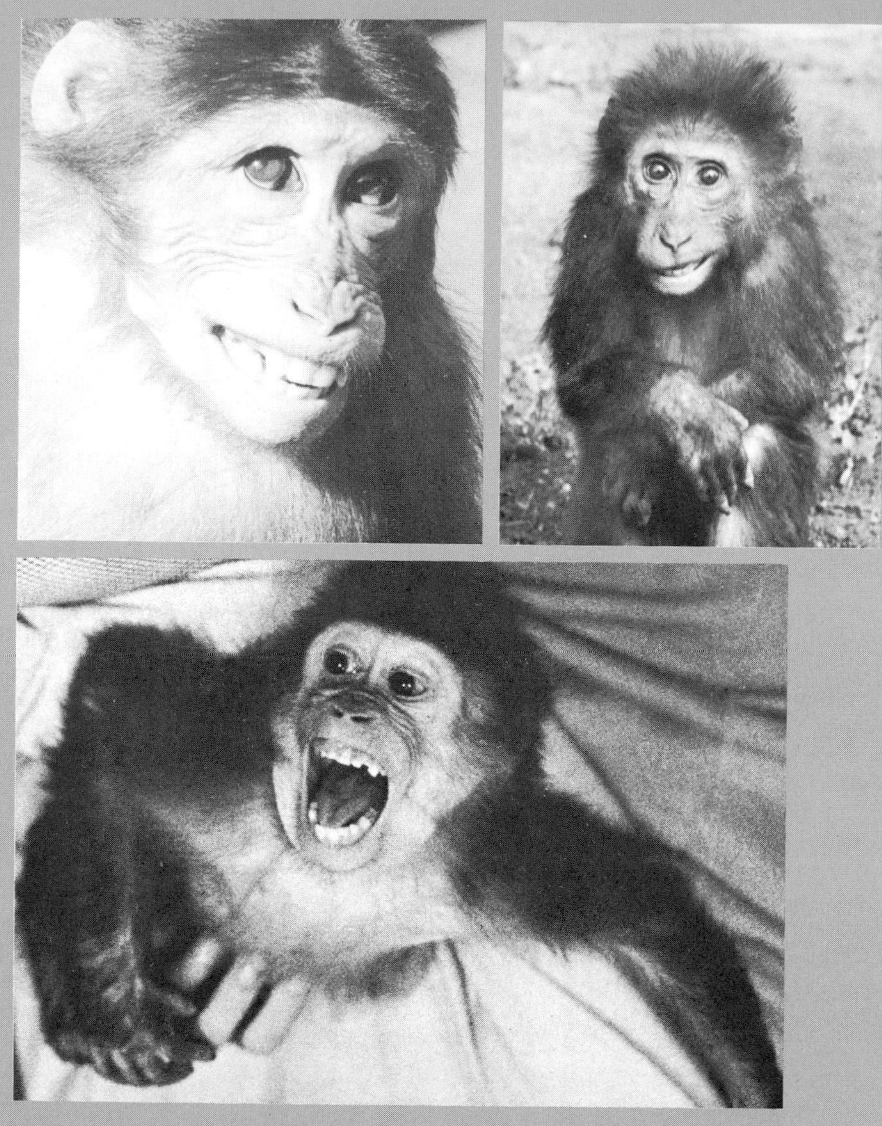

Figure 73 (above) Grin faces in the stumptailed macaque. The fear grin (top left) is clearly related to the grin of submissive greeting (top right). At bottom is the play face of a juvenile being tickled. (From M. Bertrand, 1969.)

Figure 74 (opposite, top) Human beings may grimace in extreme emotion or physical tension. Tony Jacklin. (Courtesy of E. D. Lacey.)

Figure 75 (opposite, bottom) The human smile is a greeting gesture, but it more often grades into our laughter and play face rather than into a fear grin or a grimace. Tony Jacklin after winning the 1969 British Open Championship. (Courtesy of E. D. Lacey.)

dominance as well as sex, particularly in marmoset and squirrel monkey, and colobus may have erections during territorial border disputes (Marler, 1969c), although this is less widespread than presenting the posterior to indicate submission.

VOCAL COMMUNICATION

The sound spectrograph gives us a means of analyzing vocal communication that is unparalleled by anything in the visual line. The spectrograph plots recorded sound by time and frequency. In theory, we should know exactly what any primate is saying.

In practice, this is much more difficult because primates produce such graded sounds. Any one type of call or noise may shade into others, so that one cannot even say how large is the repertoire of a single animal—it depends on the observer's preference for splitting. It is cheering that different observers of, say, macaques at least agree what the major groups of sounds are. Grimm's (1967) catalogue of the sounds of the macaque is particularly interesting, as he had workers unacquainted with macaques draw up a list, simply from a vast number of tape recordings. The major calls and their variants, thus classified in isolation from other behavior, also turned out to be those used in nearly similar behavioral situations by the macaques. There are now behavioral repertoires drawn up by different authors for several species of macaque: Japanese, stumptail, pigtail, rhesus, bonnet, and crabeater. However, it would take a specialist who knows the animals to analyze the similarities and differences.

Marler (1965) emphasizes that clear pure-frequency sounds, so typical of birds, are not typical of primates. In fact, many New World monkeys, such as titi and marmoset, give remarkably trilled, birdlike calls. However, grunting, harsh noises over a wide frequency band are very common. It may be that harsh noises provide more possible intermediates between major kinds of vocalization than do the clear calls. Andrew takes this rather further, pointing out that our speech is a kind of harsh grunting, affected by the shape of the buccal cavity on its way out. Baboons but not macaques (Lieberman *et al.*, 1969) make much the same sort of "hominid grunt" that we do, and changes in their facial expression, such as grinning or lip smacking, similarly affect the quality of the sound. Thus, a baboon or chimpanzee can vocally communicate the shape of its face.

An important difference occurs between the short-range signals discussed and the long-range vocal systems of a few primates. The short-range system is typically variable, whereas long-distance spacing calls are far more stereotyped. Long-distance signals may also be *purer* in frequency, more highly structured, either pure in

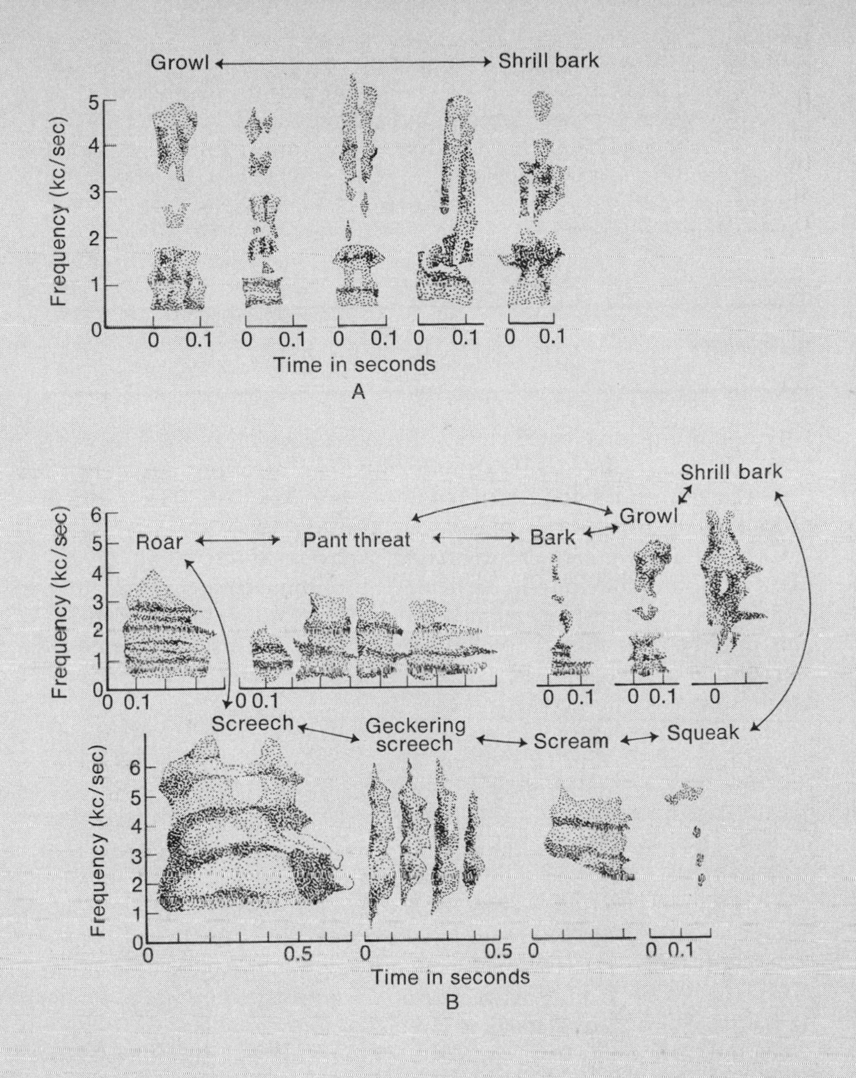

Figure 76 Graded vocalizations of rhesus macaques. The sound spectrograph transposes calls into a visual record, with time on the horizontal axis and frequency on the vertical axis. Blackness of the tracing indicates intensity. A tone of pure frequency is a single horizontal line, whereas overtones appear as higher horizontal lines above the fundamental. White noise is a vertical blur; a noisy click is a vertical line. These typical primate vocalizations have a fundamental and overtones blurred by much noise; that is, they are harsh noises, not clear calls. Note how the vocalizations grade into each other in the detailed series (*A*) and throughout nine agonistic vocalizations (*B*). (After T. E. Rowell, 1962; T. E. Rowell and R. A. Hinde, 1962; P. Marler and W. J. Hamilton, III, 1966.)

tone like a gibbon or an indri's wail or pulsed like the roar of colobus and howler. This may eliminate confusion due to distance or confusion between species. Epple shows that marmoset adult calls are more stereotyped than those of the young, and again argues that the adults must communicate at a distance, whereas the young are always in bodily contact (*cf.* Altmann, 1967; Marler 1965, 1968, 1969c; Winter, 1968).

SUMMARY

Any communicative act includes the signal, which is the transient form of the act, the sender's motivation, the meaning apparent to the receiver, and a long-term evolutionary function. These often do not relate in a simple one-to-one manner.

Communicative signals originated as by-products of single aspects of other behavior—in particular, autonomic changes, intention movements, and displacement behavior. During evolution, the signals may be "ritualized" to eliminate ambiguities by exaggeration, stereotypy, and repetition. There may also be external constraints on the form of the signals.

There are fundamental logical problems in choosing the size of a communicative unit to analyze. This matters in the time dimension: the animal determines meaning by integrating over an unknown amount of previous acts. It also matters in type: classifications by compound face differ from classifications by eyes or lip. Primate gestures and facial expressions grade into each other over a continuum; different species make different breaks in the continuum or center on different modal expressions. This is analogous to a linguist's problem in analyzing a foreign language—he cannot "objectively" determine what words are equivalent to each other; he has to ask a native speaker.

Quantitative analysis of animal communication, although promising, is in its infancy.

Status 10

DEFINITIONS: ANGER, INTERSPECIFIC CONFLICT, TERRITORIAL CONFLICT, AND STATUS

Anger, status, territoriality, and *predation* are four terms that often, wrongly, are lumped together. They are not even the same *kind* of word. Anger is an emotion, the other three are relations. Status and territoriality are intraspecific relationships and subject to quite different selective pressures than interspecific predatory relations.

This chapter is chiefly concerned with status, which is a set of long-term relationships among individuals who know each other. Although status is often connected with aggressive acts, the connection may be fairly remote in the history of either individual or species.

In ethology, agonistic situations are situations of conflict between conspecifics. We recognize agonistic situations, at one extreme,

Figure 77 A specialized threat gesture, the baboon yawn. (See Figures 62–70 for threat faces that occur throughout the primate line.) (Courtesy of S. Skulina.)

where animals actually damage each other and, at the other extreme, where one animal approaches and the other avoids. We learn to recognize ritualized antagonism in situations where the animals' gestures bear a close temporal relationship or a formal similarity to either physical conflict or approach–avoidance. The rhesus head-bobs in threat, in a clear intention movement of lunging. Conflict, as noted earlier, is often more difficult to recognize—for instance, Ellefson thought the morning display of male gibbons a sequence of joyous acrobatics until he saw one territorial male actually pursue and bite his rival (Ellefson, 1968). Similarly, the territorial "battles" of the sifaka seem like nothing at all to the unfamiliar observer—the troops leap toward or through each other in close formation, each side facing outward from its own territory. Only when one knows the animals is it clear what is relatively fast or slow movement, tight or loose grouping, and which animals belong to which territory.

Granted that we can recognize conflict situations, what is *anger* or feeling aggressive? It is emotion, motivation. We do, in fact, know what we mean by feeling aggressive ourselves. It seems to me perfectly legitimate to say that animals in many conflict situations also feel aggressive.

Aggression, in the sense of a propensity to intraspecific conflict, is common in the majority of vertebrate species. That is, most individuals of most species, brought up under most normal conditions and a variety of abnormal conditions, will show a range of agonistic behavior. In this sense, Lorenz' recent book, *On aggression,* is salutary precisely because it points out, and brings home, the fact that man as well has a strong tendency to aggressive behavior. This is not a return to the doctrine of original sin—original sin was an absolute, visited on all under all circumstances (Ashley Montagu, 1968). Aggressive behavior is a product of circumstances, and it is shaped in man or the swinging gibbon through evolution and through learning. A few rare tribes of men, the Arapesh, the Lepchas, the Congolese pygmies, do not hurt or kill their neighbors (Gorer, 1968). Having stated that aggression is at the innate end of our behavioral spectrum, one is then left with the interesting questions: in what situations does it appear, in what ways is it ritualized, what is its normal ontogeny? If the Arapesh are "abnormal," how could the rest of us learn to be abnormal like them?

The other three terms describe types of situations in which conflict behavior occurs.

Interspecific conflict, or competition and predation, is not usually classed with intraspecific conflict. It is related mainly because the weapons of predation—claws, canine teeth, hand axes—can be used on one's neighbors as well as on one's prey. There is no need to attribute angry feelings to the predator, tiger with sambhur or man shooting pigeon. Perhaps we are angry at a member of another species when it becomes competitor, not prey. It is not the target fowl or the squab on toast we hate, but the pigeon gobbling lettuce seedlings out of the back garden.

In *territorial conflict* aggressive behavior has a geographic aspect. Animals defend particular areas. This may result in a kind of community. Territorial animals typically recognize neighboring individuals and know how far they can go, in both literal and social senses. As discussed in Chapter 7, territorial defense has arisen over and over by convergent evolution in unrelated lines of primates as an adaptation to particular ecological niches, whereas even closely related species may differ in their territorial behavior. Territorial defense also shades into "status".

In troop-living primates, it is usually fairly easy to divide or "dominance" and "territorial" relations—neighboring troops space themselves out, and this spacing generally has some reference to geography, whereas members of the same troop move about close together and are therefore said to stand in a dominance relationship to each other. However, when animals change troop frequently, or troops join and divide, the distinction may become arbitrary or useless.

The idea of *status* or dominance has a checkered history. Schjelderup-Ebbe, who discovered the pecking-order of hens, enlarged his findings to a Teutonic theory of despotism in the structure of the universe. For instance, water eroding stone was "dominant" (Gartlan, 1968b). Schjelderup-Ebbe called animals' ranking "dominance," and many workers, with an "aha," recognized dominance hierarchies in many vertebrate groups.

Among the primates, dominance soon seemed even more baroque. Baboons and macaques mount each other in a gesture of assertion or present their rumps to be mounted as a gesture of submission (Maslow, 1936). Rarer variants are the stronger animal backing up to the weaker and forcing the weaker to mount, which happens among bonnet macaques (Simonds, 1965), or else juvenile males (playfully?) mounting adult males, as in hanuman langurs (Jay, 1965). This sexual gesture, transferred into threat-submission situations, combined with Zuckerman's (1932) description of zoo hamadryas baboons fighting to the death over females and the general influence of Freudian theory, all led to a view of aggressive dominance as a universal primate ranking, inseparably bound to sexual priorities. Of course, Carpenter's (1934 in 1964) howlers rarely threatened each other at all and mated promiscuously within the troop, but people then said New World primates might best be ignored.

At last, DeVore and Washburn (1960) pointed out that in a savanna baboon troop a recognized hierarchy stabilizes the society. Far from a continuous pecking down the line, the hierarchy makes it possible to avoid fights in most situations, for each animal knows the other's strength and respects his rights.

Finally, with much more analysis of differing species, dominance has been sorted out into component parts (Bernstein, 1964–1969; Gartlan, 1968b). It is perhaps better called "status" ranking or even "role playing," as the word "dominance" is so contaminated with the notion of a single rank-order established and maintained by threat.

FREQUENCY OF AGGRESSION: DIFFERING SPECIES

Threat behavior differs among species both in absolute frequency and in the form of the resulting hierarchies. Whereas it is clear that frequency differences are important, field techniques are such that one can only compare species by loose subjective categories—in Table 18 those of "none," "rare," "common."

Davis *et al.* (1968) have made an attempt to directly compare the frequency of aggressive behavior among species in the laboratory. They released adolescent animals into the center of a runway 9 feet by 1 foot by 2 feet high, with an animal of the same species

Text continues on page 178.

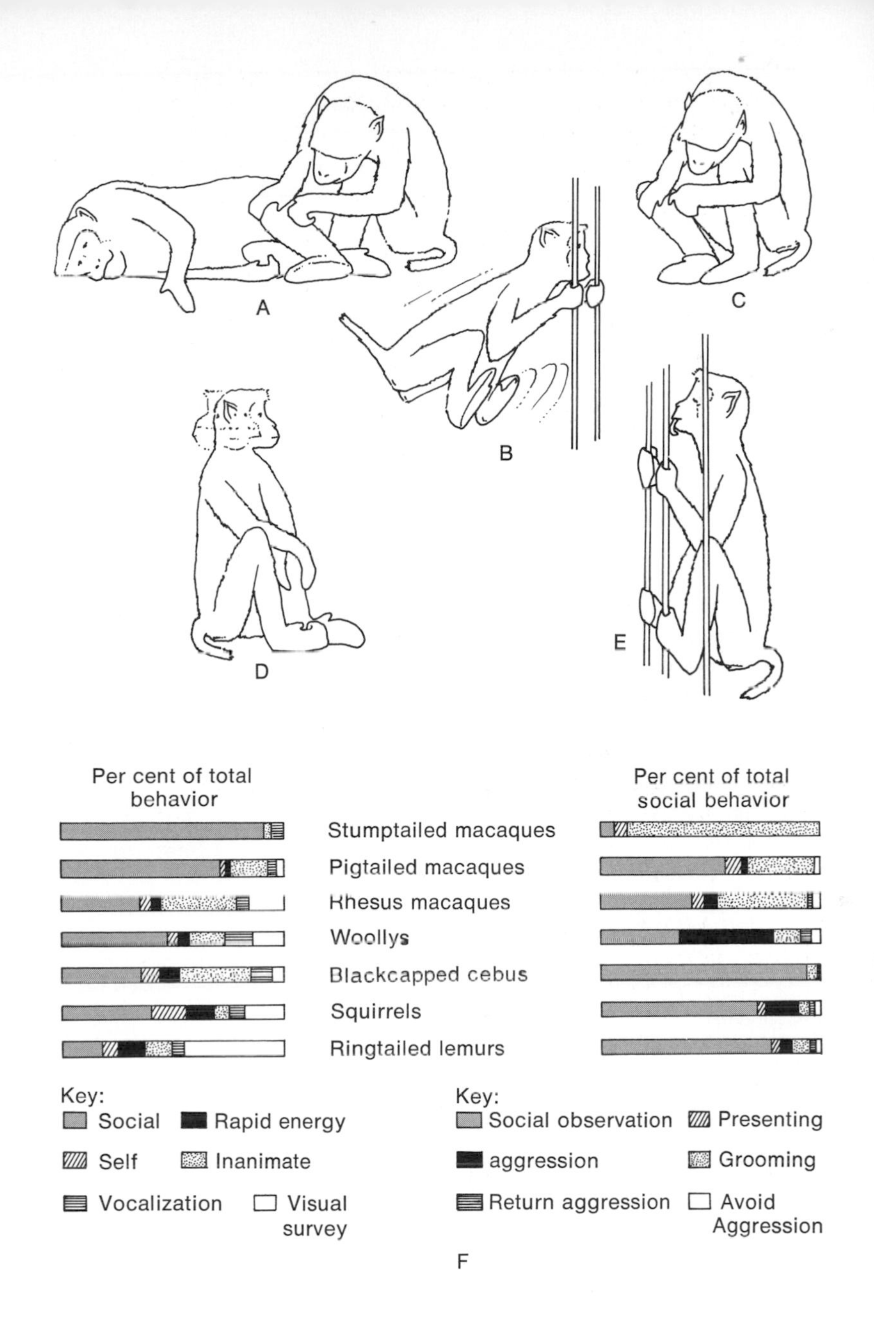

Figure 78 Species differences in gross behavior. Major categories of behavior included social behavior (*A*), rapid energy expenditure (*B*), self-directed behavior (*C*), visual survey (*D*), and inanimate object or cage manipulation (*E*). This study, in a standardized artificial environment, indicated major differences between species (*F*). Note that differences between macaque species were as great as those between unrelated genera or between macaque and lemur. (After R. T. Davis *et al.*, 1968.)

TABLE 18 MALE STATUS FUNCTIONS

Species	Priorities		Approach-Avoid		Agonistic	
	To food	To estrus females	♂ > ♂ stable	♂ > ♀♀	Fights	Threats
Grade B: Arboreal leaf-eaters						
Sifaka	–		–	–	Rare?	–
Howler	–	–	–	–	–	–
Nilgiri langur			+	+	–	Rare
Lutong langur		Harem	–	+	Rare	Rare
Black-and-white colobus			+	+	–	Rare
Grade C: Arboreal omnivores						
Dusky titi	–	Pair	–	–	–	Rare
Squirrel		–	–	Seasonal	Seasonal	Seasonal
Cebus		Often harem	–	+	–	Rare
Spider		Often harem		+		Rare
Lowe's guenon	Rare	Harem	+	–	–	Rare
Lar̂ gibbon	Rare, unstable	Pair	–	–	–	Rare
Grade D: Semiterrestrial leaf-eaters						
Hanuman langur, N India	+	+	+	+	–	Rare
S India	–	Often harem	+	+	+ With troop change	Common
Mountain gorilla	–	–	+	+	–	Rare

– means no ranking or not present.
\+ means clear ranking or commonly present.
Blank means no data.

Species	Troop Coordination				Opting Out			
	Intergroup challenge	Predator challenge	Stop aggression	Control movement	Spatial separation subordinates within troop	♂♂ troops	Solitary ♂♂	Exchange troops
Grade B: Arboreal leaf-eaters								
Sifaka	+	♂ + ♀	–	–	–	–	+	–
Howler	+	All ♂♂	All ♂♂	All ♂♂	–	–	+	
Nilgiri langur	+	–	–	–	–	+	+	
Lutong langúr	+	+	–	+	–			
Black-and-white colobus	+			–				
Grade C: Arboreal omnivores								
Dusky titi	+	♂ + ♀	–	–	–	–	–?	
Squirrel			–	–				
Cebus	+	+	+	–	–	–	–?	+?
Spider		–	Rare	–			+?	
Lowe's guenon	+	+	Rare	–	–	+?	+	–
Lar gibbon	+	+	–	–	–	–		
Grade D: Semiterrestrial leaf-eaters								
Hanuman langur, N India	–	+			–	+	+	
S India	+	+				+	+	– Exc. ♂ group
Mountain gorilla	±	+	+	+	–	+	+	+

TABLE 18 MALE STATUS FUNCTIONS (continued)

Species	Priorities		Approach-Avoid		Agonistic	
	To food	To estrus females	♂ > ♂ stable	♂ > ♀♀	Fights	Threats
Grade E: Semiterrestrial omnivores						
Ringtailed lemur	♀ > ♂	Unstable	+	–	Seasonal	Seasonal
Macaques, rhesus	+	+	+	+	+	+
Japanese	+	+	+	+	+	+
bonnet	+	+	+	+	+	+
crabeating	+	+	+	+	+	+
pigtailed			+	+	+	+
Savanna baboon, plains	+	+	+	+	+	+
forest		–	–	+	–	Rare
Vervet, plains	+	+	+	+	+	+
patchy forest						
Chimpanzee	+	–	+	+	–	Rare
Grade F: Arid-zone forms						
Hamadryas baboon	+	Harem or 2 ♂ team	+ Within team	+	Rare	+
Gelada		Harem		+		+
Patas	+	Harem	–	–	–	Rare

– means no ranking or not present.
+ means clear ranking or commonly present.
Blank means no data.

Species	Troop Coordination				Opting Out			
	Intergroup challenge	Predator challenge	Stop aggressicn	Control movement	Spatial separation subordinates within troop	♂♂ troops	Solitary ♂♂	Exchange troops
Grade E: Semiterrestrial omnivores								
Ringtailed lemur	–	♂ + ♀	–	–	+	–	–	
Macaques, rhesus	–	+	+	+	+	–		+
Japanese	Subaduet ♂?	+	+	+	+	–	+	
bonnet	All ♂?	+	+	+	–	–		
crabeating			+	+	–			
pigtailed		+	+				+	
Savanna baboon, plains	–	+	+	+	–	–	–	Rare
forest	–	–	+	–	–	–	–	+
Vervet, plains	+	–		–	+	–	–	+
patchy forest	+		+	–				
Chimpanzee	–	♂ + ♀	+	–	Fluid spacing			
Grade F: Arid-zone forms								
Hamadryas baboon	–		+	+	–	–	–	–
Gelada			+	+	–	+	–	
Patas	+	+	–	–	–	+	–	

in a carrying cage at either end and nothing to manipulate except the iron bars of the runway. They then scored visual survey, cage manipulation, social behavior, rapid energy expenditure, and self-directed behavior. Their results (Figure 78) were highly consistent, with five to nine individuals of six different primate species. In many measures, the scores of different species did not overlap at all, and in a majority the scores differed at the 5 per cent level. However unnatural the situation, it is a first attempt at standardized comparison.

The ringtailed lemur showed the lowest proportion of social behavior, and a large amount of this was only social observation. However, before jumping to phylogenetic conclusions, we should note that differences among the three species of macaque were as great as among the more distantly related primates. Stumptailed macaques were particularly affiliative, spending nearly all the time in social grooming.

What emerges most clearly is that each species has its own profile—its own quantitative preferences for various sorts of activities, at least in this very restricted situation.

Turning to field studies, can one make any generalizations about frequency of aggressive interaction? Two points seem to emerge from Table 18. First, the macaques and baboons, as a group, are by far the most aggressive. Macaques and baboons are adapted to semiterrestrial life in more open country than other primates. It has often been argued that man's aggressiveness is also related to life in the open. However, as there are data from only the one phylogenetic group, the case is hardly convincing. Forest-living baboons, the drills and mandrills, are only now being studied, and preliminary results indicate that they have similar group size and dispersion to their savanna cousins. The guenon–patas group, which also ranges from forest to savanna, tends to have a low level of intragroup aggression in either place, and so do chimpanzees. Although some differences in status hierarchy occur *within* species in differing ecologies (see following), it does not seem clear whether one can really attribute macaque–baboon aggression to savanna life.

Second, among forms with ritualized long-distance spacing behavior, the level of aggression is very low within the group. This is more convincing as such species occur in every line of primates: sifakas among the lemurs, titis and howlers in the New World, leaf monkeys in the Old World, and gibbons among the apes. Three of these forms are leaf eaters, and all live in smaller groups than other primates, or even in monogamous pairs. It is not clear whether one should argue that the *general* level of aggression is low in these animals because many of their ritualized battles seem perfectly calm to the naïve observer, or whether one should argue that the battles are highly aggressive and that they somehow "take it out on" their neighbors instead of behaving aggressively within the troop. The question is probably not useful to ask, because we can have little insight into the feelings of a langur or sifaka as he whoops or scent-marks. It is more useful to ask why we ask it. Many people

Figure 79 Ritual chest beating in the gorilla is a gesture of either threat or generalized excitement; it occurs in no other primates. Note adaptation of the fingers for knuckle walking. (Courtesy of D. Sorby.)

do, in fact, still often think of aggression as a unitary drive—a fixed quantity of energy that could somehow be channeled into either territorial display or intratroop bickering—whereas the whole effort of this book is to show how each species' pattern of behavior is complexly adapted to its own particular pattern of life. Indian rhesus macaques are probably aggressive toward either troop members or troop neighbors with the same feelings, as they literally act the same way toward both, with the same threat gestures and expressions. But one can hardly conclude that the leaping, great-calling gibbon, displaying in a tree top at his male neighbor, is aggressive in anything like the same sense as when he glances at his mate and reaches first for a fig—his feelings quite likely differ not only in intensity but also in kind.

FREQUENCY OF AGGRESSION: DIFFERING ENVIRONMENTS

Even within a species, the quantity and kind of aggression vary enormously with circumstances. These can be considered under two headings: changes under experimental manipulation and differences among wild populations in different habitats.

The most naturalistic experiment on primate aggression has been that of Southwick (1967), who caged a group of rhesus monkeys as large as many wild troops: three males, fourteen females, and ten juveniles. The animals were released into a cage 40 by 30 feet and allowed 15 weeks to settle down to a steady level of aggressive encounters. Of course, this could never really approximate a natural troop whose relationships had been built up over a lifetime, but as with humans put in prison or the random encounters of a holiday camp, a fairly constant social structure emerged rapidly. After this initial baseline period, the group was subjected to various stresses.

Far and away the most extreme procedure was the introduction of strange rhesus the group had not known before. The group attacked the strangers. Interestingly, group members were most aggressive toward strangers of their own sex and age—males fought males, females fought females, young fought juveniles (*cf.* Bernstein, 1969b). Two juveniles, two males, and four females were introduced, two at a time. The level of agonistic behavior dropped in each case by the third day, but two of the females had been badly bitten and had not eaten in 3 days, so that the experimenters had to nurse them back to health.

Other experiments varied the amount and distribution of food. When all food was concentrated in one place, the number of threats rose—such as happens at any winter bird table. However, when the quantity was simply cut by half, the threats decreased, as did all social interaction. The starving animals moved about in apathetic lethargy. In fact, this parallels reports from prison camps and a Wisconsin experiment on starving humans. The hierarchy really did determine priority to food. Dominant animals ate their fill, much as usual. After 5 days of half rations, the two lowest-ranking subadults almost died from starvation and had to be removed and hand-fed to save them. Southwick's results are confirmed by a study of provisionized rhesus macaques in Cayo Santiago Island, when a monkey chow shipment was 3 weeks delayed. Not only fighting but all social behavior lessened dramatically while the monkeys foraged for natural food (Loy, 1970).

However, changing the environment had little effect: either scattering rice to be hand-picked from the dust, introducing a paddling pool for play, or erecting a partition nearly across the cage. But reducing total cage space by half resulted in a highly significant rise in aggressive acts.

Other experiments have tested different variables. For example,

Plotnik *et al.* (1968) tried squirrel and cebus monkeys in a competition situation, wherein the group had to pass one at a time through a narrow tunnel either to obtain food or to avoid shock. In both cases and both species, the frequency of aggression rose. Plotnik *et al.* pointed out that in contrast to Bernstein's (1965) study of cebus in a large open cage, their study clearly identified a boss cebus with priority to everything, although the rest of the hierarchy was unstable. They finished with the important point: "It appears there is a continuum of aggressive behavior [in different circumstances]. The kind of aggressive pattern observed depends on what part of the continuum is selected for measurement."

This is clear in the study of wild populations as well. Many of the formative ideas of primatology have come from the study of savanna baboons in the harsh conditions of thorn savanna. Rowell (1966a) observed baboons living in riverine gallery forest. Although they foraged during part of the day in adjacent grassland, the troops could retreat for safety to the trees and found most of their food among the lush, if bitter, fruits of the forest. The adult males formed a coherent cohort, constantly aware of each other's movements—but with scarcely any aggressive interactions.

Among vervets on Lolui Island in Lake Victoria, males changed troops fairly frequently. One of the most consistent roles of the adult males was loud "territorial" or "spacing" vocalization at neighboring troops. There, it seemed unreasonable to talk of a hierarchy within the troops—much better to calculate the frequency with which each animal gave certain threats and gestures, such as the spacing call, characteristic of adult males (Gartlan, 1968a). In savanna, however, there was a perfectly clear-cut threat hierarchy among troop males and less frequent, unritualized bickering among all the members of adjoining troops (Struhsaker, 1967a).

The most dramatic case is the hanuman langurs. In the troop Jay (1965) watched in Central India, six males lived in perfect harmony, rankable only by the slightest gestures. When the beta male became alpha, he marked the change by whooping at the far end of the grove. In Sugiyama's crowded South India population, all-male bands attacked and fought the harem males for possession of harems, then fought each other, exiling the weakest of the male band as well as male juveniles and children of the harem.

In Sugiyama's (1964, 1965a, 1965b, 1966) case, there is perhaps the clearest sexual selection for male dominance. The new harem leader gained exclusive right to his females. Then he commonly bit young infants after the takeover. Their mothers hung them on a branch to die and came into estrus, ensuring an even higher proportion of the new lord's children. One of the few parallels in other mammals is the Bruce effect in mice. Pregnant female mice exposed to the presence or even the odor of a strange male abort their litter and come promptly into estrus. Slater (personal communication) suggests that this may conceivably be of advantage to the female as well as the male, if it reduces inbeeeding. It might also be of advantage if the male mouse or langur tends to be antagonistic to a female he has not mated, to such an extent that she would be likely to lose her infant or litter anyway, after putting still more time or effort into it. Some such advantage to the female might at least make it more understandable in mice, where the female's own physiology must play some role in the abortion (Parkes and Bruce, 1961).

A final, less gruesome, but still more important example is the town-living rhesus monkeys of India. Singh (1968) paired urban rhesus monkeys with their counterparts from forest habitats. The town monkeys were far more aggressive than the rural ones, both among each other and toward the strange forest monkeys.

Thus, any description of "the" level of aggression in a primate individual or species must specify which level in which circumstances.

MEASURES OF STATUS

Status may be measured first by an animal's priority to a desired object, usually either food or sex. This, after all, is the selective advantage to the individual of being dominant: to survive when resources are limited and to have a high percentage of offspring.

However, such priorities are only one dimension of status. A second criterion is frequency of threats—of conflict situations and who won them. Measuring threats as such tends to emphasize the role of the argumentative animal; furthermore, different threat gestures are not perfectly correlated with each other. A more telling category is "approach-retreat" situations (Rowell, 1966b; Eisenberg and Kuehn, 1966). Rowell points out that it is really the subordinate's reaction that shows whether the situation contains potential conflict. If one animal just walks toward another, this means little. The second may stay put and groom the first, making it a friendly interaction, or the second may choose to step aside or run away, thus defining a status interaction. Eisenberg and Kuehn (1966), studying captive spider monkeys, arrived at different rank orders in the two calculations of per cent of times an animal retreated and per cent of times the animal was retreated from. This complexity is not confined to primates. For instance, Baenniger (1968) found no correlation in rats between priority to food or water and spontaneous threats, and even chickens have no single, simple pecking order if given space to express themselves (McBride *et al.*, 1969). Presumably, the threats, or prevalence and stability of approach–avoidance situations, have evolved away from the original priorities. Instead of fighting for food or mates, social animals have evolved ritualized means of self-assertion and self-abasement. Instead of even self-assertion in each new situation, they have become capable of recognizing their station in life and have evolved self-assurance and deference.

Figure 80 A male chimpanzee charges the photographer in aggressive display. He brandishes a branch in his left hand (photographic detail of this is blurred by the speed of the arm's movement). (Courtesy of H. van Lawick.)

OTHER ROLES OF THE DOMINANT

Males of nearly every primate species protect the troop. They threaten predators, particularly predators holding or approaching an infant. This is true even in species whose males do not pay much other attention to infants. Bernstein (1966b), in a series of tests with a confined troop of pigtailed macaques, showed that the males differentiated between their own troop members and other monkeys. They attacked an experimenter who held a member of their own troop, but if another monkey was held, in the same circumstances, they sometimes attacked the strange monkey instead. Male defense is not universal. Among Rowell's forest baboons, the males galumphed fastest to the trees. Spider monkey males are often not with the troop, and lemur and sifaka females mob as energetically as their consorts. However, in general where there is real defense it is the function of males, and particularly of the dominant males in the internal threat hierarchy.

Territorial defense against other troops is also frequently a male role and in many species particularly that of the dominant male.

Another common pattern is stopping fights among other members of the troop, even literally punishing one or both of the combatants. This appears in many species and is consistently directed down the threat hierarchy, never up (Rowell, 1966b; Tokuda and Jensen, 1968).

Leading the troop in geographic movements is often harder to analyze. It certainly occurs in many distantly related species. In macaques and langurs the alpha male stalks off first. In gorillas, however, the troop ambles off amoebically (Schaller, 1963). If the main silverback male comes along, the troop makes progress, if not, they all subside again. One male of the fifty to one-hundred talapoins in a troop, scattered green and invisible through the obscuring forest, gives a "leader call"—and the others move accordingly (Gautier-Hion, 1970). A gorilla troop changed its range when a new male took control (Fossey, 1970), and the Japanese monkeys of the Takasakiyama troop abruptly changed their ranging times when Titan took over from Jupiter (Itani, 1963b; Mizuhara, 1964).

In this last case, there is a suggestion of more subtle influences. The provisionized Takasakiyama troop contained five-hundred animals at the time, with twenty-four leading males. They all recognized a single male hierarchy, with Jupiter as alpha—an animal Itani called "violent to the point of cruelty." However, Jupiter weakened and died, and Titan took his place. With the gentler Titan in control, the whole troop became more gregarious, with much closer spacing and more frequent contact among animals. Although other factors might have operated as well, it is possible that here the personality of the leader affected the whole level of social interaction within the troop.

TROOP HIERARCHIES

As Table 18 shows, there are among the primates all possible variations of dominance hierarchies. The sharing of food, and priority to it, may be accomplished only by territorial behavior among groups, with no priorities inside the group. There may be no priority to females. Group structure itself differs widely—the boss of a harem certainly has sexual priority to his females, but by the system of keeping all other males at a distance, not living in continuous rank order with them.

Three groups of examples can illustrate some of the possible variants: the squirrel monkey and ringtailed lemur; the macaques and baboons; and the chimpanzee. The first two are examples of extreme dissociation of measures of dominance. The second two approximate classic single hierarchies, but even here the measures do not correlate perfectly, and there are the added complications of coalitions and respect. The chimpanzee, finally, introduces new factors of display suggesting the multicriterion status roles of human beings.

1. Noncorrelated: Squirrel monkey and ringtailed lemur

Ringtailed lemur males had a clear-cut rank order of threats and supplanting, reinforced by glance and posture: dominant males swaggered, subordinates cringed. Females took little part in the threats. Although they occasionally threatened or supplanted each other, it seemed more a hasty impulse than the continuous male posturing. (There were too few observations to be sure if the females had a stable rank order. In fact, all these remarks are based on a single troop in a single season.) However, females were dominant over males, both in threats and in priority for food. Females at times bounced up to the dominant male and snatched a tamarind pod from his hand, cuffing him over the ear in the process. When females came into estrus, mating was not determined by the established threat hierarchy. Instead, males fought around the females, slashing with their canines, and in three of four observed cases one subordinate won the battle. However, after mating he resumed his former low rank. These lemurs are an extreme example, but they show that it is possible for the different criteria of rank to be almost completely dissociated (Jolly, 1966a).

In "Monkey Jungle" of Miami and quite likely in its native jungles as well, squirrel monkeys' behavior is equally offbeat (Baldwin, 1968). In the birth season, males were thin and apathetic, interacting little with anyone. They often traveled near each other, but if they approached too close to the hundred-strong group of females and young, the females threatened and chased them away. Even the youngsters threatened them, peeping and thigh spreading, or, if male, displaying the squirrel monkey threat of erect penis.

Figure 81 A squirrel monkey male, Scar Eye, who intermittently led the threat hierarchy in the Monkey Jungle troop. *Top:* With "fatted" shoulders during the mating season. *Bottom:* Six months later, with thin shoulders and forearms, in nonbreeding condition. (Courtesy of F. V. DuMond, Monkey Jungle, Miami, Florida.)

In the mating season, all changed: the squirrel monkey males grew fat about the shoulders, which is related to seasonal spermatogenesis. They developed a rigid hierarchy of penile display and urinating toward each other's faces, which could turn into a "pile-up" of all four males displaying at each other and landing physically on top of each other. The pile-ups might, in turn, lead to violent

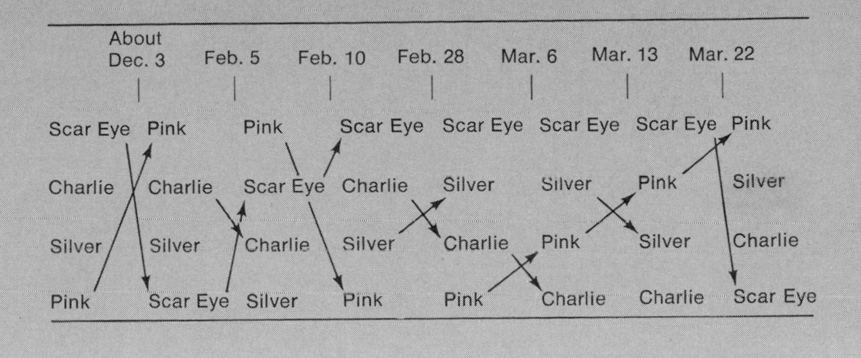

Figure 82 Rank changes in squirrel monkeys. The ascending arrows indicate successful dominance challenges that led to changes in the hierarchy; descending arrows indicate the loss of status of the deposed animals. Males were often demoted after damaging fights. This fight-and-threat hierarchy was not correlated with mating success or with the males' generally apathetic behavior outside the mating season. (After J. D. Baldwin, 1968.)

fights, which not only reversed the threat order but damaged the current alpha so badly that he had to rest for several days at the bottom of the hierarchy (Figure 82).

The threat hierarchy, in turn, bore no relation to mating success. The males were attracted to smell even nonreceptive females, and females were attracted to pile-ups, so Baldwin speculates that the males' excitement helped bring the females into mating condition. (Communicated excitement and scent may similarly synchronize the mating season in lemurs.) However, all the observed matings were by Charlie and Silver, neither of whom were ever alpha male. The two contenders for alpha male became so excited and aggressive that they roused the female to aggressive, not sexual, behavior and attracted female "hecklers" who chased them away. (Ringtail females occasionally leap on a mating pair as well.)

It is possible that the squirrel monkeys behaved abnormally in their tourist-populated "Monkey Jungle." However, the parallels with wild lemurs suggest that there is good evolutionary reason for this dissociation of aspects of status, although very difficult to know what the reasons may be.

2. Well correlated: Macaques and baboons

Macaques and savanna baboons approximate the original conception of dominance. They have well-defined, stable rankings, in which all the measures of status correlate moderately well and in which frequent threats underline the importance of status in social life. Most troops have a linear hierarchy of males, males dominant over females, and a clear hierarchy of females as well.

Above all, priority for food is nearly the same as priority for

Figure 83 Hamadryas baboon male threatens another with open mouth and canines displayed. The second male head-flags, looking aside and presenting the side of his neck to the aggressor. Seeing the dispute, the females of each harem line up behind their harem leader. Although this is obviously a conflict situation, what occurs is not one animal's hurting another but ritualized gestures of attack and submission. (From H. Kummer, 1968.)

females at the height of estrus and is the same as the direction of most threats. However, Conaway and Koford (1969) have thrown doubt on the effectiveness of sexual priority, even in macaques. Subdominant males, mating with a female before she reaches peak estrus, may actually father her children. However, with finer analysis, the measures are not perfectly consistent even here. Rowell (1966b) shows that different threat gestures vary in their use down the hierarchy within a captive group of savanna baboons.

Bernstein (1969b) has directly compared the threat hierarchy and the feeding priorities of a group of pigtailed macaques. There was close correlation between the threat hierarchy and success in obtaining grapes from a chute that delivered grapes one at a time into the compound. However, feeding ranks in other situations with restricted access

> may be assumed to favor bold juveniles who rush in, snatch a piece of food and flee; females enjoying the toleration of high ranking males, and the more highly food-motivated animals . . . . Whereas feeding order is certainly related to dominance, it is not a direct measure of it. The use of a feeding order to indicate rank may lead one to believe that female ranks change with the estrus cycle, since estrus females are tol-

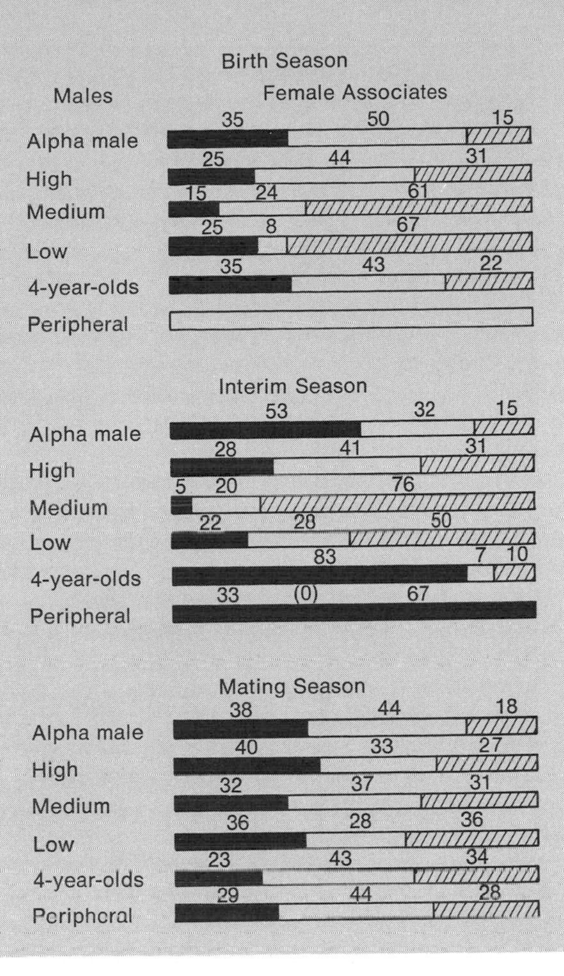

Figure 84 Male and female hierarchies and social relations of free-ranging rhesus. These data are for the tattooed troop of rhesus on Cayo Santiago, where identification and sampling can be reasonably complete. Each bar represents 100 per cent of adult female associates for that season of the males in a given rank group. High-ranking females are given on the left, medium-ranking females in the center, and low-ranking females on the right. High-ranking females tended to associate more with high-ranking males during the birth and interim seasons, and low-ranking males associated with low-ranking females. In the mating season, high-ranking males associated with females at peak estrus, and class differences disappeared. (After J. H. Kaufmann, 1967.)

erated by dominant males. Furthermore, since estrus females may be more active in aggressive encounters, they may also appear to have improved their dominance position, if aggressive frequency scores are used. An analysis of dyadic interactions, however, failed to show any reversals in the matrix in terms of which animals the female aggressed against and submitted to and therefore the female's dominance rank was assumed to be unchanged despite her more frequent involvement in agonistic episodes. (Bernstein, 1969b, p. 455)

3. Coalitions and respect

Some macaques and baboons form coalitions, which greatly affect the balance of power. A savanna baboon troop watched by DeVore (Hall and DeVore, 1965) had an alpha male and a beta male as the "central hierarchy." One was very old, with worn-down canines, the other younger. The old male disappeared; the gamma male formed a new coalition with an outsider from the next troop and took over. Similarly, Southwick's temple-living rhesus troop formed

Figure 85 A tense moment between gorillas. The younger gorilla play-bites the older one while the older one seems to be moving from a play face to an aggressive expression. These two caged males live together without real fighting. (San Diego Zoo Photo by Ron Garrison.)

two subgroups: the two leading males of one subgroup were collectively superior but individually subordinate to the male of the other.

In Bernstein's caged pigtails, there was a dramatic shift of rule where a rising young male took over the group. He fought the alpha male, whose wounds became infected so that he died 3 weeks later. The young male remained subordinate to the previous beta for 2 months more, when he fought and defeated the beta, killed the highest-ranking female, and at last became alpha himself. During the following few days there were many minor fights among group members, but essentially the new alpha and his alliance had replaced the survivors of the old ruling alliance.

Again, the violence of fighting and the closeness of the coalitions presumably reflect the smallness and bareness of the enclosure: "As soon as an encounter began, participants could be seen visually checking the location of other group members, and larger animals fled smaller ones long before supporters arrived on the scene." But there is ample evidence for similar coalitions in the wild.

Respect for older animals, or perhaps just a habit of giving way to them, is also a crucial factor. Bernstein's beaten alpha male maintained his status until a few days before his death—in spite of having previously lost one eye and broken three of his four canines. According prerogatives to aged animals has been seen in Japanese macaques, savanna baboons, hamadryas baboons, chimpanzees, and gorillas. In one small wild rhesus troop, the alpha male was wounded by a villager. The troop remained in a tiny portion of their range with the incapacitated leader until he died, then resumed their former habits (Southwick and Siddiqi, 1967). In a free-ranging troop, it may be an advantage to keep an experienced leader, even if he is not physically the strongest animal, thus the evolution of habitual respect (Rowell, 1969). Furthermore, the disruption of changing leader, with its attendant troop instability, can be avoided for as long as possible.

4. Chimpanzees

Chimpanzees, although they move in shifting, fluid bands, still have an obvious status hierarchy. However, the hierarchy, in the ordinary way, is little expressed. Males hoot with excitement, but they also reassure each other with a pat on the shoulders or the groin. Females may be timid, but a ritual touching of hands and kissing bids them into the group. Systematic provisioning with bananas in closed boxes has drastically raised the observed levels of chimpanzee aggression. However, what impresses one is not so much the hierarchy as the vast number of greeting gestures, reassurance gestures, and appeasing-begging gestures among chimpanzees.

Reynolds and Luscombe (1969) have quantified status interactions among the Holloman Air Force Base chimpanzees. The colony is a concrete-moated island in the Arizona desert, filled with overcrowded, underamused leftovers of space-research experiments, many of them plainly psychotic (Kollar *et al.*, 1968). Thus, the results seem plausible only because they confirm what one already suspected is true of wild chimpanzees.

Reynolds and Luscombe found that priority to food did not correlate with quantity of aggressive behavior. However, food priority did correlate with "popularity," as measured by the amount of grooming animals received: not only the dominant male was popular but also the very young infants and juveniles. Grooming, in turn, correlated with the big males' displays: jumping about bipedally with bristling hair, then running to drum or jump on some resonant object: in the wild, a buttress of a rainforest tree. At its highest, Jane Van Lawick-Goodall describes male chimpanzees rushing downhill flailing trees and hooting in the rain dance.

Reynolds concludes, following a hypothesis of Chance, that at least in chimpanzees the structure of attention is a more relevant measure than the structure of aggression.

ATTENTION STRUCTURE

Chance and Clifford Jolly (1970) have proposed a major theory of the evolution of status hierarchies and social groups. They consider only terrestrial primates: the patas, the hanuman langur, rhesus and bonnet macaques, savanna and hamadryas baboons, and the chimpanzee.

They propose a fundamental distinction in the structure of attention between *acentric* social groups and *centripetal* social groups.

The patas is their type of acentric species. In moments of crisis the females save themselves, while the male bounces about on a bush, diverting the predator. Thus, the females' attention is directed away from the male, and the troop loses coherence. Further, the male's dominant position is hardly secure: females may gang up to threaten him.

The contrast is the macaque–baboon form, where in any excitement or threat from a troop member or from a predator subordinates turn toward more dominant animals. Thus, the high-ranking male or males provide a constant center for attention.

A more democratic form of centripetal structure is exemplified by the chimpanzee. Again, attention is directed toward the dominant male, but often in a "hedonic mode" of dancing, banging display, and friendly association.

This seems an immense contribution, in that it rephrases the whole of status, and much of the rest of social structure, in terms of direction of attention.

However, one immediately wants to add weakening qualifications, "more-or-less" clauses to their major categories.

For instance, predator defense versus acentric troop flight from predators depends on the situation: plains baboons are more likely to try defense than are other species, but this is only a fairly weak statistical probability, whereas the most effective defense seen yet, the males pursuing a jackal and making it drop a monkey infant, was actually made by the type "acentric" species, the patas.

The hedonic mode, i.e., predominant direction of grooming, seems separable from the threat hierarchy in rhesus (Chance and Jolly, 1970) and in pigtails, crabeaters, Celebes black apes, sooty mangabeys, gelada baboons, and green (vervet) monkeys (Bernstein, (1968b). Thus, the "hedonic mode" of organization of chimpanzees

Figure 86 Human aggression. Although human beings do fight and kill each other, most aggression, as in other primates, is mediated by gestures of threat and submission. (Courtesy of N. Blurton-Jones.)

seems to be widespread and independently determined from the agonistic mode, even in apparently dictatorial species groups.

These may seem cavils—but when the hard edges of the categories have been blurred by enough statistical qualifications and attention structure has been analyzed as such, it seems likely that the categories themselves may crumble.

Chance and Jolly conclude that the directing of attention toward adult males as leaders and protectors has been passed from a prehuman ancestor to human beings—hence, in times of stress, we blindly follow charismatic leaders. But they conclude that we can at least choose our mode of response. We can respond to those who threaten us themselves and encourage us to redirect our fear at other races or nations—that is, the dictators and war mongers. Or we can respond in the hedonic mode, to those with the loudest display who can attract most grooming. Pop drummers may seem then the best hope of mankind, as well as perpetuating the best of the social structure of the chimpanzee.

SUMMARY

Anger, status seeking, territoriality, and predation are too often lumped together as "aggressive." Predation by one species on another is quite different from relations within species. Anger is an emotion, the others are relations, and ritualized and codified within society. Conflict behavior varies widely in both frequency and kind in different species. In comparisons of primate species, status threats within the troop seem inversely correlated with territorial threats, although it is not clear what this means in terms of motivation. Troops of the same species in different environments differ in conflict frequency: in general, the harsher the environment, the more threats, although real starvation leads to social apathy. Artificial crowding (including crowding at the food supply) can lead to violence; strange conspecifics may also be violently attacked.

Status may be measured by priority for mates, priority for food, direction of threats, approach–retreat behavior, and other roles in the group such as protection against outside threat. The different measures of status may correlate fairly well, as in macaques and baboons, or have practically no relation, as apparently in squirrel monkeys and ringtailed lemurs. They are complicated by coalitions (or friendship) among animals, and respect for aging leaders.

Chance and Clifford Jolly suggest studying "attention structure" in the group rather than starting with the "status" of individuals. Status based on threat does not correlate perfectly with grooming attention or with status based on display; it also relates to different troop reactions to predators. "Attention structure" is useful if only because it focuses on the group as a whole.

Primate status roles do not exist except in the social group and can usually be seen as benefiting the group, not the unbridled aggressor.

Affiliation and Sex

11

Structure of attention channeled through the status hierarchy accounts for much of the formal structure of primate troops. Status formalizes aggression, makes it possible for animals to live in close contact, and organizes the roles in the troop to mutual advantage.

However, this does not really account for the unifying of the troop: the fundamental attractiveness of primates to each other.

Sir Solly Zuckerman (1932) suggested, nearly 40 years ago, with immense influence, that year-round sex was the underlying primate bond: the ever-willing female attracted the ever eager male to remain with her throughout their adult lives. A mass of subsequent research has shown that Zuckerman was wrong about the nonhuman primates, although right by all the data available at the time. It now seems that many higher primates breed seasonally; individual females may be willing to mate for only about 2 weeks out of 2 years.

However, he was more nearly right about man. We are indeed the sexiest of primates, mating at any season, at any stage of the menstrual cycle, and even in advanced pregnancy. Clearly, sex is one of the major bonds linking our own social unit: the married pair or polygamous family, which in primates would be called a harem (Morris, 1967).

This chapter will first consider grooming and contact: behavior that is probably derived from mother-infant care but that is one of the major affiliative bonds in primates and reflects the social relations of status, sex, and friendship. Next it turns to group structure—the temporal associations of adult males and females—then breeding seasons and courtship and mating patterns among primates. Finally, it speculates about the origin of the human family.

GROOMING

Most mammals groom each other. At the very least, a mother licks her newborn infants.

Primates, however, have developed grooming to a fine art, parting each other's fur with their fingers and extracting tiny grains of scurf with fingers, lips, or teeth. Primates have evolved specialized adaptations for grooming each other. The toothcomb of lemurs and lorisoids is formed of their lower canines and incisors, flattened, forward-pointing, arranged for fur scraping. It is quite possible that the saltiness of our sweat is evolved to reward the diligent groomer with crumbs of salt!

Grooming has probably evolved directly from mother-infant behavior, as have associated pleasure gestures such as lip smacking (Anthoney, 1968). In adults, however, one can only say it represents friendship, reassurance—although we see as well the mother-infant emotions of trust, dependence, solicitude.

However, levels and uses of grooming vary enormously among species. Many New World monkeys manage to remain as a mated pair or social group with little or no grooming, except as a prelude to copulation. Then one is forced back to some tautology, such as that primates stay together because they like to, as "the" affiliative bond.

In the Old World monkeys and lemurs, however, bouts of grooming clearly reflect the daily events and relationships: which females are friends with which, which males prefer which females, or which tiffs can be smoothed over.

In many cases, grooming reflects rank order: male baboons or rhesus loll in front of a female, who is expected to groom them adoringly. The males groom back, but for much less time than the female. When the female is in estrus, the male grooms her far more attentively. Conversely, when a new male thicktailed bushbaby was introduced to a social group, the resident male approached repeatedly, urine-marked in front of him, and forced the stranger to submit to being groomed.

Figure 87 Black lemurs groom using their specialized toothcomb. (Courtesy of J. Buettner-Janusch.)

Among bonnet macaques, however, males groom as much as females, males groom each other, and there seems no relation at all to dominance status. Again, then, differences among macaque species are as great as among many genera (Simonds, 1965).

Therefore, grooming can be one of the most important indexes of the structure of attention within the troop.

Figure 88 Savanna baboons groom using their hands to pick over their fur. (San Diego Zoo Photo by Ron Garrison.)

SEX AND SOCIAL STRUCTURE

In Part I we saw some of the factors that lead or allow primates to be gregarious animals. There are many ways to be gregarious, however. In the commonest primate system, males group with females for long periods. It could be reasonably said that the commonest ungulate social group is a nursery herd of females and their offspring. Males, as they mature, leave their mothers or are driven away by the older males. Thereafter, they form various sorts of mating relations, often involving only temporary association with any female or group of females. The relation may be "driving" an estrus cow during the rut, herding a harem for the rutting season, or establishing a breeding territory into which willing females may come. Each of these patterns has appeared independently in major phylogenetic lines.

Of course, one must put in a word of caution about considering any pattern "typical." Primates, and ungulates, include species that exhibit every possible social structure, from solitariness through very casual association through tightly knit multimale troops. For instance, peccaries run in multimale troops much like baboons, whereas spider and squirrel monkey males are semi-independent of the female group. Among Lowe's guenons, subadult males seem to leave the harem, although the dominant male does not drive them out (Bourlière *et al.*, 1970). Eisenberg (1966), who has done the major survey of mammalian societies, prefers to emphasize the similarities among different orders of mammals and the fact that one can draw no hard and fast phylogenetic distinctions in behavior.

It is only the bulk of research that makes it seem that artiodactyl males are more usually in an extraneous relation to the coherent group of females and young, whereas, among the primates, males of many species are incorporated within a group throughout their lives.

I can see no obvious environmental reason for this difference. Perhaps it is a phylogenetic "accident," some legacy of the ur-ungulate and ur-primate ancestors. However, the male presence affects much of primate life, both in relations between the sexes and in the upbringing of the young.

SEASONS

Many or most primates have a breeding season. For much of the year no females are in estrus, whereas for a period on the order of 3 to 4 months in many species females come into estrus. In many monkeys a female breeds only every other year, unless she loses her baby. As Lancaster and Lee (1965) point out in their review, a great deal of data is necessary to distinguish between a *season* of births, in which breeding is strictly confined to one part of the year, a *peak* of births, in which the majority of births are clustered in a few months but others occur throughout the year, and *random* distribution throughout the year. Much more evidence is needed to distinguish between a slight birth peak and truly random distribution than is needed to note a sharp birth season.

It is clear that true seasonality exists in guenons, langurs, macaques, savanna and hamadryas baboons (and geladas), malagasy lemurs, and most lorisoids. It seems established that howlers among the New World monkeys have either random distribution of infants or only a very slight peak, and births may be random among chimpanzees as well.

Seasonality depends very strikingly on external conditions. Rhesus monkeys or bushbaby species in the laboratory may breed throughout the year, with estrus cycles following each other without interruption, just as in humans (Manley, 1966). In the wild, both breed seasonally, with several months' anestrus. There is even some evidence that both greater and senegal bushbabies have two breeding seasons per year at the equator, whereas the more southern species breed once a year—but often have twins. There is clearly much lability in individuals taken from wild to captive conditions, and quite probably selective divergences among populations (Butler, 1967). Petter-Rousseaux (1968) shows that the widely divergent birth seasons of lemur species are understandable as the young of each species are *weaned* during the wet season when there is abundant food.

There has been little work on the external causes of seasonal breeding in primates. By analogy with other vertebrates, the changes in day length probably play a role, and this is certainly true in mouse lemurs (Petter-Rousseaux, 1969). It is possible that other clues, such as temperature, are also effective. It seems likely that, in the highly synchronized mating of ringtailed lemurs and of squirrel monkeys, social communication plays an important part in bringing all the animals into estrus at once—their frantic scent markings may serve as sexual pheromones (Jolly, 1966a; Baldwin, 1968; Evans and Goy, 1968).

Humans, as well, have very slight seasonal differences in birth frequency. Cowgill (1966) has reviewed census data from many countries and historical data from baptismal records. In Europe more conceptions tend to occur in spring and early summer—May, June, July, with a minor peak around the festivities of Christmas. In the Southern Hemisphere the major peak occurs in October–November, blurring into Christmas. The United States resembles the south, with most conceptions in October–December. It may just be that most people except Americans exuberantly make love in spring—but any simple hypothesis can be confused by the case of Puerto Rico, which switched between 1940 and 1960 from the European pattern to the American one!

COURTSHIP AND MATING

Having duly laid emphasis on the point that most male–female bonding is not directly sexual, if only because the females of most primates are unlikely to be in estrus for as much as 20 weeks of a 20-year life span, how do primates court and copulate?

Female primates, like many other mammals, have a repeating estrus cycle of 20 to 35 days interval. At the time of ovulation conception is possible, and the vagina is maximally prepared to receive the fertilized ovum. If the ovum is not fertilized, the vaginal wall breaks down or decreases in complexity until the beginning of the following cycle. Ovulation does not usually take place all year, but instead females may have three or four cycles, then cease to ovulate for the remainder of the year. (This is called being *seasonally polyestrus.*)

The Old World monkeys and great apes menstruate, although

Figure 89 The vervet male has a bright red penis and blue scrotum that show against his gray and white fur in nearly any position he adopts. (Courtesy of M. D. Rose.)

Figure 90 The gorilla shows maleness in his heavy build and high skull crest. (Courtesy of Zoological Society of London.)

there is very little flow of blood in guenons. New World monkeys have a microscopically visible menstruation. Rowell (1963a) suggests that because there are far more striking changes in the behavior of rhesus macaques when a female is menstruating than when she is ovulating, their cycle should be properly called a menstrual cycle. In contrast, baboons and pigtailed macaques change much more clearly during the estrus phase (Tokuda, Simons, and Jensen, 1968).

Females possess various ways of signaling approaching estrus. Baboons, pigtailed macaques, mangabeys, and talapoins have prominent sexual swellings, as do chimpanzees, when the vaginal lips puff out and turn pink. At least in genus *Lemur,* and possibly other malagasy lemurs as well, the vagina opens, flushing bright pink, at estrus. In bushbabies, the vagina opens and flushes at estrus, but closes completely between estrus periods, with the skin joining over the opening. The size of vaginal swelling differs in different conditions: wild ringtails swell more than those in cages, whereas caged savanna baboons swell more than wild ones (Rowell, 1966b). There is some doubt how much communicative significance the purely visual aspects of the cycle possess. Rowell found that caged baboon males paid little attention to caged females at the end of their cycle, after conception, although the labial swelling was as large as ever. Presumably, the cues of other behavior, or of smell, signaled that the female was no longer receptive.

Scent communication may play a far larger role than usually

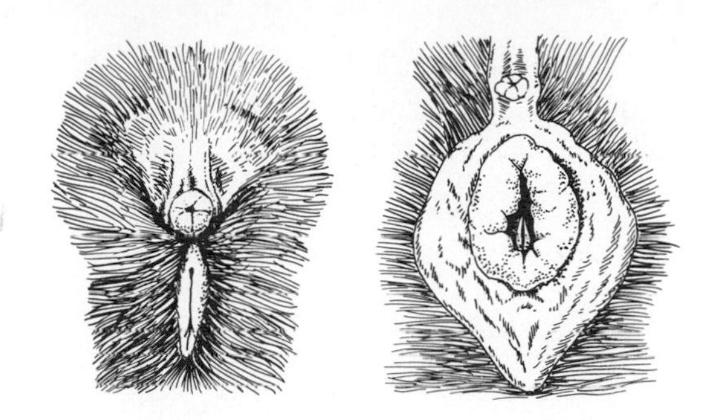

Figure 91 Anogenital region of a female tarsier. Left, when quiescent; right, with estral swelling. (After W. Wickler, 1967.)

credited. It is obvious in lemurs that glandular scent-marking rises to a frenzy before mating. The sternal glands of many New World primates from marmoset to spider monkey may also play a major role in courtship (Epple and Lorenz, 1967). But subtler scent communication exists. Michael and Keverne (1968), in elegent experiments, has shown that female rhesus' attractiveness to the male depends heavily on vaginal odor, which is stimulated by estrogen and blocked by progesterone. (These experiments must be done with well-known couples—otherwise, individual preferences and mating patterns would mask the effect of the hormone.)

Not only the look and the smell of female primates may change with sexual condition. The whole pattern of behavior changes. This has been best studied in rhesus monkeys and in savanna baboons,

Figure 92 The chimpanzee indicates estrus by swelling of the vaginal lips or "sex skin." Captivity exaggerates the swelling in baboons and may do so in chimpanzees. (Courtesy of Zoological Society of London.)

Figure 93 The chest patch of the female gelada baboon mimics the pattern of her rump. It also flushes red and develops a necklace of white tubercles during estrus. (San Diego Zoo Photo by Ron Garrison.)

Figure 94 (opposite) Mating and female cycle in wild baboons, caged rhesus, and humans. *A:* Frequency of mating in a wild baboon troop when genitalia are inflating, swollen, flat, and pregnant (I, S, F, P) adjusted by number of females in each state. Mating is here correlated with sexual swelling, although not perfectly so. (After T. E. Rowell, 1967b.) *B:* Individual cycles of mounting frequency in caged rhesus. Although mating reaches a peak at presumed time of ovulation (day 0), there are wide individual variations. In many cycles there is a drop after ovulation, then a rise before menstruation, followed by a sharp drop (not shown) at menstruation. Rhesus behavior changes more at menstruation than at estrus, and rhesus macaques have little or no sexual swelling or reddening at estrus. (After R. P. Michael, 1968.) *C:* Percentage of women in the North Carolina sample reporting intercourse and orgasm by reverse day of menstrual cycle. There were 40 women and 73-115 cycles. The pattern resembles the rhesus pattern, with a peak at probable ovulation and a secondary peak before menstruation. (After J. R. Udrey and N. M. Morris, 1968.)

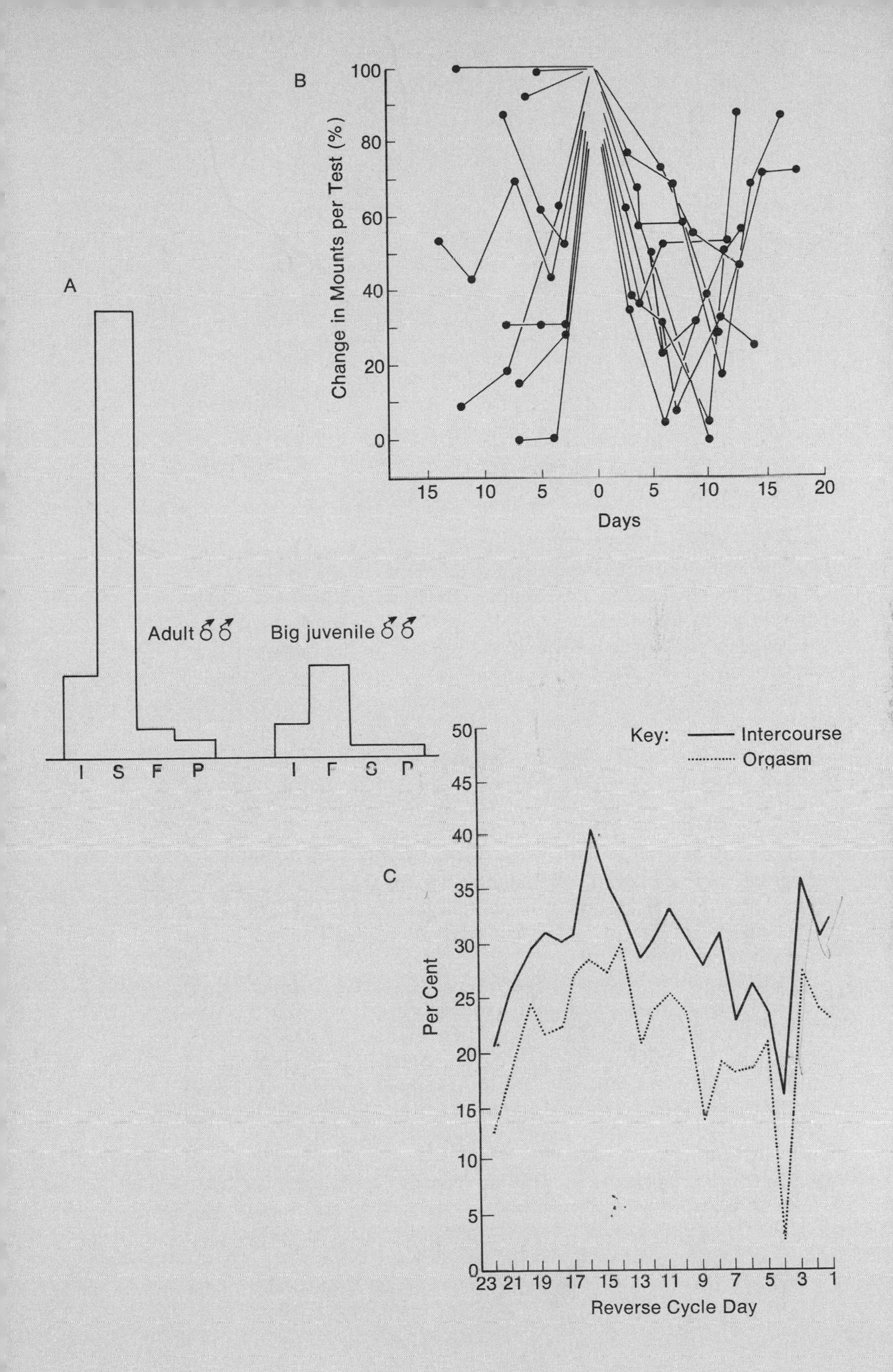

A
Adult ♂♂
Big juvenile ♂♂
I S F P
I F S P
B
Change in Mounts per Test (%)
100
80
60
40
20
0
15 10 5 0 5 10 15 20
Days
C
Key: Intercourse
Orgasm
Per Cent
50
45
40
35
30
25
20
15
10
5
0
23 21 19 17 15 13 11 9 7 5 3 1
Reverse Cycle Day

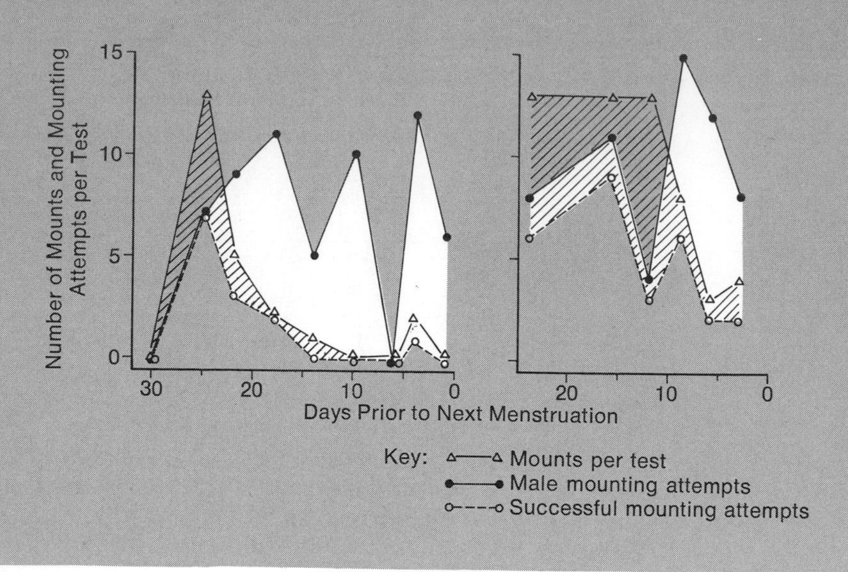

Figure 95 Male and female initiation of mating in caged rhesus. The female contributes positively during the first parts of the cycles by initiating mounts (hatched area) and negatively during the second parts of the cycles by actively refusing (white area). Where hatched and white areas overlap, the female is inviting and refusing in the same test. (After R. P. Michael, 1968.)

which differ from each other in that the rhesus have little sexual swelling and very unstable color change whereas the baboons' swelling is all too obvious. During the cycle, there are changes in grooming, aggression toward the female, and aggression by the female—it is clear that with these primates (as with people) the menstrual cycle can shift the balance between affection and irritation. External social stress in baboons increased the length of the menstrual cycle, whereas social isolation increased the size of the estral swelling (Rowell, 1970).

Figure 94 shows some patterns of observed copulation in Michael's caged rhesus and wild baboons. It is clear that the patterns of various species differ sharply. In humans, Udrey and Morris (1968) have reported on frequency of copulation in a group of Southern Negroes (as with all such studies, there are methodological queries!). They found a frequency like some but not all of Michael's pairs of macaques, with a peak at about estrus and a secondary peak just before menstruation. They concluded that hormonal changes have an influence on human mating—it would be extraordinary if hormones did not. But as Michael's, Herbert's, and Rowell's work has shown, even in macaques the hormonal stimuli to mate are mediated through a complex set of behaviors that appear in the approach, avoidance, attack, and grooming of males and females, as well as in mating itself (Figure 95).

Figure 96 Gorillas copulating. (Courtesy of D. Sorby.)

CHANGE OF MEANING IN SOCIAL INTERACTIONS: DOMINANCE MOUNTING AND HAMADRYAS PAIRS

Wickler (1967) has reviewed many cases of the change in meaning of gestures that evolved in one context and came to be used in another—in particular, sexual signs that have taken on a different meaning in the social context. The classic case is dominance mounting, in which an animal of either sex asserts his authority by mounting his subordinate, sometimes even with thrusting. Mounting of this sort may be a kind of punishment, as when a subordinate has been fighting or threatening near a dominant and the dominant breaks up the fight and mounts one of the participants. It may also involve a kind of permission. When a subordinate wishes to take a piece of food, he may "present" his rump to the dominant, who briefly mounts and then allows him to take the food. Bonnet macaques mount in any dominance order, but even in other monkeys mounting is not strictly tied to the direction of dominance. Oddly, the excitable estrous females are quite likely to mount as well. The presenting and mounting, although clearly sexual in origin, are now just as clearly ritual signs of excitement, self-assertion, appeasement, or even—for bonnets—friendship, in a wide social context.

However, Wickler points out that the underlying motivation may well be as complex as the gesture itself. Presenting, after all, appeases *because* it is the gesture of a sexually receptive female.

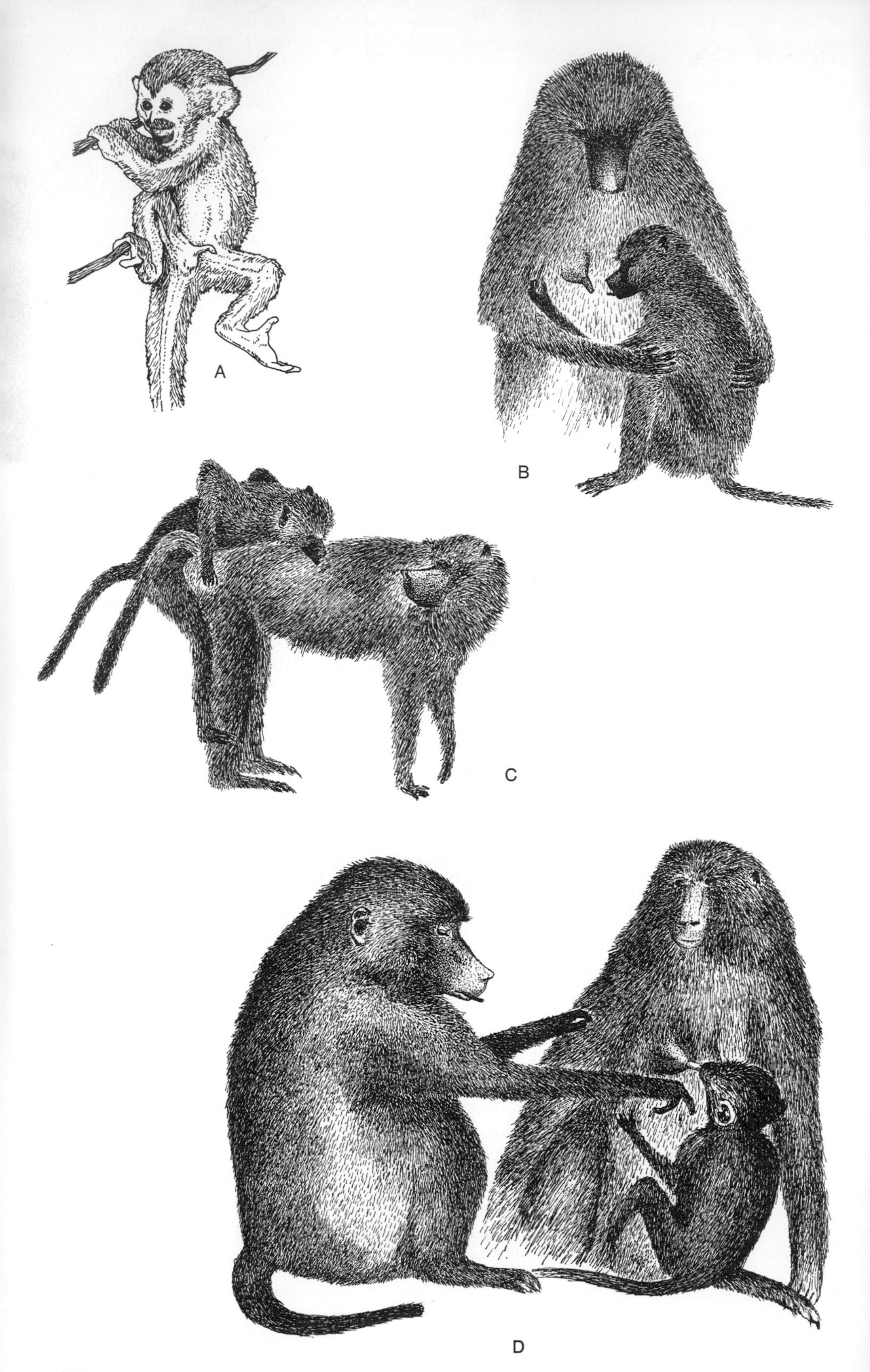
A
B
C
D

Figure 97 (opposite) Semisexual displays: squirrel monkeys and baboons. Penile erection and display are commonly used by squirrel monkeys in threat or dominance interactions. *A:* This infant monkey is already displaying in the adult manner. Thus an originally sexual act has taken on dominance functions. Lip-smacking in baboons probably originates from infant suckling but matures into greeting, begging, and sexual contexts. *B:* A juvenile lip-smacks on a adult female's nipple during an embrace. *C:* He lip-smacks on the fur of an estrous female during mounting. *D:* An adult female lip-smacks at and touches a nursing black infant. (*A:* After D. W. Ploog, 1967. *B–D:* After T. R. Anthoney, 1968.)

Dominance mounting should divert an animal from aggressive, potentially injurious behavior to sexual behavior. It is an advantage both to "fool" and be "fooled" in this situation. Given the possibility of using sex in potentially aggressive situations, the device works best if it stays fairly close in feeling and form to real sex. Being anthropomorphic, if we pity the gibbon's nearly sexless monogamy, the macaque might well pity our dull set of status symbols. Board meetings would be so much more amusing with vice-presidents mounting each other down the line . . . .

The intial pair formation of hamadryas baboons is a completely different case of a set of gestures evolving away from their original function while probably retaining much of the original emotion. Kummer (personal communication) has shown that hamadryas

Figure 98 A hamadryas baboon disciplines his mate for straying too far by biting the back of her neck while she screams. At the disturbance other females run to their leaders. (From H. Kummer, 1968.)

Figure 99 A juvenile female hamadryas baboon cuddles against her subadult male leader during a fight. (From H. Kummer, 1968.)

respect each other's priority to wives. If one captured hamadryas male is introduced first to a strange female, other stronger males do not attempt to take her away. A maturing male, then, cannot steal an adult wife. Instead, the young male "adopts" a female juvenile, hugging and carrying her, protecting her from outside aggression for a year or so until she grows up enough to mate. The male gives the gestures of maternal care to his child bride, while throughout a female's life she depends on another stronger animal—teasing her family from that animal's side, enlisting her defender's aid in feuds, and expecting punishment if she strays too far herself. She shifts all this juvenile dependence directly from her mother to her mate (Kummer, 1968; Kummer and Kurt, 1965).

We know all these complexities of behavior in ourselves, of course. We know how many marriages also contain a parental-infantile relation, how mothers may love their sons with different emotions than in their love for daughters. All of psychoanalytic theory is based on the transformation of child-parent love into sexual love as the normal pattern of development of our species. We know, as well, how even a single gesture combines motivations.

The macaque presenting to be allowed a piece of food is much like the secretary batting her eyelashes to be allowed typing mistakes—not just sex involved, but a measured proportion of sexiness, appropriate to species and situation.

MARRIAGE

It is only by comparison with the primates that we see the major human innovation—to a pair bond, or marriage, maintained in large part through sexual relations. Of course, many other factors enter in, including attraction to children, shared experience, economic dependence, and, not least, force of social custom. Many societies put taboos on intercourse during pregnancy and lactation, as well as during menstruation, which may mean maintaining marriage without sex for much of a woman's adult life.

Rhesus paired in cages, with half an hour to get on before they are separated again, mate at all stages of the menstrual cycle. Wild rhesus and chimpanzees mate during early pregnancy. Macaques and many other primates that are seasonal in the wild may breed year-round in captivity. Therefore, one could argue that the physiological changes may not have been very drastic to produce our more continous sexiness—a mere change of environment can do the same to other primates (Van Wagenen, 1967; Vandenberg, 1969).

Similarly, studies of primates in the wild (Kaufmann, 1965) and in cages (Michael and Saayman, 1967; Michael and Herbert, 1963) indicate that there are strong personal preferences in choice of mates, even among fairly promiscuous species; so again personal bonding might have easily arisen with slight social and environmental changes.

Stephens (1963), in his cross-cultural survey of the human family, concludes that man is indeed basically a marrying type, although not necessarily monogamous. By this Stephens means that *every* culture has a rite of marriage, and rights of marriage—we all recognize a sense in which a particular woman and children belong to a certain man, and vice versa, and we formalize this relation. As Desmond Morris (1967) remarked, we say "I'd like you to meet my wife," not just "This is my mate." In the cultures that Stephens (1963) surveyed, there were only two striking exceptions. One Indian tribe of the Pacific Northwest was said to practice true promiscuity. Men visited a woman's house, leaving gifts for her, and individual men had no rights apparent to the anthropologist over either the woman or her subsequent children. The other exception was orthodox Muslims. Arabs could take a recognized wife for a temporary stated period, perhaps the duration of a pilgrimage or business trip. This contractual temporary relation is, Stephens stresses, quite different from marriage in a society with high divorce rates. Although a realistic couple may know their own marriage has a fair chance of dissolving and reassorting with other partners, it is extremely rare to contract for the end of a partnership at its beginning.

There are at least four possible selective advantages of the human pair-bonded family, which may have combined to reinforce each other (in any order). First, many modern primates that form exclusive pairs or harems are those that live in areas of scarce resources. We, like the gelada or hamadryas baboons, might have adapted behaviorally to forage in small groups in arid conditions and have had elaborate means of pair bonding long before we shared food or developed a conception of future time.

Second, we may have gone over to an economic bonding very early on, such that males shared food with their females or even hunted food to bring back for their wives and young. Red foxes and wolves pair and support their young, and hunting dogs regurgitate food not only for the young but for the "baby sitters" who remain in the lair (Eisenberg, 1966; Kühme, 1965). It may be that food sharing is feasible only with meat, which comes in large, scarce, transportable packets. We do not know how far back in evolution man became a hunter, but hunting would surely have tied in with and reinforced the man's responsibilities to his own family or to the troop.

Third, males could protect females. If we foraged in arid country, like the hamadryas, or traveled independent-mindedly, like the chimpanzee, then the smallest male-protected group would be the pair or harem.

Fourth, whenever human children began to grow too slowly for their mother to provide for them alone, a semipermanent bond would have become economically crucial.

Note that much of this could be provided by a well-knit troop or pack. Aunts for the young, protection, and food sharing would be feasible or even easier in a reasonably sized troop. This means that *before* the human pair bond we probably lived in small units, either a very early harem structure or the loose social structure of modern chimpanzees. This again would fit Clifford Jolly's hypothesis that the earliest hominids ate seeds, whether the seeds of grasses or of dry woodland trees.

In any case, human behavior has probably always been fairly labile, so that even our early societies may have taken different forms in different circumstances.

SUMMARY

Primates stay in groups because they like to, not for any single kind of bond.

Grooming may reflect kinship, friendship, and status roles. However, some New World monkeys only groom during courtship or when tending newborn young. Lemurs and lorisoids use a specialized toothcomb; higher primates groom with hands and teeth.

Most primate females are sexually active for only a small fraction of their lives. Most primate species breed seasonally, mating in a limited period of the year. However, there is a tendency in species of every branch of the primates for males to associate with females throughout the year and throughout their lives.

In the female primate estrus cycle, visual, olfactory, and behavioral cues may attract the male and signal the female's readiness to mate. With wild primates, females tend to mate only during estrus, when able to conceive. However, in caged primates (and caged mammals), receptivity may be much prolonged. This is, of course, very much true of human beings, in whom sex is one major factor holding together the marriage.

Sexual signals may take on other functions in society, as with "dominance presenting" in macaques. Sexual bonds, as well, may blend with other relations, as in the male–harem bonds of hamadryas baboons. It is not strictly true to speak of "mixed feelings" in these cases—the whole point is that the feeling appropriate to one situation, e.g., sex or parental protection, can occur, and be normal, and be in fact very useful in other situations.

We ourselves have a huge variety of mating patterns, but almost all human cultures have an institution of marriage, in which particular individuals are assigned to each other "permanently" (or at least not explicitly temporarily) and assume joint responsibility for bringing up their children. There are a number of primates that also form exclusive pair bonds or harems, and even among troop-living macaques or baboons particular individuals have a marked preference for each other's consortship and company. However, the primates give us no unequivocal picture of early man. It may be that our ancestors formed small one-male family groups, in arid-country ecology, like the present-day hamadryas and gelada baboons, even before we began extensive hunting and food sharing. It might equally well be that we had an open, chimpanzee-like community, and males did not commit themselves to particular females and children until food sharing made it advantageous for the male to provide. In any case, human behavior has probably always been fairly labile, and even at a very early stage families may have taken different forms in different circumstances.

Mothers and Infants

AGE STRUCTURE

The life span of primates is long. It is by no means uniquely long. Elephants probably live as long as men, and the Galapagos tortoise may live 200 years. Absolute length in any case only matters in relation to other species with whom the animals come in contact.

Figure 100 indicates that lengthened life span is a progressive trend throughout the order. The relative length of different phases of life is very different from that of other mammals. The immature phases form a relatively large proportion of the primate's total life. This is important for the individual. He has a long period of dependency on his elders and a long period in which to learn the appropriate behavior for an adult of his species. It also is important from the point of view of the troop and its social composition. In troops of most species there are many infants and juveniles who must be cared for. The infants and juveniles as well contribute to the life of the troop, forming a center of attraction that may strengthen the social bonds among adults. Juveniles usually make the few innovations in behavior that can be incorporated into the culture of the troop. All these points will be discussed in later chapters, but all relate back to the physical stages of growth.

Napier and Napier (1967) divide the primate's life into gestation, infancy (during which the child is closely bound to his mother), the juvenile phase before puberty, and the adult phase. In most species it is convenient to distinguish a subadult phase when the animal, although sexually mature, has not yet achieved full adult stature. Primates may also have a postreproductive phase, in late adulthood, although very little is known about this in the wild.

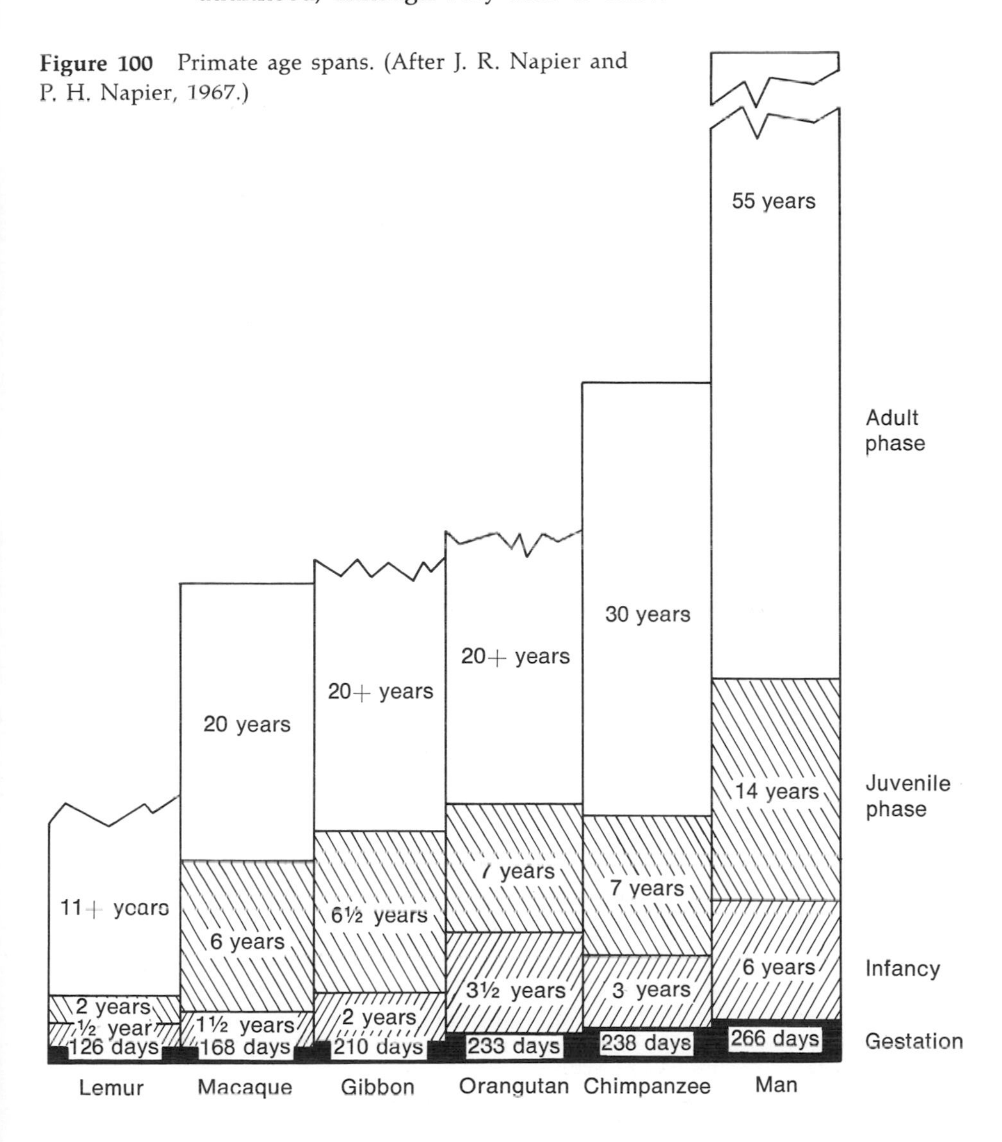

Figure 100 Primate age spans. (After J. R. Napier and P. H. Napier, 1967.)

Primates as an order have a very long pregnancy. Even in mouse lemurs pregnancy lasts $3\frac{1}{2}$ months and in true lemurs for $4\frac{1}{2}$ months. (Compare this with 3 weeks in mouse-lemur-sized mice and 3 months in lemur-sized cats.) Pregnancy length in higher apes is about the same as our own. However, our own newborn are much less advanced than monkey or ape newborns, either in motor control or in percentage of growth. The length of human pregnancy seems to be the result of two opposing tendencies. The human brain is much larger in proportion to the body than an ape's, and a large part of the growth of the brain takes place early in life. However, the child must be delivered through the mother's pelvis, which in turn is constrained by the demands of bipedal walking. Therefore, much of the brain growth must take place after birth: "The gestation period is terminated in man and other primates when the size of the head is consonant with a safe delivery" (Napier and Napier, 1967).

The infantile period, during which a child is physically and emotionally dependent on his mother, also grows progressively longer as one ascends the primate order. Unlike gestation, it doubles in length from ape to man. In part, this relates to the immaturity of our newborn. The first part of our infancy is really what Ashley Montagu calls "exterogestation"—a nearly helpless stage in which the infant is still transported and nourished like a fetus, although he can see and hear and feel the outer surface of his mother. The more active primate baby, like our preschool children, is still emotionally bound to his mother. Much of the initial social learning takes place in this prolonged period of dependency.

The juvenile phase, lasting until puberty, is still more prolonged. In this phase, as in infancy, much must be learned by the growing primate, and there has to be time to learn it. Puberty and menarche come just before or during a spurt in physical growth. Very little is known about just what the juveniles in wild troops are doing during this long period. The Freudian theories of human development lay great stress on our "latency period," during which we are supposed to be becoming human. Wild juvenile primates are obviously playful and obviously initiate many interactions among themselves, but few that influence adults of the troop. However, few detailed comparisons have been made with human youngsters.

Human subadults may have a period of adolescent sterility when conception is unlikely to occur, even though sexual relations take place. The same stage is obvious in many primate species whose females may not conceive during their first estrus period. In some species, such as the savanna baboon, young males are much slower to reach full growth than females, which leads to an apparent imbalance in the sex ratio. There are usually about as many males as females in a savanna baboon troop, but fewer of the males are apparently adult or fully adult. One can see the advantage in this if the males are more aggressive and argumentative. If fewer adult males contend for dominance status, the troop may be more peaceable as a whole.

The longest absolute increase in a phase of life from primate to man is the adult phase. While the zoo-cossetted chimpanzee or gorilla may spend 30 years as an adult, a man can look forward to about 55 years of adult life. Preservation or elaboration of a body of culture by adults over several generations of growing young is essential to perpetuate tradition as we do.

One of the most influential overall theories of human development points out that adult men retain many characteristics of juvenile or even fetal primates. Man anatomically resembles an orangutan or chimpanzee child. His face does not have brow ridges and his skull is set vertically on top of his spinal column without flexing forward as in quadrupedal mammals. Behaviorally, he retains the curiosity and inventive play common to other mammals' obstreperous young. This theory was elaborated by Bolk (1926, in Napier and Napier, 1967). Aldous Huxley (1939) took it to the logical conclusion by imagining that an enlightened savant of the eighteenth century found the secret of immortality. After 200 years he, alone among men, had lived long enough to grow up—into a gorilloid, glowering from under his massive brow ridges at a world of no interest to him. On the whole, though "foetalization" may have been one of the mechanisms of human evolution, it seems that each of the traits has a clear selective function, not least of which is the contribution of human curiosity to human society.

SYSTEMS OF MOTHERING

Mammals, by definition, depend on their mothers. However differently young mammals grow up, all begin by needing their mother's milk, her licking and grooming as they enter the world.

Figure 101 Precocial and altricial young. *A:* Newborn European hare. *B:* Newborn European rabbit. (After F. Bourlière, 1964.)

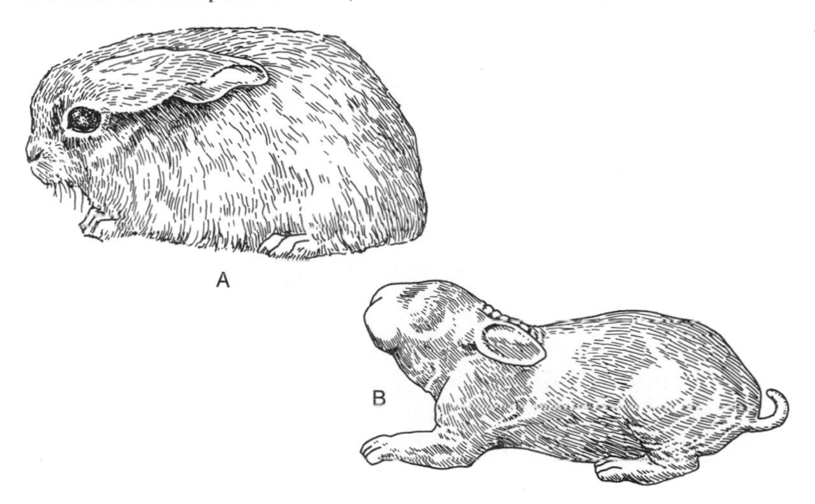

However, there is a vast difference in the preparation for life. Some species have *precocial* young: the young are born with eyes open and are fully furred, perhaps able to walk or run from the first day. Some have *altricial* young, naked and helpless. The terms, of course, are relative—the hare is more precocial than the rabbit (Figure 101, page 217), but the acouchi, which runs on the first day of life and nibbles food on the second, is more precocial still. Further, not all the aspects need go together. The naked, helpless young of the tree shrew are left alone in their nest from birth and manage their own thermoregulation. The kangaroo, an inch-long, acephalic embryo, 1 month after conception crawls unaided the long 8 inches from the womb to its mother's pouch, where it can settle for 8 months more to finish gestation. In one animal the temperature regulation and in the other control of the forelimbs have developed out of all proportion to the rest (Bourlière, 1964).

Portmann (1965) and Martin (1968a, 1969) have considered the likely origins of mammalian mothering. They conclude that the present-day placental mammals probably descended from a nest-building ancestor. The ancestor might have had a fairly short gestation, of perhaps 30 days, a large litter, and young born with eyes and ears closed, teeth not yet through, and no fur. Portmann believes that in forms with no nest, the nest phase is compressed

Figure 102 Senegal galagos carry their young in their mouth when it is necessary to move them outside the nest. (Courtesy of T. Bekker.)

Figure 103 An adult male Senegal galago adopting the carrying posture of an infant. Infants of species that are usually carried in their mother's mouth reflexly bunch up and hold still when lifted by a fold of skin. (Courtesy of S. Bearder.)

Figure 104 The slender loris parks its baby on a branch for the night and returns to pick it up in the morning. (Courtesy of Zoological Society of London.)

Figure 105 The rarely photographed woolly lemur carries its baby on the fur as higher primates do. (Courtesy of R. D. Martin.)

into the intrauterine phase. The young of precocial, nidifugous species begin gestation with open eyes, then close them *in utero,* then reopen them before birth. Furthermore, species which seem "primitive" in other respects—insectivores, rodents, most lagomorphs, carnivores, prosimians—seem to build nests. However, the rats and mice may have secondarily shortened gestation, to their mere 16 to 22 days, after developing their extensive shelter systems.

Martin (1968b) is suspicious of this sort of argument, as species that are primitive in some respects can perfectly well be specialized in others. However, the early care of the young is obviously related to ecology. Martin follows the argument that pre-Paleocene mammals were probably arboreal. They could well have built tree nests, like some present-day prosimians, then the older juveniles might have clung to the parent's body, like many modern arboreal mammals (primates, sloths, bats, opossums, colugos, pangolins). One of the crucial bits of evidence, here, is that the hind foot of very many mammalian embryos has an opposed big toe, although it closes again to make a running or walking foot in ground-living forms.

Primates, as a group, either have their young in nests or carry them on the body from birth: none have truly precocial babies who can follow after their parents. However, only some prosimians and people, among the primates, build birth nests and can afford to

Figure 106 An infant black lemur. The grip in fur of baby prosimians may have been a preadaptation for fine control of the hand. (From J. Buettner-Janusch, *Science,* 136 [April 13, 1962], cover photo. Copyright 1962 by the American Association for the Advancement of Science.)

have naked immobile young. Monkeys and apes are born open eyed and furry, with at least the capacity to climb up their mother as far as the nipple.

The amount of care that mothers give varies widely. At one mammalian extreme is the tree shrew, with an "absentee system" of mothering. The litter of two or three is born in a separate nest from the parents' sleeping nest. The mother cleans and feeds them after giving birth, and then abandons babies and nest for 1 or 2 days. She returns at 48-hour intervals, goes directly to the spot marked with the babies' urine, squats over her young, squirts milk into their mouths for approximately 10 minutes, then is off again. She does not groom her young, cover them, or retrieve them if they have moved from their urine spot. If she does not find them within 2 minutes of entering the brood nest, she leaves and never returns. All this is unprimate (although rabbits behave in a similar way), and it seems highly likely, on this and other grounds, that tree shrews are not closely related to the primates (Martin, 1968a). However, the lorises and pottos have been repeatedly seen to park their infants on a branch for the night and pick them up to sleep

Figure 107 (opposite) The young infants of most species are carried ventrally. A proboscis mother and baby. (San Diego Zoo Photo by Ron Garrison.)

together in the morning (Charles-Dominique, 1966a, in preparation; Walker, personal communication; Hall, personal communication).

The nest-building primate whose maternal behavior has been most closely studied is the senegal bushbaby, in seminaturalistic conditions. Again, the mother builds a separate nest in which she raises the young, but, at least in captivity, other animals occasionally groom and cuddle the young (Doyle *et al.*, 1969).

Among the primates that carry their infants on their fur, there is a huge spectrum of behavior. Chimpanzee and gorilla mothers support their babies with one hand for the first month or two, as the babies are too uncoordinated to cling during fast movement.

Figure 108 Older infants are carried dorsally. A night monkey and its half-grown juvenile. (Courtesy of Zoological Society of London.)

Squirrel monkey mothers aid their babies very little. In fact, they seem to pay no attention for the first 10 days, while the newborn climbs over them and puts itself to nurse. However, if the baby is incapacitated, they hold it and help it as other primates do. Newborn marmosets crawl over to their father, who carries them, except for brief nursing sessions, until they can run alone.

As with everything else, even related species differ widely. The ringtailed lemur has a precocial infant who can scramble from its mother onto other animals in the first few days of life and who rides longitudinally under its mother's belly. The brown lemur is much slower developing, and rides transversely wrapped around its mother like a belt. The variegated lemur is born still more helpless and is left in a nest, or is carried, when necessary, in its mother's mouth (Petter-Rousseaux, 1964). Even populations and races differ in breeding season and size of litter. Many parameters of behavior differ although they are not obviously correlated with physical development: hanuman langurs groom their babies frequently and rescue them if they cry, whereas nilgiri langurs almost never groom and leave their month-old young screaming, precariously stuck on a branch (Poirier, 1968b).

PREGNANCY AND BIRTH

Primate mothers may be lethargic and visibly swollen during pregnancy. Senegal bushbabies increase activity, irritability, and nest-building behavior in the day or two preceding birth (Doyle *et al.*, 1969). Savanna baboons conveniently indicate pregnancy by flushed ischial callosities (not the sexual skin). Often, however, the birth surprises the primatologist, who could not tell physically or behaviorally that the female was approaching parturition.

Primate births follow the same general pattern as our own. They may or may not begin with the "breaking of the waters"—the amniotic sac of fluid that surrounds and cushions the baby. There is a first stage of contractions while the cervix dilates, a second stage while the baby is expelled, then, after a brief pause, the third stage of expelling the placenta or "afterbirth."

In two respects, their births differ from our own. First, the total period of labor, from first contraction to delivery of infant or placenta, is much shorter, typically on the order of 2 hours. This varies from complicated deliveries, such as breech presentations, which may last for 2 or 3 days and result in death of at least the infant, to deliveries in which no change in the mother is noticed until a few moments before the birth itself.

Next, birth in New World and Old World monkeys commonly takes place at night, in the species for which there are records. Such a rhythm is well known in other mammals, including horses and cows. Bowden *et al.* (1967) suggest that nocturnal birth has

Figure 109 A pseudopregnant gorilla. Pseudopregnancy occurs in many mammals from mice to human beings; because a baby is never born, it can be taken to extremes. (Courtesy of D. Sorby.)

two functions: the mother does not have to keep up with a moving troop for protection from predators, and she is as well insulated from overeager attempts by friends and "aunts" to groom her new baby. Occasionally in laboratory colonies babies are killed by the frantic efforts of their cage mates to reach and hold and groom them.

The great apes, at least according to the statistics available, seem to give birth at any hour of the day or night. However, with the really large series of statistics available for human beings, a peak again appears, between 12 midnight and about 7 AM. Interestingly, the nocturnal peak can only be found in records of normal births—for premature babies, stillbirths, and abnormal presentations there is if anything a slight peak during the daytime. Labors ending in nocturnal births, even measured on objective criteria, tend to be shorter than daytime labors (Kaiser and Halberg, 1962; Jolly, in press).

RECOGNIZING A BABY

Primate mothers' reaction to their babies seems to vary as much among individuals as among species. Some mothers assist their babies, helping them to climb up to the nipple; others virtually ignore their young, letting the little one climb almost by itself up her fur to take its first feed. Nearly all mothers lick off the baby and eat the placenta. In fact, G. E. Hutchinson (personal communication) has suggested defining the human species as the primate that does not normally eat the placenta.

On the whole, primiparous mothers are more fumbling, less apt to give the normal repertoire of maternal responses; multiparous mothers, even in human beings, seem more competent. However,

Figure 110 The cute response. Babies have large rounded heads, large eyes, small noses and chins; adults are elongated and angular, with smaller heads and eyes. The similarity of young vertebrates may result originally from the cephalocaudal gradient of embryonic development. Many vertebrates have probably evolved a recognition of this generalized baby shape, the "cute response." (After K. Lorenz, 1950 in K. Lorenz, in press.)

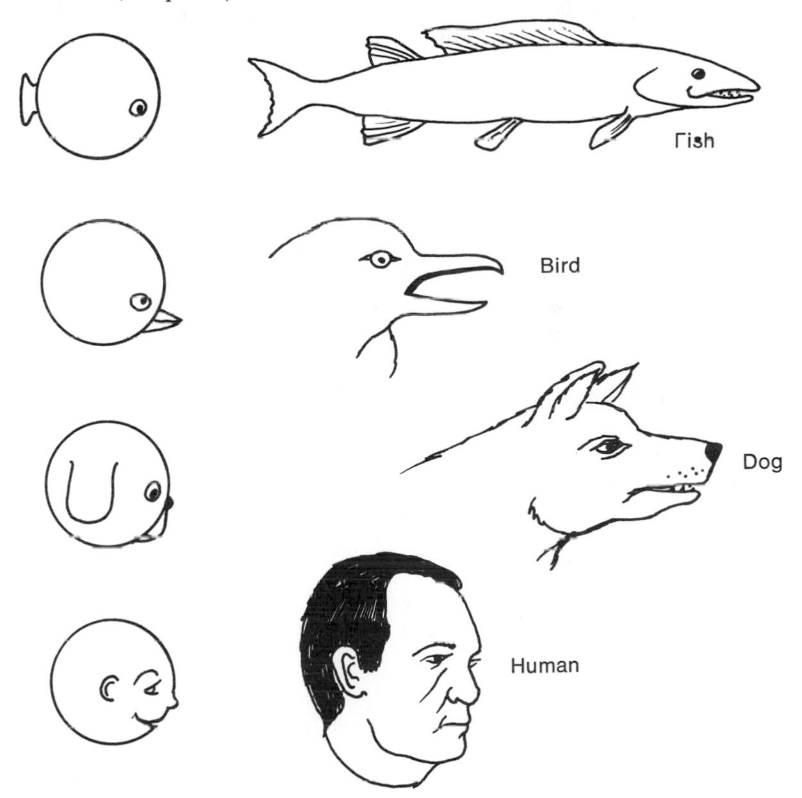

one must measure either quite a large series of mothers or have quite sophisticated measuring techniques to show the differences, because individual differences among monkeys as among people overwhelm most differences among recognizable groups.

How does a mother recognize a new baby? Among primates as among people, experience must play a major role. Most troop-living monkeys have met or even held and cuddled other infants before they have their own. (The attraction of juvenile females for new infants will be discussed in the next chapter.) Infants of many species are clearly marked; in many the natal coat is a different color than the adult's: black-and-white colobus have white babies. The baby rhesus monkey has a dull brown coat like its parents, but a pink parting in its hair seems to be particularly attractive to the females. Our own children are of course a markedly different shape than adults. Lorenz has made a beautiful diagram of the so-called cute response (Figure 110, page 227). Children or animals or cartoon characters with very large heads and short legs in proportion to their bodies look cute to us, the more so if they have large eyes in their large heads. This applies to baby fish, baby birds, baby dogs, artificially babified dogs such as the Pekinese, and babies. Gardner and Wallach (1965) experimented with silhouettes of real babies' heads and "super babies," which had even larger foreheads and smaller chins, as well as more adult faces with receding foreheads and protuberant chins. They presented a series of these silhouettes to college students, both male and female, and asked which looked the most babyish. The students, and particularly the

Figure 111 The cute response. The smallest of primates, a baby mouse lemur, whose large head, large eyes, and short limbs should provoke a cute response. (Courtesy of R. D. Martin.)

Figure 112 A newborn rhesus macaque. (Courtesy of R. Zimmermann.)

female students, consistently picked a super baby rather than the real, normal baby head. Like a herring gull chick pecking at a larger, redder beak than would be conceivable in its own parent, we respond to an exaggerated cartoon baby as being more real than the real thing.

Recognition of the baby would seem a likely thing to need no prior experience. The primiparous mother must be assured of treating her first young as an infant, not a stranger. One interesting sidelight on this is that human mothers, after a normal birth when they have not had too much anesthetic, say that they are overcome by a feeling of joy and tranquility after the baby is born. Obviously, culture tells them they ought to feel so, but the physical wash of emotion, rather like that after completed sexual intercourse, may have much deeper sources. Such a physiologically determined feeling of joy and tranquility in primates, who have not been nattering and knitting for the baby for the previous 9 months, may allow them to accept the infant without the resentment that would normally greet a total stranger squirming about their bodies.

In summary, it is not really known how mother primates recognize their young. There are plenty of physical markers of the newborn and every likelihood that unlearned processes are deeply involved, but experience certainly plays a considerable role as well. The qualitative aspects of a mother monkey's care are very similar in most species. A baby monkey simply does not survive unless his mother reacts to him as a baby, not a stranger, allows him to climb on her and suckle, cleans him off, and to some extent cuddles and supports him. However, the quantitative differences among species, individuals, or mothers in different situations are enormous.

MOTHERLESS MONKEYS

H. F. Harlow (Harlow and Harlow, 1965; Seay *et al.*, 1964; Mitchell, 1968b) began a famous series of experiments on monkeys by a simple attempt to find out what some of the parameters of mothering were, what in fact were the essential stimuli for a baby monkey to cling to its mother. Baby rhesus monkeys were given a choice of a "pseudomother" covered with soft terry cloth or a bare wire pseudomother. One of the two dummies had milk bottles attached

Figure 113 A baby rhesus monkey keeps contact with his soft pseudomother even while reaching for milk from the hard pseudomother. (Courtesy of Wisconsin Regional Primate Research Center.)

Figure 114 A motherless monkey rejects her own child. (Courtesy of Wisconsin Regional Primate Research Center.)

as teats. It made no difference to the baby monkey which had the milk; what mattered was softness to cling to. Each baby attached itself semipermanently to its terry cloth pseudomother. (Harlow gave the dummies particularly horrible faces with bicycle-lamp eyes to make quite sure that the face had small resemblance to that of a rhesus monkey.) Harlow at first thought he had cracked the problem: mother essentially is fur, or at least some sort of softness and comfort. The "cupboard-love theory" that mother merely is a set of conditioned stimuli associated with the source of milk was promptly thrown out.

But then the motherless baby monkeys grew up. They turned out to be strikingly abnormal in their behavior. One might perhaps have suspected as much, from their totally abnormal upbringing and the fact that while growing up they sat and rocked in the corners, a stereotyped rocking typical of human mental defectives as well as isolate monkeys. The motherless monkeys could not mate. Males mounted with impossible orientations, obviously with some degree of sexual excitement but little hope of reproductive success. Females would not accept mounting by males. Harlow arranged that several of these females be more-or-less raped by experienced males, so they became pregnant and gave birth. They mistreated their offspring; in fact, they treated their own newborn babies much as they would treat a rat that entered their cage, hitting it away, stepping on it, and grinding its face into the cage floor. Rhesus babies have a fair degree of motor control, and some of these infants succeeded in nursing by their own efforts, although their mothers continued to reject or ignore them. More of the first babies eventually had to be removed. However, motherless monkeys were considerably better with their second and succeeding babies, so that even they learned from experience.

Since Harlow's original experiments many more have been done on this type of gross deprivation of young monkeys. The periods of deprivation range from 3 months to 6 months to a year or two. This is long past the period of infancy and well into that of young childhood, even for so short a time as 6 months. It is not surprising that monkeys with such treatment turn out psychotic. What is more surprising is how short a period of contact with other monkeys will in part obliterate the subsequent effects on mating and recognition of the young. Even an hour a day with a peer group, that is, with monkeys of the same age, will help a great deal, but Harlow writes: "I am now quite convinced that there is no adequate substitute for monkey mothers early in the socialization process" (Bowlby, 1969).

However, this contact must occur during the first 6 months of life. Contact after the first 6 months, after the period of isolation, is very slow to make these changes. Visual contact alone is not enough, at least in Harlow's laboratory. There has to be an opportunity for touching, grooming, rough-and-tumble play. In Meier's (1965) laboratory in Puerto Rico, where animals are raised in close visual and vocal contact, but without physical touching, these gross

Figure 115 Contact with other juveniles can in part make up for lack of mothering. Harlow calls these "together-together" monkeys. (Courtesy of Wisconsin Regional Primate Research Center.)

abnormalities have not seemed to develop, so there is still much to learn about the etiology of the deprivation effects. However, it is clear that the longer the period of isolation and the more complete the isolation, the more severe are the effects.

Motherless, isolated chimpanzees show much the same syndrome as rhesus—social apathy or aggression and inept sexual behavior. However, chimpanzees seem able to learn from social companions, even after 2 or 3 years' initial isolation. Their greater behavioral flexibility gives them some chance of recuperation (Mason *et al.*, 1968; Rogers and Davenport, 1969; Turner *et al.*, 1969).

Isolated rhesus and chimpanzees are abnormal not only in their reaction to social contact but also to novel situations. They hold onto themselves and rock, so-called stereotyped, repetitive behaviors, or "autistic behaviors." The syndrome of childhood autism, often considered a kind of schizophrenia, combines hyperactivity and hypersensitivity to stimuli with a withdrawal from contact with the outside world, as though the child could only cope with the sensory bombardment from outside by a total cut-off. When released in a new situation, chimpanzees lay prone or crouched rather than sitting like a normally reared chimpanzee (Menzel *et al.*, 1963a, 1963b). They moved close to the wall and kept there, which autistic children also do, rather than venturing into the free space of the room. They were terrified at first of novel stimuli, would not touch them or approach them, or went up and sat sucking their thumbs and rocking a few inches away without daring to touch. Gradually they overcame their fear and played with the stimuli, the new objects, just as normal chimpanzees do, but after a much greater length of time. Menzel explained this by saying that the isolates were overresponsive to the new situation; they were terrified of a mild stimulus just as a normal monkey or chimpanzee would be terrified of a very large or rapidly moving stimulus.

On a milder level, isolates seem to perform worse on tests of learning and delayed response because they do not pay attention to the test situation; they are distracted. This recalls many deprived children who are distracted in school and do not pay attention to the learning situation, although this is of course complicated by social interaction with the teacher (or sometimes by the lack of social interaction). The frightening part is that these differences in learning remain among adolescent chimpanzees who have been "normally" caged with others for 5 or 6 years after their early isolation.

Isolate monkeys are deficient in the very materials of social communication. Miller (Miller *et al.*, 1967) runs a closed-circuit television testing system (see Chapter 9) in which one monkey is shown a conditioned stimulus portending food or shock while a second monkey watches the televised face of the first and presses a "deliver food" or a "turn off shock" lever. Early isolate monkeys are inconsistent as both senders and receivers of the messages. They neither grimace reliably so that a normal monkey can press the appropriate lever, nor do they respond to the terrified face of the normal sender and release both of them from the shock.

When isolate rhesus are first tested in a social situation they react with either exaggerated fear or exaggerated hostility, depending on their age. Three-year-old isolates, who have been isolated for either the first or second 6 months of life or the first year, show extreme fear, whereas 4- or $4\frac{1}{2}$-year-old isolates become extremely aggressive and, as Mitchell (1968b) says, make suicidal attacks against huge adult males or brutally beat up infants. Their behavior, above all, is inconsistent, for the facial expressions of fear may occur along with the gestures of aggression. Monkeys reared in individual wire cages form unstable dominance orders, for the normal expression of dominance depends on consistent communication and appropriate restraint of aggression (Mason, 1968a).

In rhesus, as in humans, abnormal behavior can be passed down the generations. Offspring of brutal mothers are themselves significantly more aggressive than normal young (Mitchell, 1968b). This is true not only of offspring of mothers who were punitive due to early isolation but even of offspring of some wild-caught mothers who, for unknown reasons, mistreated their infants. These infants displayed high levels of peer-directed aggression before 1 year of age and became violently aggressive during adolescence and maturity; in fact, two of the males killed one of their female cage mates. Interestingly, the total amount of hostile behavior in Mitchell's normally reared group and his brutally reared group was about the same, but the normals redirected a great deal of hostility toward the experimenter or it appeared as displacement yawning and cage shaking. The brutally reared group redirected much less and took out their hostility in actual attacks on each other. Although aggressive, they also showed more fear and social submission. Again their behavior was not just extreme, but inconsistent (Møller *et al.*, 1968).

In summary, it is possible to produce many kinds of psychotic behavior by grossly abnormal treatment during infancy. Stereotyped behavior reminiscent of childhood autism, disturbances in sexual behavior, and even murder among monkeys can appear in this way, and, once established, abnormality can be passed from generation to generation. Undoubtedly, this establishes the importance of sustained early contact and love.

SHORT-TERM SEPARATION

Young children who are separated from their mothers often react to the separation with surprising intensity, going into a period of depression when separated, sometimes apparently refusing to recognize mothers or parents on returning home, and then clinging, whining, and following their mothers around for a long period after the separation. Human beings who have been totally isolated like monkeys in wire cages are fortunately rare, but short-term separations are very frequent, for instance, when the mother goes to hospital to have another baby or when the child itself is hospitalized. John Bowlby (1969) was the first of current scientists to recognize the emotional impact of short-term separation, flying in the face of medical practice as well as the nurses' observation that children seemed to become terribly upset and cry when their mothers visited the hospital. Bowlby's conclusions have been criticized both on the practical ground that it is inconvenient to have mothers around cluttering up hospital routine and on the theoretical ground that it is extremely difficult to prove his case with data from human beings, on whom deliberate experimental isolation is unthinkable. Several investigators have turned to the primates to illuminate Bowlby's work.

Hinde removed mother rhesus monkeys for 6 days. Their infants remained in the home cage group surrounded by "aunts," that is, other females with whom they were well acquainted, one adult male, and sometimes other infants. The infants at 32 weeks of age were really independent, spending about half their time off the mothers in any case and perfectly well able to care for themselves. However, the infants were at first hyperactive and then depressed without their mothers. Then, when their mothers returned to the cage, the infants flew to them and clung, even as much as 90 per cent of the time on the first day. The amount of time spent off the mother increased in the first few days after her return, largely due to her own initiative as she rejected the overdependent clinging of her infant, then regressed, then slowly returned to its preseparation level. However, even as much as a year after separation, two out of four of Hinde's initial group of infants showed marked differences from the group norm in the amount of time they spent near their mother.

Kaufman and Rosenblum (1967) removed pigtail mothers for a whole lunar month, 4 weeks, when their infants were 24 weeks of age. Here the period of depression was marked. The infants turned to "self-directed behavior," sitting in a corner and clutching themselves and rocking, then went into a period of almost complete passive depression during the first 7 to 16 days of separation, then gradually came back to normal playing with their cage mates. Again, reunion was dramatic, infant and mother clinging to each other. Again for some, but not all, of the infants the differences persisted for at least several months after the separation. Mitchell *et al.* (1967), with a different experimental design of repeated separation, but for only 2 hours each time, came to the same conclusion. In at least some of the experimental infants differences persisted for a year after the final separation, well into the second year of life.

STAGES OF GROWTH

Mother–infant interaction is a continuous process between two individuals, modified from day to day, in terms of the biological state of mother and child, and in terms of all that they have done and felt for each other. However, it is possible to distinguish some qualitative shifts of emphasis, particularly in human infancy.

The most potent theoretical model comes from the work on imprinting in birds. Lorenz (*cf.* 1970) described imprinting. What is more, he practiced it—he drew himself hopping through the spring grass, quacking, with a train of baby mallards behind him (Lorenz, 1952) to the bewilderment of the neighbors. The mallards accepted him as their mother as long as he remained of a reasonable size, crouched not more than 3 feet high, and made an intermittent noise, such as quacking. From this beginning came Lorenz's categorization of *imprinting:* (1) It was a process that occurred in early youth, the so-called *critical period,* and after that stage of life could no longer occur. (2) It was a process in which the young duck or bird learned the characteristics of its parents' species, not so much the characteristics of mother as an individual, but the generalities that would later allow the young bird to identify its own appropriate sexual partner. (3) Further, the process seemed at the time to be irreversible. (*Cf.* Lorenz, 1970.)

Since Lorenz's original work the definition has somewhat softened and broadened. It is now realized that nearly any kind of learning occurs more easily at one stage of life than at another. The learning of species' characteristics may be reversible; it depends on the circumstances. It also depends on the species—even fairly closely related animals may differ in the degree to which their adult sexual preferences are unlearned behavior, or learned during a kind of imprinting, or learned fairly broadly throughout the period of growth. Further, as in most important biological processes, there are redundancies of control, so that a bird is far more likely to learn right than to learn wrong.

However, with this wider definition it is possible to see a common process occurring in very many young birds. When the bird is newborn it has a tendency to approach, follow, and cuddle against any conspicuous object, particularly if the object is moving or flashing and making an intermittent noise. This sort of object has the properties of a reinforcer: the young bird will work to turn on a flashing light. It seems to reduce distress when the bird can cuddle up to a conspicuous object, or even see one; it makes quieter calls, stops distress calling, and slows down activity unless the object is moving away, in which case it follows the object. After the first unspecific period when almost any conspicuous object will elicit approach, the young bird learns very rapidly the characteristics of its own particular object and will no longer respond to other objects. Following this comes a period of rising fear when the chick actively avoids strange objects, running to its own "mother" if that is present. If the chick reaches the age of fear responses with no imprinting object, it will no longer imprint but will flee from all novel stimuli. In this case, it may in fact be imprinted on the gray walls of its cage for want of a more adequate mother. In the wild this system normally leads to learning one's own mother's characteristics—a duckling that hatches and sees a fox as its first imprinting object might as well follow the fox, as it is lost anyway. By and large, the system works fairly well. The duck is apt to learn that a duck is its mother.

Hinde (1966b) warns that birds and mammals have been phylogenetically separate since they were derived from their reptilian ancestors. As the reptiles presumably had no maternal care, maternal and infant behavior in birds and mammals must have been separately developed and any similarities can be no more than analogous. However, mammals as well seem commonly to go through a period of approach to any conspicuous object, in the likelihood that it will be their mother, followed by a period of learning ever more particular characteristics of their own mother and then of rising fear of all novel situations and stimuli and strangers. Whether or not this early learning channels sexual responses in the adult mammal is still being studied. Oddly then, as far as I know, there has been no adequate set of experiments in mammalian species that would show that imprinting, in the classical sense, has occurred and sexual responses have become directed to an alien species solely due to learning at a restricted early period of life. In many species this is clearly not so, and animals may be raised in total isolation from conspecifics, yet still mate normally as adults (Scott, 1968).

For present purposes, we are concerned only with infant–mother development. One might outline a few general stages of development of attachment in young mammals and young primates.

The helpless stage

The first stage would be that directly following birth, when the infant's behavior is largely reflex and the mother's behavior is crucially important in drawing the two together. The infant may be physically unable to do much in the way of approach. Perhaps of more interest in this period is how the mother recognizes, if she is primiparous, that her baby is a baby and not a strange creature, and as well how the mother knows what actions are appropriate with the new baby. The mother cleans off the newborn and makes some effort to draw them together and to allow it to nurse. In different species, of course, such a period may last very different times. For acouchis the period of infant helplessness and total dependence on the mother may be so compressed as to be almost nonexistent. At the other extreme are our own children, in whom this period lasts at least for the first 6 weeks of life. The infant, except for crying, can make almost no attachment to its mother; its first clear attachment sign comes with the beginning of social smiling, at approximately 6 weeks old. This stage, according to Harlow, might last for about the first 3 weeks of a rhesus monkey's life. It is questionable whether the stage really lasts so long in rhesus monkeys, as Rowell (1963b) has observed a young infant rhesus of 8 days following its mother about the cage with its eyes in preference to watching other females.

Recognizing a mother

The second stage would begin when the infant begins attachment, or, if you like, imprinting behavior. This is the period when the baby learns to recognize his mother, her species and herself. In the human baby, this recognition shows with social smiling. Smiling is at first directed to very general stimuli—two black eye spots on a sheet of paper are enough to evoke it, and in fact so are many simple changes in the environment. But it becomes narrowed first from general changes, to eye spots, to something resembling a human face, although grossly distorted faces and masks will evoke smiling for a time, to at last the mother and familiar people alone. This is what seems to the theorists to resemble imprinting in the duckling, the narrowing from any conspicuous change to species-specific stimuli to recognition of the mother herself.

Many people have studied attachment behavior in human babies: the smiling response (Ambrose, 1963); separation of young babies sent to the hospital during this period (Schaffer and Emerson, 1964); development of attachment in Ugandan children (Ainsworth, 1967); differences in attachment between babies in normal families and those in institutions (Spitz and Woolf, 1946). Schaffer's work is particularly clear on babies sent to the hospital; under 2 months, infants seem to show no effect of either separation from their mothers or reunion with them; from 2 to 7 months, a baby separated from its mother lies in the hospital neither crying nor vocalizing very much, just quietly scanning the environment, and when sent home is also markedly unresponsive, even limp at first (from 20 minutes to 4 days after reunion with the mother), then rather suddenly picks up again. Still older babies, who fear strangers, may protest and scream at separation.

It is in this attachment or imprinting period that the child first becomes cute. A newborn Caucasian infant is pink, if not red, wet and wrinkled, and scrawny, in fact incredibly attractive to the mother, but not the sort of round-faced eye-to-eye contact smily baby who sells soap flakes to the troop at large. (African newborns are often also pinkish, but their dark eyes give an early impression of eye-to-eye contact.) The round smooth face, the large head, in short the "cute" gestalt, indicate really not a new baby but an attaching baby.

In primates there has been very little direct work on the early period of attachment. The infants are still clinging to their mother most of the time as they have since birth, and are still physiologically dependent on her, so there is not much overt behavior that could be compared with the human smiling response. The first new calls that appear after birth are the greeting growl, in rhesus at 6 weeks, and elaborations of a short call to be picked up that has been present since birth—nothing that seems to correspond with the human smile. Probably the rhesus baby does not need such a thing, as it is clinging anyway and the smile is a way of drawing the mother near to a helpless baby lying in a carriage or on a blanket on the ground. Harlow reports that a rhesus at about 45 days begins to pay much more attention to the faces of other monkeys, but because he is talking about grossly institutionalized infants this might come much earlier in a wild group.

Fear of strangers

The third stage is the stage of rising fear of novelty and specificity to the mother. Perhaps too much has been made of fear of strangers in human infants because this might fit so neatly with ducklings' imprinting if it were true of all babies. A few babies, at least, in the second half of the first year, begin anxiously to reject strangers. Others do not cry if a stranger picks them up, but look repeatedly back and forth from the face of the stranger to the face of the mother, obviously aware of and comparing the differences. Schaffer (1966) shows that the child can in fact recognize the differences as early as 3 or 4 months: it is not until 8 months or so that he becomes fearful. In rhesus monkeys the comparable period perhaps appears at about 9 or 10 weeks in a laboratory group situation, when a group of new calls appears: lip smacking, which is a social attraction signal among monkeys, pleasure noises, social grooming, and as well the beginning of the fear grin and the fear call, the so-called geckering screech that goes with the grin. By this age the monkey baby has typically lost its distinguishing infant marks: the hair parting of the rhesus baby or the black coat of the young baboon.

Growing independence

The final stage is one of increasing independence. In this period the young monkey either leaves its mother more and more or is rejected by her more and more, but remains in association with her, sometimes for years. Thus, the final stage, although one can point very roughly to a beginning, may trail off or continue into the adult life of the young monkey. A great deal of research work has concerned developing independence: the measurements of Hinde and Spencer-Booth (Hinde and Spencer-Booth, 1967b; Spencer-Booth *et al.*, 1965; Spencer-Booth and Hinde, 1969) on rhesus in groups; of Kaufman and Rosenblum (1966) and Bobbitt, Jensen, and Gordon (1964) on pigtailed and bonnet macaques; of Jensen *et al.* (1967) on pigtails; and of Rowell (1968a) on the savanna baboon. All these studies measure such parameters as time on the mother while suckling, time off the mother, time within arm's length of the mother, whether the mother or the infant initiates approaches or departures, and active rejection or punishing by the mother. Unfortunately, almost none of the studies are strictly comparable:

Figure 116 A spider monkey mother makes a bridge for her child over a difficult passage, in Panama rainforest. Behavior in the wild during the stage of growing independence probably differs sharply from behavior in laboratory situations. (Courtesy of D. J. Chivers.)

Figure 117 A hamadryas mother makes a bridge for her child on an Ethiopian cliff face. (From H. Kummer, 1968.)

they have used different caging situations or slightly different measures. Barrenness of the cage or slightly richer environments enormously affect mothers' and infants' contacts (Jensen, 1968). Thus, it is impossible from the published graphs to get comparable data on the different species and animals used in different experiments. However, all agree that, for perhaps the first 20 or 25 weeks of young macaque monkeys' life, the amount of independence, time off the mother, and time farther away from her is increasing fairly rapidly, and that then this trails off in most species.

All the observers who work with caged animals are struck by how much the development of independence depends on the mother's behavior. She may actively reject, wean, even hit her youngster. Hinde has a useful index of the number of contacts that are due to the mother's or infant's initiative. This is the difference between the percentage of approaches that were due to the infants' movement and the percentage of leavings that were due to the infants. If the infant leaves its mother more than it approaches, that is, if the infant is trying to get away by and large, the index is negative. If the infant is approaching the mother more often than it is leaving and the mother is in fact doing the wandering off, the index is positive. Figure 118 shows this index for Hinde's group of young rhesus monkeys. For monkeys under about 20 weeks the index is negative. The youngster is constantly trying to get away

Figure 118 Maternal influence on the development of independence in caged rhesus. Dots show mean and shaded area shows range of six infants. *%A* − *%L* is the difference between approaches to the mother (from more than 2 ft to less than 2 ft) that were due to the infant and leavings from the mother (from less than 2 ft to more than 2 ft) that were due to the infant. Thus if the infant tended to leave the mother and be retrieved by her the index is negative, whereas if he followed her when she left the index is positive. In this situation, where small social groups of about five adults and young were caged together, the infants made increasing bids for independence up to 10 weeks, but after about 20 weeks it was the mother who initiated most separations and the infant who made most approaches. (After R. A. Hinde and Y. Spencer-Booth, 1967.)

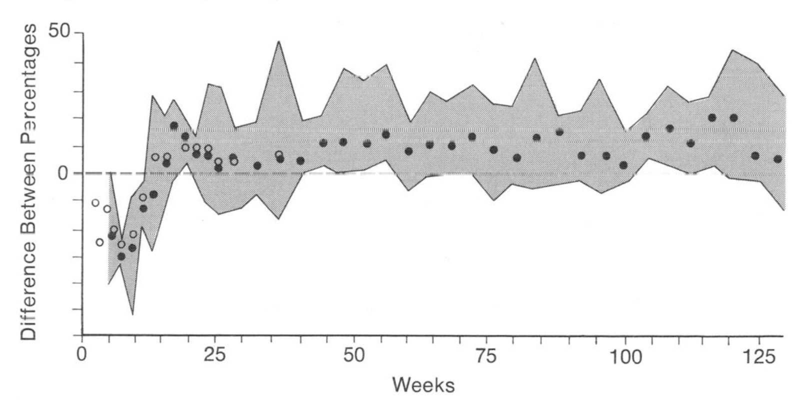

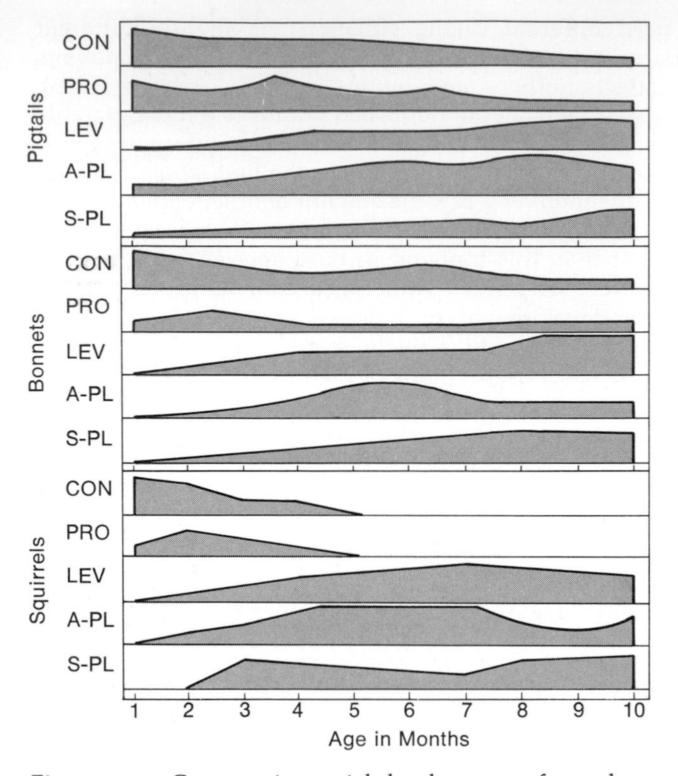

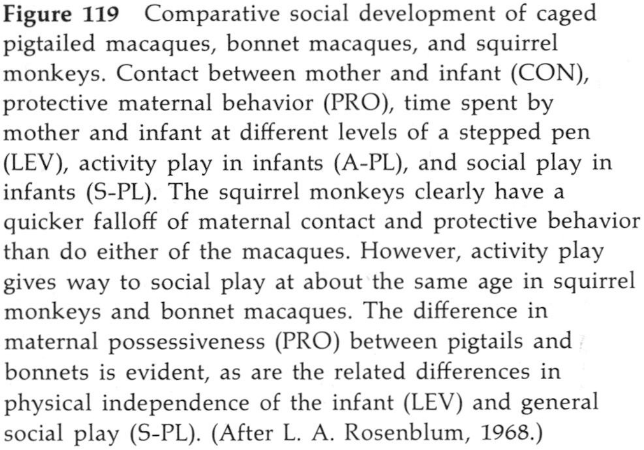

Figure 119 Comparative social development of caged pigtailed macaques, bonnet macaques, and squirrel monkeys. Contact between mother and infant (CON), protective maternal behavior (PRO), time spent by mother and infant at different levels of a stepped pen (LEV), activity play in infants (A-PL), and social play in infants (S-PL). The squirrel monkeys clearly have a quicker falloff of maternal contact and protective behavior than do either of the macaques. However, activity play gives way to social play at about the same age in squirrel monkeys and bonnet macaques. The difference in maternal possessiveness (PRO) between pigtails and bonnets is evident, as are the related differences in physical independence of the infant (LEV) and general social play (S-PL). (After L. A. Rosenblum, 1968.)

and explore while mother pulls him back by his tail or a hind foot. After this period the infant is responsible for most of the contacts they make, and the mother does not restrain him so much. The period of maximum infant attempts to get away may correspond in some sense to our 2-year-old period of aggressive independence, when human children are constantly saying "no" and "I want," and a tail for pulling them back out of trouble might be quite an asset.

The development of independence varies enormously with species and environmental situations. Kaufman and Rosenblum (1966) (Figure 119) compared pigtailed and bonnet macaques. The bonnet macaque mothers let their infants stray farther, longer, earlier than the pigtails. The pigtails both restrain their infants and punish and hit them, treating them much more roughly than the bonnets. As adults the pigtails continue to maintain an individual distance from each other, even sleeping at arm's length, while the bonnets sit in happy clumps, lumped around each other, taking care of each other's babies because the bonnet baby that is allowed to wander usually winds up being cuddled by one of its mother's female friends.

The punishing of young infants by the pigtail mothers does not make the infants less attached to their mothers. On the contrary, laboratory studies seem to show that punishing or even quite brutal treatment of infants leads the infants to cling ever closer, not only in the early stages but later in life. Harlow rigged up one of his surrogate mothers with a row of jets of air down her belly so that when the infant clung it could be blasted in the face with air, which rhesus hate. It could turn the air off by ceasing to cling, but of course in great distress it cried and clung ever louder and harder and was blasted more and more. Sackett (Sackett *et al.*, 1967), doing choice experiments with rhesus raised in various conditions, has

Figure 120 A chimpanzee mother tickles her child. (Courtesy of H. van Lawick.)

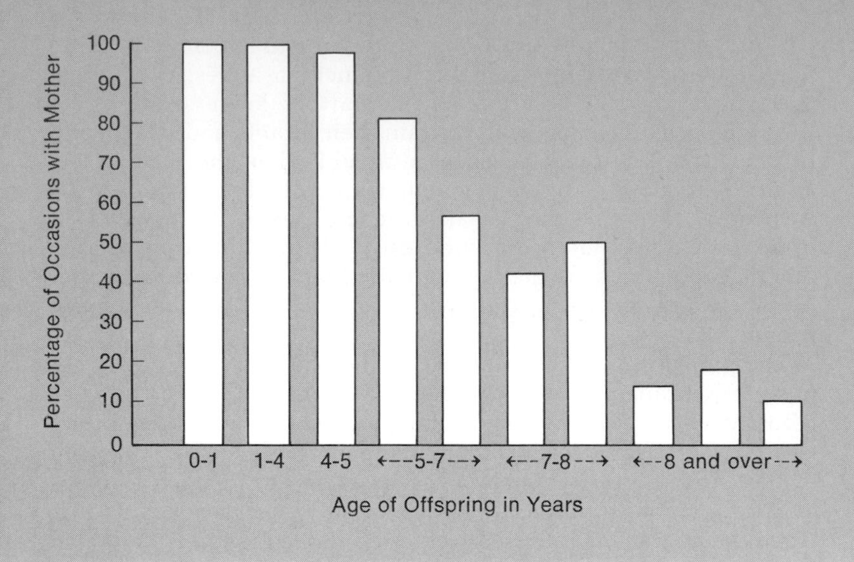

Figure 121 Development of independence in wild chimpanzees. The number of occasions when mother and offspring were seen traveling about together as a percentage of occasions when either or both were seen. (After J. van Lawick-Goodall, 1967a.)

found that the infants allowed to choose among different females reliably chose their own mother if they had had anything like normal mothering but chose their mother even *more often* if they had had brutal, punishing mothering. The punishing pigtail mothers as well have their infants clinging, staying closer to them on the infants' initiative as well as the mothers'.

Rowell (1968a) has compared the amount of time that young baboons cling during the rain and during sunny periods, as a cautionary tale. During rain infants shelter underneath their mothers in a kind of tent formed of their mothers' arms and long side hair. This is quite useful, as their own natal coat is not waterproof. Rain increased the amount of clinging time by about a quarter and could therefore have a very noticeable effect on the amount of time left for social and exploratory play.

The social environment is of course even more important. Subordinate mothers whose babies risk being stolen by a dominant tend to become overprotective, in cages. The effects of this pathological protectiveness can greatly override any other aspect of the environment (Rowell, 1968a; Spencer-Booth, Hinde, and Bruce, 1965).

Free-ranging rhesus monkeys almost never reject their babies, which again means that the laboratory studies which show how maternal rejection leads to independence of the young are highly biased and comparable mainly with other studies in similarly constructed laboratories.

INFANTS' SEX AND PARITY

While primatologists are beginning to study the differences in mothers' treatment of their babies in different circumstances, they have also suddenly discovered that children are different, that they exert their individuality. One can presume that some infants are more tranquil and some are more aggressive and that this is one of the major variables in the apparently precise laboratory studies.

Mothers clearly do treat their infants differently by sex (Jensen *et al.*, 1968a; Hansen, 1966; and Mitchell, 1968c). Boy rhesus babies are allowed more independence and are also treated more aggressively, whereas female babies are cuddled closer to the mother and are also restrained more. Two male babies of overprotective mothers were restrained more than a male normally would be and seemed in some respects feminized, that is, less aggressive and more subordinate than most males. The sample is insignificant, but it is interesting in any case, particularly as human beings have long been known to treat males and females differently from birth, and it has been presumed that a great deal of the adult sex role is learned through early childhood from this differential treatment. Among Thelma Rowell's (1968a) caged baboons, the adult male as well took a great deal of interest in the male babies but not the female babies, inspecting the male babies' genitalia as well as grooming them and allowing them more contact with him.

Mitchell and Stevens (1969) are currently working on a study of the differences between primiparous and multiparous mothers. They come to the conclusion that at least for the first 3 months of an infant's life a primiparous mother is consistently more anxious. She restrains her infant more and reacts more violently to novel or slightly threatening situations. Quite probably among rhesus monkeys, as among human beings, there are consistent differences in the behavior of first- and second- and lastborn children in a family, due in part to their differential treatment.

SUMMARY

Young mammals may be *precocial* or *altricial*. The earliest mammals may have been nest-building tree dwellers with relatively altricial young, which, when older, clung to their parents' fur. Many prosimians follow this pattern; other prosimians and all higher primates (except man) carry their young on the fur from birth. Birth follows the same stages as in man, although labor is usually shorter. Old World and New World monkeys generally give birth at night; man has a slight statistical bias toward nocturnal birth.

Many primate newborns can climb to the nipple themselves,

although mothers generally help. Many primates have distinct natal coats, and all share the "cute" characteristics: big eyes in a big round head. The baby is "cutest" some weeks (or in humans, months) after birth: it may be that the cute gestalt functions chiefly toward troop members, whereas the mother's initial recognition arises largely from her own physiological state.

Monkeys raised on dummy mothers choose a soft, clingable surface rather than a pseudomother that gives milk. Motherless monkeys, when adult, mate abnormally and, finally mated, may reject their first young. A peer group of other infants can largely, but not wholly, compensate for lack of mothering.

Infants sometimes react to short-term separation and reunion with their mothers by clinging, overdependent behavior of very long duration.

Human infants show stages of attachment that resemble imprinting in birds: first reflex clinging, then recognition of one's own mother, followed by unease at strangers, and then increasing independence. These stages are clearest in people, but probably also exist in primates. Social smiling plays a major role in human babies, both to show the infant's attachment and to attract a mother to her immobile young; clinging primate babies lack the smile.

Rhesus mothers, like human mothers, seem to treat first and second children differently and boys differently from girls.

13 Growing Up in a Troop

FATHERS

Most primate fathers could not claim their own children. A few species live in pairs, or one-male harems, where the available male is presumably the father. However, in large troops any one of a number of adult males might have fathered any child.

In some primate species such as hanuman langurs, males almost entirely ignore infants. However, if an infant is threatened by danger, males will respond by challenging the attacker and if possible rescuing the infant. Males commonly allow young infants to take liberties. Babies play with or even hit an adult male with impunity. Commonly, other animals are punished for being rough with an infant; this is part of the general male behavior of punishing animals that cause a disturbance in the troop, and being rough with an infant generally leads to a loud, crying disturbance. Young juveniles are often disciplined in this way. As usual, there are wide differences in the amount of defense or tolerance or punishment, and very wide differences in the amount of grooming or other contact that the adult male will direct toward the infant. At one extreme are the marmoset males, which actually carry their twin young until the young are about half grown. Adult male baboons groom and come close to young infants, although less than female baboons do; adult male sifakas eagerly cluster around and groom new infants as much as do the females. There is the whole spectrum from the marmoset's behavior to that of ignoring the young.

Figure 122 Marmoset males offer the extreme in paternal care. This pygmy marmoset will carry his twin young until their combined weight equals his own, only handing them over to their mother for feeding. (San Diego Zoo Photo by Ron Garrison.)

Figure 123 Infants form a center of attraction in many species. Here a male barbary macaque sits close to the female and her young. (San Diego Zoo Photo by Ron Garrison.)

Mitchell (1969) has recently reviewed father-like behavior in primates, and Beach (1967) has pointed out that quasimaternal behavior appears in many mammalian males, given the right environment.

Mitchell points out that father-like behavior may be very much influenced by the mother's treatment of the young male baby. If in fact she treats males rougher, there is plenty of experimental evidence to show that rough or brutal treatment increases aggression, in a rhesus monkey at least, and this may be part of the normal development of male aggressive behavior. Isolation destroys normal paternal behavior as it does normal maternal behavior: Harlow's motherless male rhesus have been known to kill infants.

The characteristics of the infant that call forth paternal behavior include age. In some species the newest infants get most attention from the males, in others it is the 1-year-olds. It includes sex: young male infants, at least among Rowell's baboons, get more attention from the male; however, slightly older juvenile females seem to be more associated with males. If a male is a mother's kin, a mother's consort, or in any other special relationship that leads him to be close to a mother, he may groom or take an interest in her infant as well. Finally, orphaned infants are occasionally, at least in macaques and baboons (Bolwig, 1959), adopted by males, and in Japanese macaques during the birth season adult males adopt 1-year-olds while their mothers are giving birth to new infants (Itani, 1959). This last seems to be a culturally propagated behavior, because it only appears in some troops, but in these it does so quite consistently.

Males may even use infants as pawns in the status game. This last is more complicated; in rhesus monkeys, males with a strong interest in the center of the troop can pick up the infants of dominant females and thus be allowed in. Hamadryas baboons use infants to protect themselves, because the dominant male does not attack them when they are carrying an infant. Barbary macaques have ritualized this to one of the commonest male interactions. They hold and carry infants from the first week of life, lip smacking to the infant's bottom, and present the infants as passport to more dominant males, even sitting in the dominant's lap with the baby between them—the polite response by the dominant is to lift the baby's tail, and, in turn, lip smack to its behind (Deag, 1970; Lahiri and Southwick, 1966). Thus, in this special case quasimaternal behavior can confer a kind of status on a young male. Deag calls this "social buffering"—a tripartite situation in which two animals' antagonism is buffered by a third animal.

There seem to be no phylogenetic trends in paternal behavior. However, there is one consistent relationship with other social behavior: in groups of all the branches of the primate order that have only one adult male, paternal behavior is more likely to occur—the marmosets, the titi monkeys, the gibbons. From Chivers' (personal communication) study of the siamang, it seems that the mother sleeps with the infant but the male sleeps with the juvenile, and during the day they transfer so that the infant is actually carried about by the male. Hamadryas baboons, with a very different system of the male and his harem, quite possibly derived from the promiscuous system of the savanna baboon, develop their groups through a quasimaternal behavior of the males. Young males, subadults, may adopt a play group of infants temporarily and particular female infants, only 1-year old and far from sexually mature, on a more permanent basis. Thus, Kummer (1968) speculates that the mane of a male has in fact developed as a supernormal stimulus for grooming, so that the infant female's preference for her mother's fur is transferred directly to her attachment to the bushy-maned male. The subadult male and his child bride eventually mature into a normal group, with maternal-seeming behavior and protection by the male of the female changing into the male's sexual defense of his female. We ourselves of course are a good example of males bonded to particular females and exhibiting outstanding paternal behavior. The correlation in other primates between one-male groups and paternal behavior supports the argument in Chapter 11 about the causal relationship between the two: that where it is ecologically advantageous for male and female to raise the young together, one tends to find not a large promiscuous troop but more limited marriages.

AUNTS

Among all the social primates it seems to be usual for females to take an interest in each other's babies. Females carry, cuddle, and groom a new baby and, if they cannot get hold of the baby directly, approach and groom the mother until they are allowed to touch and take care of the baby. Hinde, Rowell, and Spencer-Booth (Hinde *et al.*, 1964; Hinde and Spencer-Booth, 1967a) call this "aunt behavior." They do not mean to imply blood relationship but that

Figure 124 "Aunt" behavior in a ringtailed lemur. One female grooms the infant of another. (San Diego Zoo Photo by Ron Garrison.)

the females are behaving like the maiden aunts of English turn-of-the-century middle-class families.

North Indian hanuman langurs pass their babies around practically like footballs from the first day of life (Jay, 1965). An aunt may carry a new baby several hundred yards from its mother, and although the mother tends to keep an eye on where the baby has gone, she does not otherwise protest. Baboon and rhesus mothers are much more restrictive, although other females of the troop take an equally great interest in the new young. Squirrel monkeys (DuMond, 1968; Baldwin, 1969), more advanced in motor development than the preceding two, begin going to aunts at about 3 weeks, when mothers first let their youngsters climb on other females. Among the social lemurs, the sifaka has extensive aunt behavior. Females, males, and juveniles of the troop take an interest in the young, and the young climb on them. Only other mothers are allowed to groom a newborn ringtailed lemur, but the mothers reciprocally groom each other's infants and may even transfer infants in the process. The one generalization that can be made is that, although there are both quantitative and qualitative differences in aunt behavior among species, the first excursions of any young social primate tend to be onto other animals of the group rather than onto branches or other exploration of the environment.

Two studies have compared the frequency of aunt behavior in different females of a troop. Spencer-Booth (1968), working with caged rhesus, found that females that had not borne live young, that is, had not themselves raised a baby, were more likely to display aunt behavior toward young infants than females who had been mothers. The single class of females most active in this way was the subadults and adolescent females. Struhsaker (in prepara-

Figure 125 "Aunt" behavior in woolly monkeys. (Courtesy of L. Williams from Williams, 1967.)

Figure 126 "The Women's Institute." Hanuman langur females congregate around a nursing mother. (Courtesy of S. Ripley.)

tion), working with wild vervets, came to the same conclusion. The class of females showing most aunt behavior was the 2-year-old females, that is late juveniles or adolescents.

Clearly the behavior of the aunts can influence the mother's own treatment of her infant. We have already mentioned cases of pathological restriction in the cage, where a mother rhesus or baboon may cling to her infant and restrain all its early attempts at exploration because a dominant female is attempting to steal, or temporarily steal, her new infant.

Aunt behavior has various functions. If a mother dies, her infant stands a chance of being adopted by other animals of the troop, and this has been repeatedly seen both in cages and in the wild. A subtler function may be that of binding together the adults of the troop. Washburn and DeVore (1960) suppose that in the baboons they watched one of the main cohesive forces was the social interest in grooming new infants, displayed by both males and females. It may also simply be convenient for the mother to leave her infant occasionally with another female. Among nilgiri langurs there is what amounts to a real babysitting system, in which one female may sit near three or four infants while the other females of the troop are off feeding (Poirier, 1968b). Most importantly, it clearly plays a major role in the learning of social behavior. The infant learns relations with other adults besides its mother, while the caretaking females may themselves be learning the appropriate behavior for a mother. Many observers remark on the ineptitude of some of the aunts: juvenile hanuman langurs that hold an infant upside down so clumsily that it squeals, whereupon the mother retrieves it, juvenile squirrel monkeys that leave the infant on a branch at the approach of danger, again with the mother rushing over to retrieve it. The learning may not be infallible. Nilgiri langurs apparently leave the infant squealing whether they are aunt or mother. However, one can see that, particularly if aunt behavior is common in the late-juvenile or subadult females, this can be important preparation for effective motherhood, without which an infant primate cannot survive. It is quite possible, although difficult to prove, that the same tendencies remain in human beings. In many parts of Africa and Asia, girl children are put in charge of young babies as child nurses, carrying the babies around on their backs. In our own society, girls take a great interest in new babies, cuddling them and playing with them. Much of this is obviously due to cultural roles, but there is no reason why there should not as well be an innate bias toward playing with babies.

KINSHIP

Because many savanna primates seem to live in fairly homogeneous troops, it was long thought that when an infant reached independence from its mother the family bond broke up and was lost in the general social interactions of the troop. Now, in every species that has been studied for a sufficient length of time, it is clear that a young animal maintains special ties with its mother, even into adult life. Ties among siblings also develop, quite plausibly simply because the older juvenile sibling is still associating with its mother when her new infant is born and therefore the juvenile and its younger sister or brother also associate. The evidence is best for chimpanzees (Van Lawick-Goodall, 1967a), Japanese macaques, and the rhesus monkeys of Cayo Santiago (Koford, 1965), because the longest field studies have concerned these species. Families of chimpanzees are now known in which a mother associates with four of her offspring born at 2- or 3-year intervals. The most famous of these is the matriarch Flo with her now adult son Faben, her second son Figan, daughter Fifi, and baby Flint. However, the kinship groups of Japanese macaques have a truly Japanese complexity, and one can see that not only the children of one mother but several generations including two sisters and their descendants or a mother and her brother still live in a fairly close sibling relationship, so that the brother takes care of his nephews and nieces. The kinds of association include moving together and feeding together in tolerance, as well as grooming relationships. Although kinship relationships can usually be traced back to the relationship of brothers and sisters to their own mother, the sibling relationships

Figure 127 Flo and her family. Flo is grooming Faben, her near-adult son (about 11 years old) while her son Figan (about 7 years old) sprawls in the foreground. Fifi (4 years old) plays with Flint, the 3-month-old baby. (Courtesy of H. van Lawick.)

Figure 128 Sibling behavior. Flo gently prevents Fifi from touching the new baby, Flint. (Courtesy of H. van Lawick.)

persist even in the absence of the mother. Examples of this are the mother's brother relationship in Japanese macaques (Yamada, 1963); another example is the orphaned chimpanzee adopted by its older sister. A young male rhesus may be more likely to change groups if he has an older brother who has already done so, and he takes up his sibling relationship with his brother with renewed vigor in the new troop (Koford, 1965; Kaufmann, 1965).

Although such kinship relationships have been traced only in very few species, the burden of proof is now on people watching the other species to see if anything of the sort happens. Field studies of other primates have simply not been adequate either to prove or to disprove the existence of kinship relationships beyond the mother and her young infant or juvenile. Where the adults are solitary or live in exclusive pairs or harems, it seems quite likely that the adolescents really do leave their parents and each other for good. However, even here the pattern may not be clear-cut. For instance, hamadryas baboons, although they live in harems, may band together with several males joining forces against several other males. What it is that determines the structure of these larger bands of males is unknown, but kinship may well play a role.

THE OEDIPAL PHASE AND LATENCY PERIOD

All the stages of maternal attachment, fear of strangers, and beginnings of independence only take the human child into his second year. Two further stages are clear in human children: First there is a period of growing concern with their own bodies, accompanied by concern with the parent of the opposite sex, which may often be expressed as blatently sexual flirtation. This early sexual, or "oedipal," period, from about 3 to 5 years of age, is followed by a "latency" period from 5 years to puberty, when children are less overtly interested in sex, at least as directed toward their parents, and spend far more time in peer group play. If the culture permits, some of this play may be erotic as well.

Freudian theory holds that the human 4-year-old's sexual attachment to one parent and jealousy of the other parent, complicated by dawning bodily fears, particularly the fear of castration, become a bottled-up, violent passion. If not suitably resolved, this may lead to emotional abnormalities. If it is normally resolved, it sets a pattern of willing respect and emulation for the like-sex parent and romantic, not just possessive, love for the other. During latency, the child drives his sexual feeling into the subconscious, where the pressure of emotion becomes the basis of intellectual curiosity. Dr. Benjamin Spock puts it:

> The emotional development of man up to the age of five or six is not—except for his overidealization of his parents—basically different from that of the other higher animals. What

distinguishes man so sharply from other creatures is the characteristics he acquires after five: his inhibition and sublimation of his sexual interests; his capacity for abstract thinking; his interest in symbols, systems, and rules; his inventiveness and creativity; his capacity for being inspired by heroes and spiritual ideals; his urge throughout history and throughout the world to define and worship a God. It is fascinating that these particularly constructive human characteristics are brought out in him by his having to relinquish his possessive yearning for one parent because of fear and rivalry with the other. (Spock, 1969, p. 12)

One may not accept the Freudian mechanism, or one may believe that Freud is far more clearly right about Middle European man than about people in more easy-going societies. At the least, though, it is true that many or most children behave quite differently during the "oedipal" phase than they do in the latency period. It would be very instructive to know if anything similar happens in primates.

However, we are still in reaction to the over-Freudian primatology of the 1930s, so there is almost no relevant data from modern studies. The Hayeses (1951) record that 2-year-old Viki in her human "family" began to notice and turn toward her father just as 3-year-old little girls do. Flint, as a 2-year-old, mounted and thrust at his mother when she came into estrus. Older chimpanzee male children and young adults did not mate with their mothers (see the next section, on incest taboos). There is, of course, a very long childhood and youth in most primate species. If a chimpanzee 2-year-old is roughly comparable in development with our oedipal 3- to 5-year-old, there remain to him 6 years before he reaches puberty at 8 years and 4 or 5 years more before he is fully adult. During this time he clearly turns increasingly from his mother to his peer group, but whether or not he at first directs sexual responses toward his mother, then away from her, is unknown.

Neither is much known about the course of juvenile play. In all species described, there is an erotic component—the patterns of sexual behavior, like the patterns of most other adult behavior, appear in play. The rudiments of a "latency period" would imply an early peak in infant sexual play, then less through midchildhood, rising again at puberty when effective coitus appears. On the other hand, if there is nothing resembling latency, juvenile sexual behavior might increase steadily in frequency and intensity, from none in infancy to full sexual behavior sometime in adolescence.

No one would claim that repressed sex underlies intellectual curiosity in the primates, and it is questionable how much the very young primate juvenile is likely to be in rivalry with his like-sexed parent, although in a number of species juveniles try to hit males who mount their mothers. However, if one is going to claim the oedipal mechanisms as unique to man, or as a means by which we arrive at intellectual ambition or romantic love, it seems ludicrous not to know how much of our childhood sexual development really is unique.

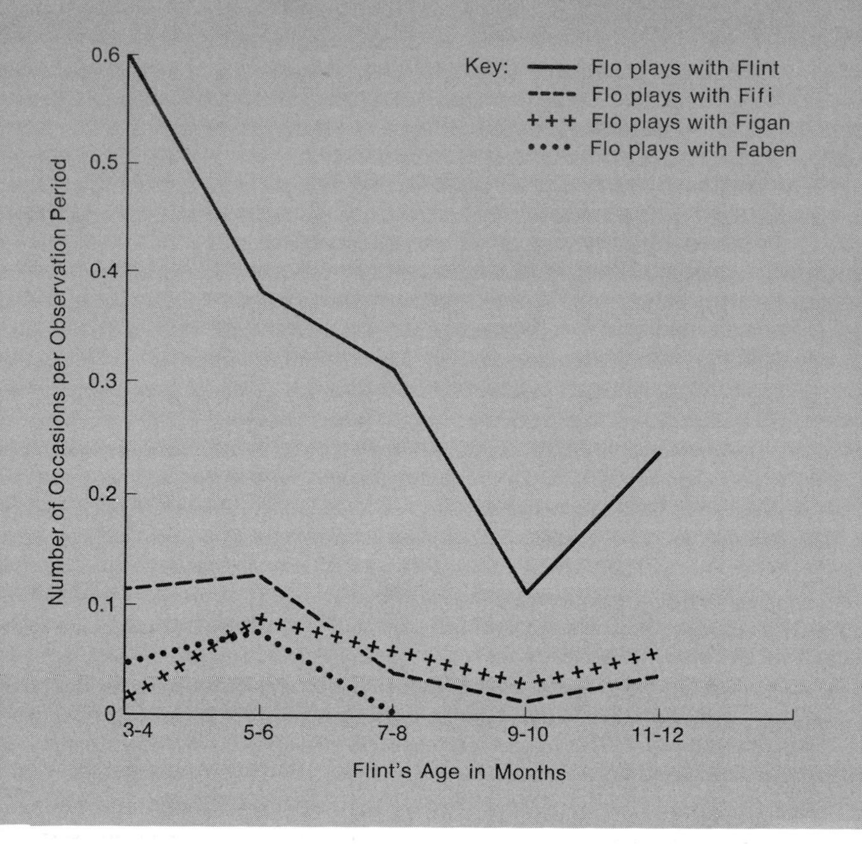

Figure 129 Mother–child play in a chimpanzee family. Changes in the frequency of the mother Flo's play with her four offspring while her infant Flint was 3–12 months old. (After J. van Lawick-Goodall, 1967a.)

INCEST TABOOS

Incest taboos are universal among human beings, the taboos against mating between son and mother, between father and daughter, and mating between brother and sister. In free-ranging macaques there is apparently very little mating between sons and mothers (Sade, 1968; Imanishi, 1965; Koford, 1963). Most of the inhibition can be attributed to differences in dominance status, for the mother long retains dominance over her adult son, and in one case of reversal of dominance the son also mated with his mother. However, low-ranking sons sit with and groom with their mothers more than with any other female, so if they mate at all one would expect them to mate with her. One could postulate a specific inhibition of incest, as Sade (1968) does, or a more general tendency to continue respecting the mother, as van Lawick-Goodall (1967a) does. Van Lawick-Goodall describes the adolescent or young adult chimps Faben and Everred letting their mothers take bananas first from the feeding place. She notes that, whereas the young adult son continues respecting his mother, the mother develops an increasing respect for her son. Flo jumped and stamped on and snatched things from her 8-year-old son Figan but never took such liberties with her 12-year-old son Faben. The persisting bonds between mother and grown son are shown in the unusual amount of time that they associate together, travel around together, play together, and defend each other; when another male attacked Flo, Flo and Faben together combined to drive off the male, Faben coming to his mother's protection. Figure 129 shows the amount of time that Flo spent playing with each of her children during the early months of life of her youngest baby, Flint. When Flint was a small infant she played more with all her children, even the nearly adult Faben.

There seems to be no incest taboo against father-daughter mating, (which is hardly surprising inasmuch as neither fathers nor observers in most monkey societies know which females are the daughters) or, so far recorded, against mating between brothers and sisters, although Fifi, in her first estrus, protested. Washburn and Lancaster (1968) suggest that these taboos originated with the nuclear family of early hunters as a way of avoiding extra pregnancies among adolescent girls, in groups heavily dependent on adult males to provide food for all.

DEPENDENT RANK

Kawai (1958a), studying Japanese monkeys, first showed the importance of the mother's position in determining the status ranking of her offspring. Japanese macaque troops when feeding at a provisioning site are generally divided into a central portion with the females and leading males and a peripheral portion in which sit the younger adults, the subadults, and low-ranking males. A male monkey whose mother is extremely dominant may never be exiled to the peripheral portion but grow up in the center of the troop, making a smooth transition from the status of a privileged infant and juvenile to that of a leading male monkey. Both male and female infants learn the behavior appropriate to their mother's status very quickly, because, as infants, they are treated with the respect or lack of it due to their own mothers. Figure 130 gives Kawai's analysis of one Japanese monkey troop, in which the young infant ranks directly below its own mother, and her juveniles of preceding years just below the new infant yet above the next kinship group of mother and her offspring. Thus, while an infant or juvenile is associated with its mother and while it can count on her support in quarrels, its rank approximates hers. Quite rea-

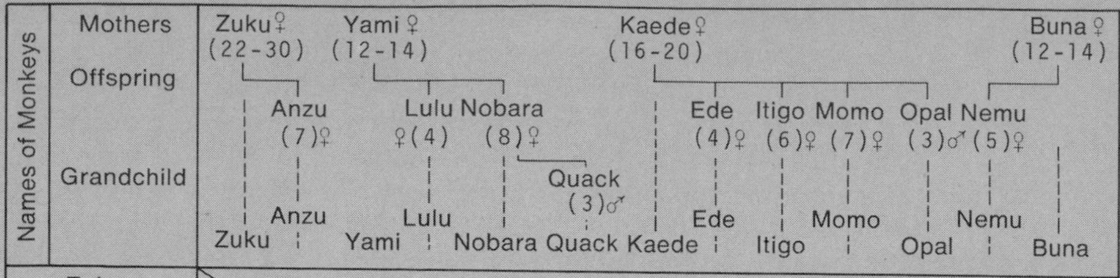

Names of Monkeys													
Mothers	Zuku♀ (22-30)		Yami♀ (12-14)				Kaede♀ (16-20)						Buna♀ (12-14)
Offspring		Anzu (7)♀		Lulu ♀(4)	Nobara (8)♀			Ede (4)♀	Itigo (6)♀	Momo (7)♀	Opal (3)♂	Nemu (5)♀	
Grandchild						Quack (3)♂							
	Zuku	Anzu	Yami	Lulu	Nobara	Quack	Kaede	Ede	Itigo	Momo	Opal	Nemu	Buna
Zuku		+	+	+	+	+	+	+	+	+	+	+	+
Anzu	−		+	+	+	+	+	+	+	+	+	+	+
Yami	−	−		+	+	+	+	+	+	+	+	+	+
Lulu	−	−	−		+	+	(±)	+	+	+	+	+	+
Nobara	−	−	−	−		+	+	+	+	+	+	+	+
Quack	−	−	−	−	−		(±)	+	+	+	+	+	+
Kaede	−	−	−	(±)	−	(±)		+	+	+	+	+	+
Ede	−	−	−	−	−	−	−		+	+	+	+	+
Itigo	−	−	−	−	−	−	−	−		+	+	+	+
Momo	−	−	−	−	−	−	−	−	−		(±)	+	+
Opal	−	−	−	−	−	−	−	−	−	(±)		+	+
Nemu	−	−	−	−	−	−	−	−	−	−	−		+
Buna	−	−	−	−	−	−	−	−	−	−	−	−	

Key: + Dominant
− Subordinate
(±) Equivocal
Numbers in Parentheses are Age of Animals

Figure 130 Dependent rank in a Japanese macaque troop. This troop is unusual in having no permanent adult male. However, it is typical in that each mother's offspring rank just beneath her, taking precedence over the next family. Younger offspring of one lineage commonly outrank elder siblings. Numbers in parentheses are age of animals. (After M. Kawai, 1958.)

sonably, the young of dominant females learn to behave in a dominant and self-assured manner, and females as well as males tend to perpetuate their mother's status (Kawamura, 1965, 1967).

To some extent, this legacy of the privileged mothers occurs in all types of mammals. A strong and healthy mother will be more likely to have strong and healthy offspring; a mother sheep that has a particularly favored bit of grazing will bequeath this pasture to her own offspring as they learn the habits of following her in her usual tracks. However, the transmission of aristocracy and privileged behavior in a dominance situation that we see in macaques is much more likely among troop-living, complexly learning animals, and has all too obvious parallels with mankind.

PEER GROUPS

Young mammals play. When we read even of a marsupial grasshopper mouse that does not play, we are astounded and think that something must be very peculiar in its development (Ewer, 1968). If anything, primates play even more than other mammals. Young bushbabies, perhaps even young pottos, indulge in locomotor play and, in laboratories, where there is nothing else to play with, object manipulation. However, the striking characteristic of young, socially living primates is their social play. Infants and juveniles play together, play with adults, play with their mothers, play with their siblings. If the troop is large enough to have a group of young monkeys, they tend to play mostly with each other; in small troops, they play in groups of very mixed ages.

Such play is in fact very serious, not, one hopes, in motivation or in the fun they get out of it, but in the training for future social roles. They learn the physical gestures of communication. If one prefers not to say "learn," the practice certainly refines these gestures and increases the sensitivity of their use, as shown by the work of Miller *et al.* (1967) on the noneffectiveness of communication between isolated animals. They eventually learn their future dominance status. However influenced this may be by their physical constitution or their heritage from more or less dominant mothers, it is worked out in the course of interaction within the peer group. Male infants and juveniles play more vigorously with more rough and tumble than females—this is true in rhesus and human beings at least, and probably many other species as well.

Loizos (1967) points out that two at least of the theories of the uses of play are not logically watertight. The theories are that practice or rehearsal of behavior improves the efficiency of behavior in adult life, when it has to be shown in earnest, and that play provides the animal with a constant stream of vital information about the environment. Loizos says that both of these functions could be perfectly well pursued by serious practice or exploration rather than by the exaggerated movements of play. However, as she makes clear, this is how in fact primates arrive at a great deal of their adult behavior, and social play in particular is a crucial part of the normal growing up of the young primate. Harlow has compared the behavior of young monkeys deprived of playmates with that of normals. Serious deficits appear, even with the best of mothering. However, this is of course the cage situation, where there are deficits in very many other aspects of the environment as well.

Thus, whereas all authors are agreed that the peer group is of extreme importance in primate ontogeny, that play with one's fellows determines in some degree at least one's behavior as an adult, there is very little systematic analysis or proof of this obvious conclusion. (Play as it affects intellectual development rather than social development will be discussed in Part III.)

Figure 131 Rough-and-tumble play between a wild adult and juvenile ringtailed lemur. (Courtesy of R. D. Martin.)

Figure 132 Pygmy chimpanzees or bonobos in rough-and-tumble play. (Courtesy of D. Sorby.)

Figure 133 Human rough-and-tumble play. The baby at 1 year is just transferring his ventroventral clinging to adults into wrestling with children. (A. Jolly.)

The groups of juveniles and adolescents take a role in the movement of a large primate troop as well. They are often on the periphery, typically the first to explore a new situation, to try new foods, or to discover new dangers. In a sense, the young males and juveniles are the most expendable members of the group and expended they are if they are the first to discover a lion. This then alerts the rest of the troop, who can flee or take other appropriate action. On the other hand, if the juveniles are the first to discover a new food source or a new kind of food, again the more conservative adults by observing the experimentation of the juveniles can follow to their own advantage.

THE ELDERLY

It has already been said that the elderly play a role in primate society, as their experience may be useful to the troop as a whole, and that aging dominants may be "respected" long past their physical prime. In at least one case, a dyed-in-the-wool Tory Japanese macaque leader saved the whole troop from being trapped, because he refused to let any members of his group approach the new object, although it seemed likely that neither he nor others had any experience of traps before. Thus, both the explorative nature of the juveniles and the more cautious nature of the adults may work together to their mutual advantage (Miyadi, 1967).

THE INDIVIDUAL

Summing up the ontogeny of behavior of an individual primate is not easy. At one extreme, one can turn to the solitary prosimians, for instance, the potto or golden potto. There, the mother bears one infant at a time, and the baby is parked for much of each night on a branch, clambering onto the mother when she returns. It lives with the mother for a period of time and then goes off on its own, apparently equipped with the full adult repertoire of behavior. The potto's behavior could thus conceivably be analyzed in the traditional categories of mostly learned or very innate, and genes and environment analyzed by the traditional methods. However, with a macaque or chimpanzee, the adult's behavior is an intricate summation of the influences of its mother, its father or the other adult males, its aunts, and its siblings and the social tradition of a group that has in a real sense a continuing body of culture. Therefore, for the macaque or chimpanzee, it is in a sense more appropriate to turn to techniques of human psychology, which must recognize that the individual is playing a role throughout his life in a complex social matrix. We must have here another kind of parsimony. Instead of assuming that all behavior is produced by the simplest possible mechanism consistent with the observations, it is more cautious to assume that behavior is produced by complex mechanisms, as complex as those that we would expect for ourselves, except where one can definitely prove that a factor present in us is not present in the primate.

TROOP FISSION

There seem to be only two species of social primate in which a social change in troop has been observed in more than one case so that one has much of an idea of how usual such changes could be. One is the hanuman langur, for which it has already been described how males from outside the troop come, take over a harem group, and oust the dominant male. Eventually, one of the new males becomes harem leader in his turn, kills the infants, drives off male juveniles and subadults, and mates with the females. The other species is the Japanese macaque. Japanese macaque troops have been provisionized and have built up to a minimum of a hundred animals before fission, so their process may be artificially complex. Furuya (1968, 1969) describes five consecutive fissions of the Gagyusan troop and nine fissions of other troops of Japanese macaques. In each case, it is easy to distinguish a main troop and a branch troop. The main troop keeps the majority of the original animals and the usual home range and movements. The branch troop goes off somewhere else on its own. Furuya concludes that fissions have no relation to the breeding season; on the contrary, they are more likely to occur in the nonmating season when the troop is more actively on the move. In the provisionized troops the question of food supply does not really come up: there is adequate food for all the monkeys at all times, although the main troop keeps easiest access to the feeding ground.

Two general social factors affecting fission are the size of the troop (in the Gagyusan troop about one-hundred and fifty monkeys before fission each time) and the sex ratio. Typically, the branch troop contains a fairly large number of males, whereas the main troop is left with the normal 1:2 ratio of males to females. Actual sparking of troop fission seems to depend on one or a very few very dissatisfied males, who act as the nucleus and leaders in the new branch troop. However, these males may be drawn from almost any social class. Two, for instance, were leaders who were declining in rank, having been surpassed in the main troop by their former subordinates. Three others were young males, who were growing up to be almost equal to the leaders and subleaders in physical stature, but who were barred in the original large troop from entering the center of the troop as subleaders. Three other cases have been reported in which the actual alpha or beta of the male troop acted as nucleus in a branch troop. In fact, there are a number of reports of alpha leaders leaving to become solitary males. In some of the fissions, solitary males from quite outside the troop have acted as nuclei, coming in, associating with the troop for varying lengths of time, and then walking off with a group of females. Once even a dominant and antagonistic female became the nucleus of a new troop. In general, Furuya concludes that the nucleus animals are those whose position is unstable in the old troop, although this cannot always be true because occasionally the alpha male of the old troop leads the breakaway group. However, Furuya very plausibly represents the fission process as one that stabilizes the troop structure, removing the young males whose growth of physical power leads them to challenge the established members of the hierarchy. Because a predominance of males are likely to leave in any such breakaway, this also normalizes the sex ratio of the main troop.

No branch troops have been studied for any length of time, but arguing from cases of artificial troops with high male–female sex ratio, Furuya believes that the social structure of a branch troop may often be unstable. It might resolve itself by throwing off solitary males until it reaches the more usual predominance of females. Although it may be possible to analyze the normal social structure of any troop and see whether that troop is likely to break up, it seems impossible to predict which animals will act as nucleus or leader for the branch troop, which animals will join the branch troop (beyond the general supposition that kinship groups may tend to move off together), or whether a branch troop will form by desertion of males from the main troop or by a solitary taking away some of the main troop animals. In fact, it is impossible to predict the exact composition of any ordinary wild troop. For instance, there are a provisionized troop of Japanese macaques (Kawai, 1958a) and a completely wild troop of Indian rhesus (Neville, 1968b) who have persisted for many months without any adult males, but simply dominant females who lead the social system and determine the movements of the troop. All of this is in the realm of individually determined behavior. We have perhaps reached the province of history rather than the province of biology.

SUMMARY

Males' attitude to babies ranges from indifference in some species such as langurs to performing the bulk of the care in marmosets. Males of most species will allow infants to take liberties and will protect them from outside threat. In baboons, macaques, and sifakas, infants form a focus of interest for males and females. Male barbary apes and hamadryas baboons carry infants to gain status, for "social buffering."

Females and female juveniles groom and carry infants not their own, so-called aunt behavior. This seems common in all social species and may be an important way for female juveniles to learn appropriate maternal care.

Siblings stay together and interact even as adults in chimpanzees and rhesus and Japanese macaques—all the species that have been studied long enough to know. The relation may persist to kinship lineages, in that blood-related uncles and aunts tend infants.

An infant's rank depends on its mother's status in macaques, chimpanzees, and probably most other species. The infant may lose status when it becomes independent or may persist as a member of a dominant lineage.

Freudian theory lays stress on the human "latency" period, when infantile sexual approaches to the parents are suppressed and several years pass before puberty. There is a similar time scale among many other juvenile primates, when much of their attention centers on the peer group, although we lack detailed data.

Rhesus and Japanese macaques and chimpanzees seem to avoid mother–son incest, although this probably depends on a mother's continuing general higher status than her son.

Peer group play is probably of major importance in learning social behavior.

Troop fission seems highly variable. Langur male groups raid and take over harems. Japanese macaque troops divide amoebically, with members of each age and sex class joining a new branch troop. The secession is led by one or a few males, who may be young adults who cannot enter the central hierarchy, intruding solitaries, or even the old troop's lead male. Typically more males than females leave in the branch troop.

The individual traits of troop members, particularly of the alpha male, vary widely in any species and influence the whole troop.

The most parsimonious principle may be to assume human complexity except where it clearly does not apply.

14 Violence and Warfare

How much of the primate remains in us, and how does our society differ? Man evolved away from the primates in several steps. First came "ordinary" small-brained primates who were, perhaps, terrestrial seed-eaters. Then followed hunter-gatherers, whose modern exemplars retain some of the ecology of the protohominids, yet have language, myth, and apparently the same mental and emotional capacities as any other men. Then there are the agriculturalists, whose economic base is transformed by the storage and propagation of food. Last comes technological man, slotted into his egg-carton apartment houses. Three aspects of human behavior—alienation, violence, and warfare—are sometimes blamed on our primate ancestry, or rather on a technology that has changed "too fast" for our inherited gamut of primate-like emotions (Ardrey, 1967).

One can turn to the behavior of other mammals in highly crowded conditions. For instance, it seems to be a perfectly normal part of the population biology of voles, and mice and lemmings, to increase vastly in numbers in favorable years or periods, then to die off in equally vast numbers during unfavorable periods. Such a population cycle is characteristic of "opportunistic species," that is, species whose total life span is relatively short compared with changes in climate or external conditions that determine their chances of reproductive success. These species bloom like algae when the conditions are right, taking advantage of the opportunities offered, then die off in bad years or seasons. Other animals seem relatively buffered to changes in their environment, with neither so high a reproductive rate or such a high proportional die-off. Clearly, this is a function not so much of the animals themselves as of relative timing. If there is a long enough period of highly favorable conditions relative to the reproduction rate of any species, that group of animals will increase in numbers, and similarly if there is a drastic enough setback, they will die off.

What becomes interesting is how the social behavior of the species functions to intensify these cyclical effects or to modify and buffer them. Crowding in very many species of mammal seems to have the consistent effect of increasing the amount of aggressive behavior. As aggression increases, the ordinary mechanisms of dispersing aggression, for instance, redirection to a third animal, function not to damp down fighting but to increase it in violence and frequency (Russell and Russell, 1968). Under severe crowding, even with an oversupply of food, the more dominant animals do nearly all of the reproducing. Subordinate animals undergo various physiological changes, such as enlarged adrenal glands. They die, often of apparently external causes such as measles and flu, as they are generally weaker. Above all, subordinates do not reproduce, but absorb the embryos, abort them, or fail in other ways to raise their litters. Most of the experimental work has been carried out with rats and mice, but there are indications that the same things work in, for instance, wild deer populations. Certainly the increase in aggression is commonly seen in any zoo colony of almost any mammal (Alexander and Bowers, 1967).

Wynne-Edwards (1962) has argued that a great deal of social behavior in both birds and mammals has evolved under the selective pressure of overcrowding. Before the food supply is reduced to irredeemably low levels, fighting, territorial behavior, and stress effects take their toll of the weaker animals and space out the stronger ones. Therefore, the population as a whole has a better chance of surviving than with unlimited competition directly for food. Wynne-Edwards' postulated evolutionary mechanism of group selection has been much disputed. However, if the mechanism is weakened to that of kin selection, his arguments should hold. Social primates live in kin groups, and there surely is differential selection among troops of primates as well as among individuals.

A second aspect of our present multitudes is alienation and loneliness. Most primates know every individual in their troop over a period of years or exchange members only among neighboring troops, where the neighbors are already at least acquaintances. In any primitive society, members of a hunting band or peasants in a village will also know most of their acquaintances throughout life. With the beginning of long trade routes, a few men wandered from place to place, as a few solitary Japanese monkeys do now. But as trade gave way to city life, it has become commonplace to sit with strangers, to speak to them over the counter, to flatten against them in the subway. Much of our behavior is a codification of relations with strangers, elaborate devices for pretending they are not really people, not really there (Morris, 1967, 1969).

To a lesser degree, most acquaintances are part-people, "kumpans" in the Lorenzian sense, who exist only in their own context—the shopgirl unrecognizable outside her shop, the dormitory mate who apparently lacks a past (no parents, no little brothers and sisters) and assuredly lacks a future (he will never turn into a rosy alumnus with false teeth).

We have seen that primate upbringing can adjust a baby to life in a group: defining its status and codes of conduct with known individuals. There are no indications among primates how we learn to live with strangers. Alienation, lack of responsibility, lack of reliance on others to help, or lack of willingness to help others are quite obviously related to the fact that there are just too many "others" to treat them all as "one's own."

The trouble with extrapolating directly from the primates is that we have evolved in so many ways away from them. The surprising part is not that we break down sometimes into violence, loneliness, or just ulcers—the surprise is that we build cities at all and that a large part of mankind apparently rushes away from peasant farms into the towns as soon as they have any choice in the matter, both for economic reasons and for social ones. We are not bazaar macaques; we have not developed complex societies on top of a set of fossilized emotions. Thus, although we can look to crowding effects in mammals as a *mechanism* that reappears within the convulsions of modern life, to understand the *degree* or the *function* of violence in society we must look to ourselves.

WARFARE

Nowhere is this clearer than in warfare, which is unique to man. Ants are said to practice "war," but only against other species that may be no nearer related to them than the thousands of rhesus whose kidneys are ground up for vaccine are to us. Many animals discriminate against and even attack strangers—a rat or honeybee who enters the wrong nest is killed. But war, the uniting of one group of a species to fight and kill another group, is only human.

Man now can kill at long distance, or shut his victims in concentration camps so that their supplications cannot be heard. Appeasement gestures, evolved to be effective face to face, do not reach up to a bomber pilot. However, although technology explains the scale of modern warfare, it does not explain its existence. Rape and murder in Vietnam would not surprise New Guinea highlanders or Amazonian Indians or a German peasant of the Thirty Years' War: massacring villages is commonplace human behavior. The undoubted cruelty of the twentieth century is more efficient, but possibly little changed in intent from the intergroup behavior of the Cro-Magnon mammoth hunter.

War depends on group loyalty. The danger lies not in personal violence but in man's altruism and self-sacrifice. Perhaps the Black Panthers offer the clearest example, for they stand just at the border between private murderers and public heroes. If they are considered as individuals within America, the general system of America, one can see their threats as brutal, their actions criminal, their recklessness nearly insane. If, however, one accepts them as champions of an oppressed, irreconciled nation, then they are a gallant few, martyred in hotel bedrooms instead of Thermopylae, Masada, the Sierra Maestra. It is not their actions but whether they seem to be defenders of a people that makes them noble or vile.

This, again, has been traced back to the primates, although group loyalty is sometimes confounded with geographic territories. We have seen that the clearest territoriality appears in forest primates, especially the leaf eaters, which are both phylogenetically and ecologically remote from man. The savanna primates—baboons, chimpanzees, macaques—seem to have no defended territories. Furthermore, their intergroup behavior is variable. Groups seem usually to avoid each other: actual fighting occurred when two rhesus macaque troops surprised each other around the corner of a temple complex, but also two savanna baboon troops or two barbary macaque troops may occasionally sleep together in the same trees (Southwick, 1962; Altmann and Altmann, 1970; Deag, personal communication). In short, it does not seem to me that the primate data explain the existence of warfare any more than they explain the other nonprimate ramifications of human society. At the most, they offer a mechanism, of troop loyalty, that has been taken over and elaborated during the evolution of man.

It does not seem at all clear when man turned to warfare—whether in defense of hunting rights, when crowded by a local population explosion of competing bands, as part of mystic ritual, or after the beginning of economic surpluses worth storing or stealing (Robinson, 1969). It is clear, in Washburn and Lancaster's (1968) *faux-naif* words, that "Men enjoy hunting and killing.... war has been far too important in human history for it to be other than pleasurable for the males involved." It is equally true that there are other options open to us—principally, accepting the world as one tribe.

SUMMARY

Warfare and frequent destructive violence are unique to man. Overcrowding leads rats and other mammals to increased aggression and to reproductive failure of subordinate individuals. Although overcrowding may relate to stressed individuals in cities, it probably has little to do with warfare, which largely depends on group loyalty rather than personal anger. It could be argued that warfare is the aberrant response to group conflict in an animal that does *not* have adequately ritualized intergroup defense, but it is probably better to look for the source of man's "inhumanity" among his more "human" characteristics.

Man emerges from the survey of the primates as more violent, yet more organized, and sexier, yet more married. What emerges most strongly is man's similarity to the primates in the force of his desire to be social and his adjustment of his own behavior to the roles demanded by his group. We see among the primates themselves how the social group has both demanded and allowed complexity: protecting individuals from sudden rigors of the environment, yet ever impinging upon them with the complexity of other individuals.

The emotions that lead man to respect his leaders, succor his children, and love his wife or wives have evolved from his primate past. But, as clearly, so has man's very flexibility, variability, creativity. We can behave as individuals only within, and because of, our heritage of social life.

III / INTELLIGENCE

Primate Psychology

Professed psychologists traditionally attempt to simplify psychological processes. The history of many fields of science can be seen as the struggle of two opposing desires: the intellectual delight of reducing complex facts to simple, crystalline theories as against a delight in complex reality itself. This is particularly true of the study of the primate mind. People choose to work with primates because they are complex animals, mysterious, quasihuman. On the other hand, the same people create out of the primate's behavior a single theory or simple dichotomy to satisfy the mind of the psychologist.

Nowhere is this clearer than in the work of the founder of primate experimentation, Wolfgang Köhler (1927), although his simplifications seem complex by later standards. Köhler spent World War I sequestered on the island of Tenerife with a colony of juvenile chimpanzees and was thus among the original twentieth century primatologists. He was attempting to prove the gestalt theory of learning. Gestalt theory argues that there are qualitative leaps of understanding, when a whole idea or a whole pattern is perceived.

This whole, or "gestalt," is somehow greater than the sum of the individual parts—a new level of understanding, not just a collection of components. Köhler's famous experiments, teaching chimpanzees to pile boxes on each other or to fit two sticks together to reach a banana, stemmed from his interest in the pure theory of understanding. He minutely observed the chimpanzee's hesitations, its trials, its errors, and then the sudden swift solution. To him, sudden "insightful" solutions proved that the chimpanzee mind, like that of man—that is, the animal psyche as well as human reason (and in fact human perception as well)—works by such qualitative jumps when a new whole becomes meaningful. And yet, unlike later abstractionists, he was delighted and fascinated by his animals. Köhler's long appendix on the social behavior of his colony remains one of the most complete and amusing descriptions of captive chimpanzees.

Köhler's school of gestalt psychology was answered from the other side of the Atlantic by the American behaviorist school. Their work stemmed from that of Watson and Thorndike. Behaviorists tried to eliminate qualitative jumps of understanding from their theory. They reduced all of behavior, human included, to minute accretions, as new acts were learned through the reinforcement of primary drives. Behaviorism was an atomistic discipline desperately eager to explain mind by a single mechanism. The behaviorists' temperament led them to ignore the quirks, or peculiarities, of the social behavior of their animals. Their experimental situations were designed to exclude every aspect of the animals' make-up except for that relevant to the particular learning problem under consideration.

A recent review of the methodology of discrimination learning by Meyer *et al.* (1965) points out the annoying fact that monkeys most easily discriminate three-dimensional objects that can be handled. They are much harder to train with simple stimuli projected on a screen or in situations where the lever or manipulandum that they touch is separated by a distance, or a border, from the cue they are supposed to be learning, and many species learn color cues in preference to form. This is precisely the sort of qualitative effect that annoyed the early learning theorists. And worst of all, primates seem to learn social relationships, dominance orders, and predator signals associated with alarm calls much more readily than any of the psychologists' carefully constructed tests with "neutral" object stimuli.

Qualitative differences in the kinds of things an animal will learn, qualitative jumps in learning, and innate bias in learning are all aspects that cannot be handled in classical learning theory, except by the roundabout means of saying that there is a stronger drive in some sense satisfied by the learning in question. The proponents of the classical theory postulated (and preferred) animals, or people, to be born blank slates on which to write the sum of learned behavior. This has led to obvious insensitivity about the nature of their animals and to the many articles published as work on "the" monkey, which is an Indian rhesus, or even "the" animal, which is an inbred albino rat.

An impressive body of work has nonetheless resulted, describing parameters of learning, effects of various schedules of reinforcement, and so forth. This eventually relates to the neurophysiology of the brain. The real goal (and excitement) of the search for mechanisms is to find out how the machine really is constructed.

This text will not consider most of learning theory, because it seems more relevant to rats, pigeons, neurons, and computers than to the behavior of primates as particular individuals or species of animals. Instead, many of the tests and concepts that began in a context of learning experiments will be treated briefly under different headings in following chapters: manipulative tests in Chapter 16 and delayed response tests and second order learning in Chapter 17.

Today, the earlier arguments have blurred and are being rapidly outgrown. However, there is just as strong a desire as ever to reduce all data to theory—the Piagetian formulation is offered in part because it seems to include even more facts in one theory than do the alternatives. And there remains the argument between those who embrace qualitative distinctions and those who loathe them. Piagetian theory, like gestalt theory, is a hierarchy of qualitative steps. To me, some such approach seems necessary in order to treat the complexity of cognition. This is not to say that we should abandon the search for atomistic mechanisms any more than studying the anatomy of the brain means that one should ignore the problems of conduction in nerve cells—only that we need some theory of cognitive levels even to begin organizing the present data in their biological context.

SUMMARY

There is an age-old conflict between the desire to understand the world by simplifying it and to convey its richness in qualitative differences. The gestalt school and Piaget's philosophy deal with hierarchical levels of thought and thus allow for qualitative differences in thinking. I believe that any fruitful theory of mind must admit some hierarchical organization of thought. However, many studies of primate learning have been carried out under the simplistic, single-level "behaviorist" theory or its variants. It is thus difficult to summarize primate learning in terms relevant to man.

Figure 134 The gorilla in captivity is reduced to playing or fiddling with the materials available. (San Diego Zoo Photo by Ron Garrison.)

Manipulation and Tools 16

Many criteria have been proposed for the change from animal to man. One of the recently current ones is that man is the tool-making animal. This has been more than a little undermined by Jane van Lawick-Goodall's observation that wild chimpanzees make tools, at least if one is willing to admit that fashioning a stick into a termite probe is making a crude tool. Clearly, though, humans are technological creatures, dependent from very early times on stones for bashing and sticks for poking. Therefore, primatologists both in field and laboratory have snapped to attention whenever their animals were manipulating objects.

In this chapter I shall first consider which primate species manipulate objects and under what circumstances, and then turn to the training of chimpanzees to see what the potential of the nonhuman mind can be. Finally, in the last section, I will return to tool use proper and its relevance to the evolution of human beings.

MANIPULATION

Among the prosimians, some species eat fruit, whereas some are largely insectivorous. The insectivorous ones catch insects with their hands, with a smash-and-grab like the bushbaby or by clamping them down to the branch like the stealthy potto. Their attention span and manipulation of "learning" or "insight" problems are related to the differences in diet. Insectivorous lorisoids observe problems for a long time before touching them and then use the hand to manipulate. "Animals whose food is likely to fly away must watch, bide their time, and pounce with precision" (Jolly, 1964a, p. 568). On the other hand, fruit-eating lemurs bounce into a problem, grabbing it with hands and muzzle, going to the goal by scent if possible, which is a reasonable way to behave if one's food waits dangling from a branch. The difference in "successes" then is not so much related to a difference in species' learning capacity as to their approaches to problems, which in turn correlate with their natural feeding behavior.

Thorington (1967) and Hladik and Hladik (1969) describe New World monkeys feeding in the wild. Cebus monkeys have been known since the work of Klüver (1957) to be extremely proficient at using and even making tools out of the materials provided in the laboratory. In the wild, the cebus monkey systematically takes apart dead branches or rolled-up leaves with its fingers, probing and poking for concealed larvae. Squirrel monkeys sharing the same forest merely stir up insects by their passage and catch them as they move. Thus again the natural diet and feeding habits correlate with manipulative skill, both in the physical actions of the hands and in the attention and patience with object problems that bring success in laboratory tests.

Figure 135 Chimpanzee rough-and-tumble play with an object. (I. Bernstein, 1962a.)

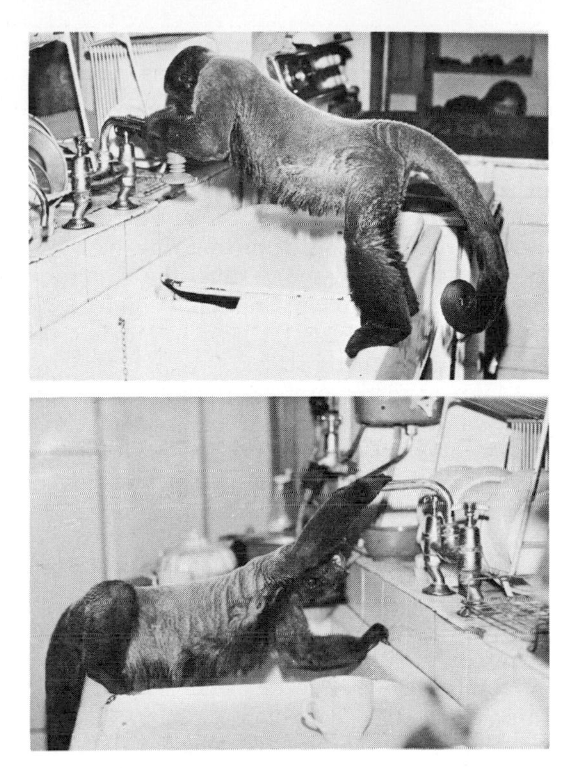

Figure 136 A woolly monkey turns on a tap and drinks. In captivity manipulative curiosity may be useful. (Courtesy of L. Williams from Williams, 1967.)

Figure 137 Manipulative curiosity may be measured on standardized tests (rhesus macaque). (Courtesy of R. Zimmermann.)

Davis *et al.* (1968), in a survey of six species of monkey and the ringtailed lemur, found that rhesus monkeys and cebus monkeys spent by far the most time exploring the environment of their standard test situation, manipulating, poking at, licking, and mouthing the cage itself and everything in it. Interestingly, the range of species included three macaques, and one macaque species, the rhesus, differed as much from its congeneric species the stumptails as the stumptails did from the tiny New World squirrel monkey or the Malagasy lemur. Thus, the differences are related to the particular environment and habitats of species, or even of populations and individuals (at least in Japanese macaques), not to any simple phylogenetic scale.

Many primates pretreat their food in some way before eating it. Savanna baboons rub roots and grasses between their hands, which takes off some of the grit adhering and saves wear and tear on the teeth. South African baboons lift rocks to find scorpions beneath, stun the scorpions with a few blows, and deftly remove the stings before eating (DeVore and Hall, 1965; Marais, 1969). In the Singapore Botanical Gardens, wild macaques rub food with dried leaves, one step further in the use of objects (Chiang, 1967). Japanese macaques actually wash their food before eating it, a behavior that has apparently begun and been transmitted from animal to animal after they were artificially provisionized with such things as gritty sweet potatoes. Thus one can go by almost infinitesimal steps from the sort of behavior pattern that would cause very little remark if a rodent showed it to patterns that are claimed to be precultural such as the sweet potato washing. Of course, all over the world monkeys have learned to take advantage of human preparation of food. One amusing case is the talapoin monkey of Gabon, which steals manioc soaked in pools by the village women. The manioc tubers must soak for a week to lose their toxic juices, but the talapoin monkeys unerringly choose those that are well soaked and safe (Gautier-Hion, 1966).

It is well worth comparing these primate performances with, for instance, raccoon behavior. Raccoons are highly manipulative animals, searching for their food by feel under rocks in streams, down holes, and in trees. The typical raccoon feeding pattern is to stick its hand in somewhere, feel what is there, seize it, pull it out, and eat it. This means that on manipulation tests and formal learning tests with manipulative operations, raccoons may outshine many primates (Thorgersen, 1958; Johnson and Michaels, 1958). As man has not evolved from raccoons, no one attaches any great significance to the manipulative behavior of the raccoon or sees in it a mystic precursor to our own society.

Thus, although wild primates manipulate food and although many such manipulations must be culturally transmitted, wild primates (except the great apes) seem surprisingly undistinguished in this line.

THE WELL-TAUGHT CHIMPANZEE

Köhler began it, with his famous chimpanzee Sultan. Let me quote him:

> Sultan is the subject of experiment. His sticks are two hollow, but firm bamboo rods such as the animals often use for pulling along fruit. The one is so much smaller than the other that it can be pushed in at either end of the other quite easily. Beyond the bars lies the objective, just so far away that the animal cannot reach it with either . . . . he takes great pains to try to reach it with one stick or the other, even pushing his right shoulder through the bars. When everything proves futile, Sultan commits a "bad error" or, more clearly, a great stupidity such as he made on other occasions. He pulls a box from the back of the room toward the bars. True, he pushes it away at once as it is useless . . . . then a good error, he pushes one of the sticks out as far as it will go and takes the second and with it pokes the first one cautiously toward the objective, pushing it carefully from the nearer end and thus slowly urging it toward the fruit. This does not always succeed, but if he has got pretty close in this way, he takes even greater precaution, he pushes very gently, watches the movements of the stick that is lying on the ground and actually touches the objective with its tip . . . . the procedure is repeated . . . . he puts the stick in his hand, exactly to the opening of the stick on the ground, and, although one might think that doing so would suggest the possibility of pushing one stick into the other, there is no indication whatever of . . . . a solution. Finally, the observer gives the animal some help by putting one finger into the opening of the stick . . . . this has no effect . . . . the experiment has lasted over an hour and is stopped for the present as it seems hopeless.
>
> The keeper is left there to watch him . . . . Keeper's report: "Sultan first of all squats indifferently on the box which has been left standing a little back from the railings, then he gets up, picks up the two sticks, sits down again on the box and plays carelessly with them. While doing this, it happens that he finds himself holding one rod in either hand in such way that they lie in a straight line. He pushes the thinner one a little way into the opening of the thicker, jumps and is already on the run towards the railings, to which he has now half turned his back and begins to draw the banana towards him with the double stick. I call the master. Meanwhile one of the animal's rods has fallen out of the other as he has pushed one of them only a little way into the other, whereupon he connects them again." (Köhler, 1927:113–115)

Figure 138 Chimpanzee Julia opens a minute lock. Note her precision grip. (From B. Rensch and J. Döhl, 1967.)

This, says Köhler, was *insight* into understanding the connection between food and the two sticks when Sultan suddenly saw the disconnected parts that he had held in his hands for an hour as a single "gestalt," a coherent whole.

Köhler's experiments were repeated by Birch (1945), who showed that previous experience with sticks contributes the animal's eventual solution of problems using sticks. Then Schiller (1957) gave naïve chimpanzees the same problems, but in play, with no rewards visible or offered, and Schiller's chimpanzees made all the same manipulations, stacking three boxes one on top of another, connecting sticks, weaving string in and out of the cage wire. In fact, they arrived at these solutions even more quickly in play, when not distracted by a banana! Köhler's own account shows that Sultan did not achieve his first solution of the problem until he had more or less given up the banana, had withdrawn, and was fiddling about with the sticks themselves. Then, having joined the two sticks, he saw their connection with the problem he had been offered and ran forward to the bars again.

Play is not confined to aimless pottering or poking or wrestling with the materials. For instance, Schiller's chimpanzees meticulously measured the distance with their hands from the corner of the box to the corners of the room, positioning their toy object with the intense concentration of a human 2-year-old arranging a play tea with plates for every doll. (Imitation and "pretense" play will be discussed in the next chapter.)

In more formal contexts, apes' manipulation of objects can be measured using the standardized children's Gesell test. Gua, a chimpanzee raised in the Kelloggs' home, was compared with the Kelloggs' own son Donald, raised in as nearly similar a pattern as they could manage. Gua, as one might expect from the chimpanzees' more rapid motor development, scored consistently a little ahead of Donald in fine manipulation in their first year and a half of life. However, Donald was somewhat superior in imitating other people and, to the Kelloggs' embarassment, became all too good at imitating the little chimpanzee (Kellogg and Kellogg, 1933).

The current manipulative genius among the primates must be a chimpanzee called Julia, who has been studied, trained, and otherwise fostered by Rensch and Döhl (Rensch and Döhl, 1967, 1968; Döhl, 1966, 1968). Julia was first taught to open boxes locked with fourteen different kinds of fastening. She extrapolated to series of different fastenings to get into the same box and to six-step series of boxes containing the tools to open the next box containing the tools to reach the banana, choosing her strategy by visually working backward from the goal. She generalized to opening unfamiliar boxes with miniature keys in miniature padlocks, tiny screwdrivers that she had to guide with the opposite thumbnail into the minute screws, or even entirely new and unfamiliar fastenings. The only fear is that Rensch and Döhl will train Julia to expert safecracking and that some limit will have to be put on her activity.

She can also solve complex mazes. She guides an iron ring along the paths of the maze by holding a magnet above the maze. Rensch and Döhl first taught her to put the ring in a slot machine that would reward her with fruit, and then she learned to move the ring along a path by means of a magnet. In the first series of

Figure 139 Julia with a complex maze. (From B. Rensch and J. Döhl, 1968.)

Figure 140 Julia studies the series of locked boxes diagrammed in Figure 141. (J. Döhl, 1968.)

definitive experiments she chose between two simple paths of a small maze, with one of them being blocked at various points. Her first movement led the ring to left or right off a small hump, so that she had to think backward from the goal to make the first choice of left or right correctly. In the next series, the paths became more and more complex through incorporation of angles and branched blind alleys. Next the paths were interlaced, the size of the maze was doubled, the paths were made narrower, and false exits were added. "In the last one hundred rather complicated mazes, the chimpanzee chose the correct path in 86% of the trials . . . . by watching the eye and head movements of the chimpanzee, we could in some cases state that the ape first looked to the exits and then to the path system near the starting point. Apparently she combined the sensations of the latter with the mental images of the goal region, a form of behavior which is very similar to that of man" (Rensch and Döhl, 1968, p. 231). Six biology students tried the same complex mazes. On the average they solved the maze in half the time that Julia did, but their scores overlapped so that in some cases Julia was the quickest!

Julia, as well as other juvenile chimpanzees, is an artist. The painting of chimpanzees has fascinated many people from Nadia Kohts (1923) and Schiller (1951), whom I believe first gave apes patterned cards to complete to see if they balanced in any esthetic or understandable way, through Desmond Morris and Bernard

Rensch. Not only chimpanzees but gorillas, orangutans, and even cebus monkeys will paint or draw given any materials at hand, even their own feces used on the wall of their cages. If one equips them with more orthodox pencil and paper or, even better, poster paints, they work with extraordinary concentration, to the extent of having tantrums if anyone tries to stop them before they are finished. They also seem to know when they are finished, ripping off a page to start a clean sheet.

Desmond Morris (1962) has analyzed in detail the stylistic differences of primate painting. Some individuals make recognizable

Figure 141 A double series of locked boxes. The chimpanzee must choose only one of the two tools she sees through the plastic lid of the first double box. Each tool opens one other box, containing one tool to open yet another box. One series of five tools leads to a box with bananas; the other leads to an empty box. The only reliable way to reach the bananas is to trace backward step by step from the goal before choosing the first tool. (After J. Döhl, 1968.)

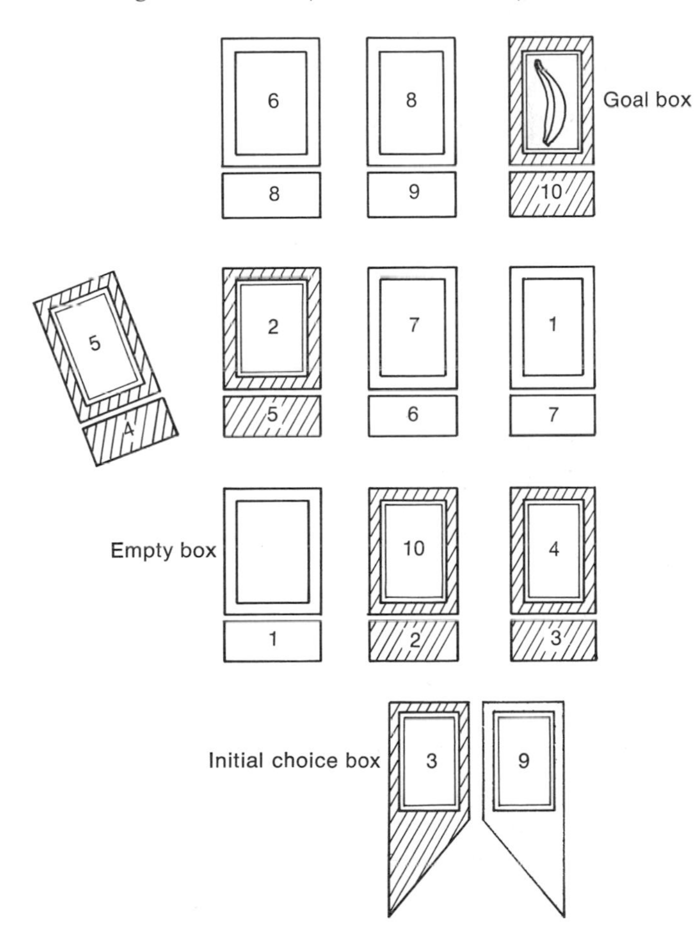

Figure 142 Congo chooses a color. (From D. Morris, 1962.)

variations on a theme, not merely a whole-arm circling motion but, for instance, a repeated fan pattern with the pencil drawn toward or away from the animal in converging lines. Schiller, Morris, and Rensch also find that the primates may attempt to complete or balance a preformed pattern, drawing around the outline of a square on a piece of cardboard or adding in color on the opposite side from a large black blot. Julia even does follow-the-dot pictures, copying square and triangle. Morris makes the tantalizing suggestion that his chimpanzee Congo stopped just before the stage when children can draw "faces." Small children, after stages of random and then more coherent scribbling, will suddenly begin to make circular patterns with spots inside. From there, the child begins to claim that the spots are in fact a face, although there may at first be no assignment of eyes, nose, and mouth. Congo's final paintings were of the form of a circle with marks inside it, but, although possessing far greater motor coordination than a child of comparable age, he never went on to recognizable representation.

It is intriguing that orangutans as a species are even more "manipulative" than chimpanzees (Benchley, 1942; Harrison, 1963; Parker, 1969; Rensch and Duecker, 1966, although no one has yet schooled one as extensively as Julia has been.

NEST BUILDING

Chimpanzees, orangutans, and gorillas build sleeping nests. They usually construct a new one every night, and sometimes rougher day shelters as well. Gorillas mainly nest on the ground, in a crudely arranged circle of vegetation. Chimpanzees and orangutans make elaborate woven structures in trees, with first large branches and then small ones broken across and interlacing.

Like other manipulative behavior, nest making improves with age, and has time to do so because the child sleeps with its mother until 3 or 4 years of age. In Bernstein's experiments (Chapter 8) wild-born chimpanzees made nests without tutoring and captive-born ones did not, but two captives with rich early environments made circular nests reminiscent of real ones. This may reflect an innate bias, but more likely the permanent damage that early isolation can do to complex manipulative ability (Menzel *et al.*, 1970) (see Chapter 19).

There seems no reason why human ancestors should not have built nests as well. One of the early Olduvai remains is a circle of stones that was perhaps a shelter. Prosimians commonly build nests. So if prosimians, great apes, and one of the Olduvai hominids constructed such things, one cannot at any rate claim confidently that earlier protohominids did *not*.

One question is how terrestrial life might have influenced nesting. Gorilla ground nests seem degenerate structures compared with the tree beds of chimpanzees. However, one juvenile chimpanzee nest and one gorilla nest actually had roofs, so it is possible to imagine transitions from simple bed to real shelter (van Lawick-Goodall, 1968b; Fossey, personal communication).

More important is the transition from bed to home. Prosimian nests are breeding as well as sleeping nests, where altricial young can be left while the mother forages. Young apes are never left behind in the nest to sleep. However, on four occasions when chimpanzees had bad colds they went to bed at 4 to 4:30 pm and slept late, until about 9 the next morning, and two made elaborate day nests where they slept for 3 or 4 hours the next morning.

Figure 143 A well-formed nest made by a chimpanzee in captivity. (From I. Bernstein, 1962a, 1–6.)

Figure 144 A chimpanzee in his day nest in the wild. (Courtesy of H. van Lawick.)

One mature male, who lost the use of both legs, probably from polio, slept for more than 7 hours a day in the nest. He made two nests in one tree and three in another, and dragged himself from the ground to the lowest nest for the day, then into a higher one for the night, during 7 days. On the last night before he had to be destroyed, he had dislocated an arm and was too weak to climb into the trees, but when his observers "broke off a pile of leafy branches he managed to work them under him, using one arm and his mouth, to form a crude ground nest" (van Lawick-Goodall, 1968b, p. 199).

In these sick chimpanzees one can see nest becoming home: perhaps, again, early humans built nest beds for other humans who were in need—small infants or women after childbirth—and thus eased the transition to settled family life.

TOOL USE IN THE WILD

Wild chimpanzees fashion tools to fish for termites as well as for two species of ants. At one season, when the winged termite adults are ready to fly, the termites tunnel near the surface of their mounds, leaving only a thin layer of earth at the end of each tunnel. The chimpanzees scrape an opening, then insert a twig or grass blade. Usually, they shape the tool first: stripping off leaves, narrowing wide blades of grass, and biting off bent ends. They insert the tool, the termites bite and clamp onto the intruding object, and then the chimpanzees cautiously withdraw the stick in order not to dislodge the clinging termites.

Young chimpanzees clearly practice termite fishing, although Hayes (1951) described hand-reared Viki playing in the garden, poking sticks into the entrance to an ant nest! Babies less than 2 years old did not fish, but small infants began to play with grass stems, to "mop" with the back of the hand like a grown-up mopping fallen termites, and even to strip and bite ends off tools (van Lawick-Goodall, 1968b). Two year olds attempted to fish with mini-tools—bits of grass 1 or 2 inches long, usually bitten or broken from a discarded adult tool (normally 6 to 12 inches long). Usually, infants jerked the tool out, which would shake off any termite that did bite, and their bouts of attention lasted less than 5 minutes, although an adult may fish for 1 to 5 hours. "On only two occasions were infants of this age group observed to 'catch' a termite, out of 22 bouts." Three-year-olds had longer bouts of attention, but still chose overflexible tools and used both hands instead of one hand. Four-year-olds mastered the adult technique, but fished only 15 minutes at a stretch. The sad exception was Merlin, orphaned at 2, whose tool-using technique had regressed if anything from the 2-year-old level.

Chimpanzees also use sticks for "olfactory aids." They probe the termite holes with thin grass blades and then smell the grass to see if the tunnel is ready for working. They also probe wasp nests, twice into van Lawick-Goodall's pocket for bananas, once at a dead python, and once at a female's genitalia. The chimpanzees also attempt to fish with sticks inside the banana boxes from which they are provisioned.

Chimpanzees crumple leaves in their mouths and then use them as a kind of sponge to sop up water from tree holes.

They also use leaves to wipe sticky substances off the body, either fecal matter or mashed banana. Once a juvenile used leaves to wipe banana off her infant sibling. Then there was the "3-year-old, dangling above a visiting scientist, Professor R. A. Hinde, [who] wiped her foot vigorously with leaves after stamping on his hair . . . ."

Two of van Lawick-Goodall's descriptions give a picture of how uses of tools can be discovered:

> A mature male, who was afraid to take a banana held out to him by hand, shook a clump of tall grass as a mild threat directed towards the human. When there was no response he shook the grasses more violently so that one actually touched the banana. He stared at the fruit and suddenly released the grasses, pulled a long soft plant from the ground, dropped it, turned to break off a thicker stick and then hit the banana to the ground and ate it. When a second banana was offered in this way he hit it from the hand with no hesitation. (van Lawick-Goodall, 1968b, p. 207)

> A 4-year-old (Fifi) used a completely adult technique when she used leaves for drinking. Once when the [tree-branch] bowl was nearly empty she let go of the leaves which she had been using and apparently had difficulty in reaching them again. After a few moments she stripped the leaves from a nearby twig, picked it, poked it into the bowl and then licked the end. She next picked and stripped a second twig and repeated the process. Finally she tried to drink with her lips and then moved away. It was not clear whether the twig-using was a tool-using pattern appearing out of context or whether, in fact, she was trying to use a second tool to reach the first. (van Lawick-Goodall, 1968b, p. 208)

Objects can be weapons as well (discussed under predation in Chapter 4). Baboons dislodge stones from a ledge on an enemy standing below. Many primates, including the methodical howlers, the tree-shaking rhesus, and the cebus, who even seem to work purposefully enough to know what they are doing, drop branches from the trees they are in to threaten primatologist or predator. None of these animals can be said to aim the stones or branches, but any predator may be discouraged by things falling from a 40- or 100-foot height in his immediate vicinity.

Chimpanzees actually aim and club with objects. Van Lawick-Goodall (1968a) describes a display called "branching" in which an excited chimpanzee picks up a branch or tears off a piece of young tree and flails it about near another animal. One of her males, Mike, generalized the display to banging empty paraffin debbies (kerosene tins) and, with the noise he made, rose to be the dominant male in the community.

She sums up aimed throwing and hitting with sticks and stones as performed by eight different male chimpanzees: in twenty cases a baboon was the target, in ten a human, and in eleven another chimpanzee. Only four out of forty-seven weapons were rocks or clubs heavy enough to do real damage, and in only five cases did the chimpanzees actually hit their targets, never with the large weapons.

Kortlandt has carried out a series of important experiments with populations of wild chimpanzees, both in forest and in woodland savanna conditions. He has put various objects in the chimpanzees' way and watched how they examine or avoid them, concluding the series with a stuffed leopard—a fairly realistic beast with glass eyes, a head that turns, a mouth that opens, and a trolley that pulls it out from its concealed lair. Some chimpanzee groups pick up sticks, usually thoughtfully provided by Kortlandt, and bash at the leopard, even clubbing it on the back, or throw the sticks from a greater distance. Some populations of chimpanzees do not respond. Kortlandt claims that there is a clear difference between forest and savanna groups and that the savanna animals are more likely to have developed adequate antipredator weapons. A more immediate difference may be that the forest chimpanzees just climb a tree, thus avoiding Kortlandt's non-tree-climbing stuffed dummy. However, Kortlandt has extraordinary films of savanna chimpanzees charging his "leopard," breaking off branches themselves from trees to hurl as they come. A strong point in favor of his theory is that chimpanzees may have ranged over far more savanna during the Pleistocene than they do now: their present-day distribution includes many relict savanna populations (Kortlandt and van Zon, 1969).

Hall (1963b), in a famous review, has pointed out how small the steps are from what might seem the simplest of operant-conditioned reflexes to this full-blown tribal attack with clubs. Again the mystery is not how much primates learn in the wild, but why they do not learn more.

One answer is that there is no one to teach them. As we have seen, so much of learning is through social contact and from social companions, and they have simply never built up the sort of nexus of culture in which even the early protohominids must have lived.

Another answer is that the learning capacity of the primates may have been selected for in other contexts than the use of tools. Washburn (Washburn and Hamburg, 1965), like Marais (1969), suggests that primates need to learn quickly in emergencies or exceptional situations such as a prolonged drought or change of habitat. Then the huge capacity of the infrahuman primate's brain will allow it the variable behavior that makes for survival. Another suggestion (Hall, 1968; Hall and Goswell, 1964; Jolly, 1966b) may be that the learning is normally not only in, but of, social situations and social connections. Then, in a way, the primate would have excess capacity that in the barren environment of the cage or the overintellectual environment of a psychologist's household it would turn toward objects as well as its conspecifics. Theories of excess, unused capacity are always suspect in the evolutionary context, so this is not wholly satisfactory either. Reynolds and Reynolds (1965), pointing out that chimpanzees know, and can remember, many different species of fruit and fruit tree or the location of many paths in the three-dimensional world of the forest, does not really solve the problem either. Finally, Kortlandt (Kortlandt and Kooij, 1963) speculates that early apes in fact used tools and weapons more than the present-day ones. Before man invented the first bow and arrow there may have been much greater advantage in tipping a stone or tossing a branch toward the enemy. According to Kortlandt, much of the mental and manipulative power of the chimpanzee is vestigial, like the appendix on its way out.

Although all of these people would argue with more or less passion and less or more evidence for their own theories, I think one must leave it as a mystery. However, one can end with the quite reasonable supposition that, even though baby chimpanzees brought up in a human home can act remarkably like human children, it is quite probable that a human child brought up by benevolent chimpanzees might show little greater intellectual prowess than the chimpanzee's own offspring.

SUMMARY

Humans are distinguished by the breadth of our interest in objects. Among wild primates, feeding methods determine much of an animal's approach to objects: insectivorous species tend to have a longer attention span and to use the hand more than vegetarians. There is very little pretreatment of food in the wild, or tool use, except among the great apes. Trained or home-raised apes make simple tools, open a series of locked boxes, or trace the path of a complex maze, in play as well as for food reward. They paint pictures, to some esthetic standard of their own, being certain when a picture is or is not finished. Wild apes build sleeping nests, and chimpanzees make stick tools to fish for termites and sponges to sop water. They also throw stones or sticks at predators and enemies. It is not really clear why apes do not manipulate objects more in the wild, when they can do so much in captivity.

Cognition

We now have a background of the manipulative abilities of primates—their achievements in the laboratory and in the wild. What can such achievements tell us about their capacity for thought? Directly, nothing. We are not even directly aware of each other's consciousness. But indirectly they can tell us a great deal, by comparison with human children solving similar tasks.

This chapter is based on the ideas of Jean Piaget. Piaget developed a biological-philosophical theory of the creation of logic and consistency in the human mind. In its light he analyzed the growth of logic in his own three children. Piaget's work was promptly ignored, particularly in America, by proponents of stimulus–response theory, but now it is increasingly accepted among psychologists of all descriptions. Whether or not Piaget's formulations go the way of all theories before them and are superseded by something else, they seem at the moment one of the most fruitful ways of organizing research on cognition of children or primates and our ideas about their ideas.

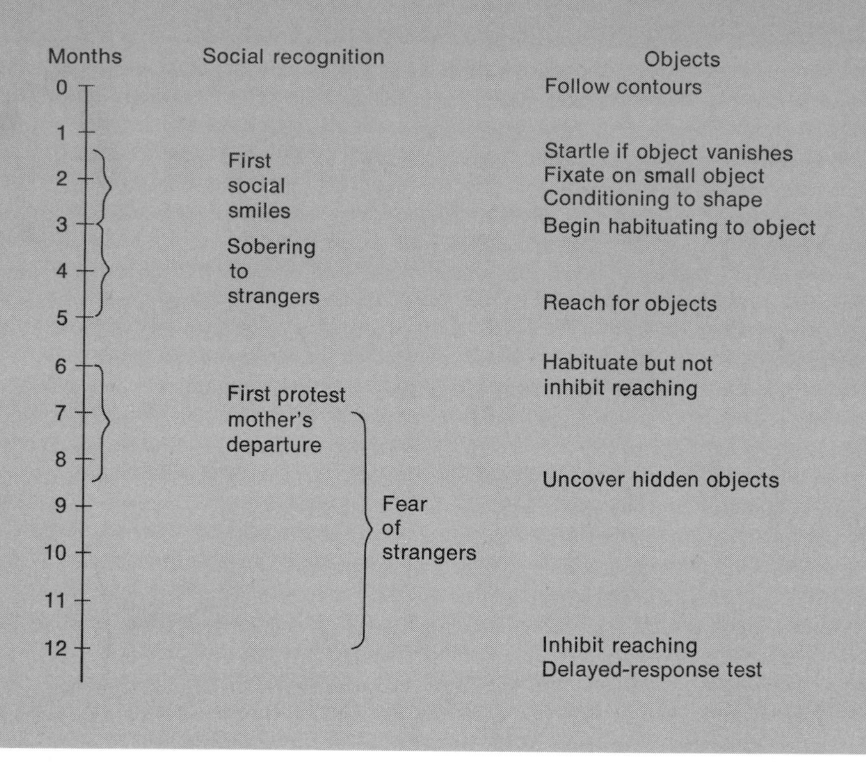

Figure 145 Human infant development: social recognition, object recognition, and object manipulation. (After H. R. Schaffer, 1966; H. R. Schaffer and M. H. Parry, 1969.)

Piaget divides human childhood into successive levels of cognitive development. Each level can be diagnosed by a few crucial experiments, although the whole is a structure of thought. Many of these experiments are those classically used with primates. Although one may quarrel with Piaget's deductions, the important point is that he has arranged the experiments in at least one *natural* order: the order in which they are solved by a growing human child.

When we compare the primates' mentality with children's, we should not make the obvious mistake of equating whole minds on the basis of a few diagnostic tests: clearly the 7-month-old baby is not a slender loris, nor the $1\frac{1}{2}$-year-old a juvenile chimpanzee! Instead, we need real comparative developmental psychology, which will tell us not just what tests a cross section of animals "succeed" or "fail" at but whether or in what circumstances they go through similar or different developmental stages as the human baby. Figure 145 shows the range of achieving some of the stages, and Figure 146 is a crude comparison of some landmarks in infantile development.

Another trap is to think that a "level" or "stage" defined by the criterion of one experiment is necessarily consistent across other experiments: this is an empirical question. We have detailed data so far only for humans and some for rhesus—but for no other primates, even chimpanzees.

This caution must apply particularly when the *mode* of response is changed. Children can respond verbally or manually or by fixating with their eyes or even by changing heart rate. We shall see that a change in heart rate at an object's disappearance comes months before a child will reach out to find a hidden toy. This may be a specifically human time lag: the primates' relatively quicker motor development could mean that they grab for a hidden object almost as soon as they "miss" objects by any other criterion. Similarly, children can order or compare or measure objects manually months or years before they can *explain* what they are doing. The verbal criterion is clearly human: but does the manual one correspond with anything in a primate's repertoire? Not only the mode of response influences results but also the materials used for testing; most children recognize mother's permanence before they comprehend object permanence.

One of the bitter lessons learned by psychologists is that the parameters of an experiment enormously influence results. Gibbons failed for years to pull in food on strings and were called "stupid"—then Beck (1967) gave them food on elevated strings, which they could easily seize with their long, hooked hands, and, lo, they had "insight" like any other ape. But if the rigor and caution of the primate psychologists were applied to the creation of a battery of Piaget-type tests, we might reach real comparison of the ontogeny of logic, like that of the ontogeny of social behavior.

Thus Piaget is important to primate research because (1) his levels are natural levels (for at least the human), (2) the levels can be defined operationally and at the earlier stages nonverbally, (3) he aims, not at some irreducible atom of learning or logic, but at an elucidation of complex thought.

INFANCY AND THE CONCEPT OF OBJECTS

Piaget's first period, the "sensorimotor period," lasts from birth through the beginning of symbolic play, at about $1\frac{1}{2}$ to 2 years. The baby develops in this time from a neonatal bit of biology to a toddling, talking, opinionated human being. Piaget divides the sensorimotor period into six stages.

1, 2. Premanipulative stage

Piaget's first stage is the "neonatal reflex period," with no adaptation to the environment, and the second stage is that of the "first acquired adaptations"—up to about 4 months of age. Recent tests

Figure 146 Early cognitive development in rhesus, chimpanzee, and human. These rates are approximate, with wide individual variations, but suggest the outlines of future comparative study. The order of trait appearance is apparently similar in all three primates. (After H. R. Schaffer, 1966; J. van Lawick-Goodall, 1968; T. E. Rowell, 1963b; J. B. Mowbray and T. E. Cadell, 1962; R. Zimmermann and C. C. Torrey, 1965.)

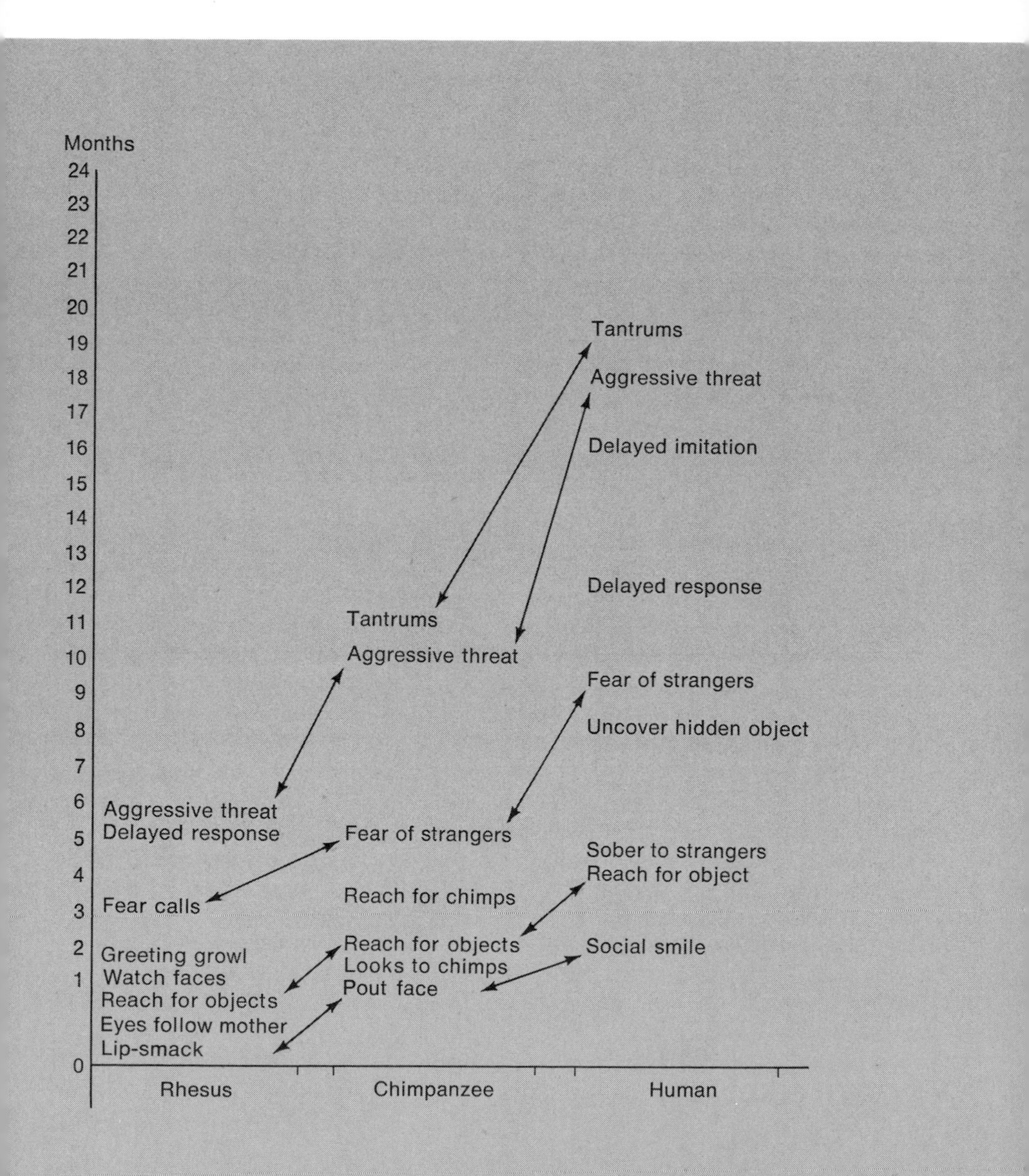

have shown that the baby can modify his reflex behavior even in the earliest weeks, so the distinction between Piaget's first two stages is now becoming blurred. In these two premanipulative stages, as the baby has not yet begun to reach reliably for what he sees, he cannot systematically change objects outside his own body.

He has, at least, the capacity to fixate objects, to *look at*; his eyes follow the contours of an object even on the first day of life (Kessen, 1967). He can be conditioned to turn his head toward a buzzer (Lipsitt, 1967; Papousek, 1967). He can modify his sucking behavior. At 3 weeks of age he can learn, in an experimental session, to suck with jaw pressure only or tongue suction only, although he "forgets" by the next session (Bruner, 1968). He can learn reliably to get his thumb (or bit of fist) in his mouth and keep it there. He can clearly modify his social communication, "conventionalizing" his crying (Bruner, 1968). The smiling response appears, and this too is modified by the mother's reaction (see Chapter 12). Sometime around 3 or 4 months, he begins to recognize objects: to watch them less if he has seen them immediately before and attend to more novel stimuli instead (Fantz, 1964; McCall and Kagan, 1967). Thus he can act on himself (his thumb), and he can direct his

Figure 147 A rhesus infant in the first days of life can learn simple discriminations of light and dark and geometric form. However, he must be tested in some form of maze, because he cannot control his hand to pick up objects in the adult fashion. (Courtesy of R. Zimmermann.)

mother to his own ends—but he cannot change the world of objects unless some adult, mother or psychologist, arranges that his minute power shall affect the world.

Of course, these first stages are much compressed in the primates. Rhesus infants begin manipulating objects at about 16 days, which would mark the end of stage 2. Zimmermann (Zimmermann and Torrey, 1965) succeeded in training infant rhesus to crawl up a wire mesh to a full milk bottle, choosing either a black or a white stimulus box. They made 80 per cent correct choices as early as 6 days of age and reached 90 per cent correct by 11 or 12 days of age. Ten- to 12-day-old rhesus can learn color, size, and form discriminations and generalize or transfer to stimuli of different size or related form. Even the *rate* of learning brightness and color discriminations does not improve much after 20 to 30 days, although shape and size discrimination improves over the first 3 to 4 months. Bower (1965) and Fantz (1964) show that the human infant can also discriminate visual cues even in the premanipulative stage.

3. Early manipulative stage

In the third stage, the child can reach for things and grasp them. Here, it becomes clear what "sensorimotor" or "enactive" (Bruner) intelligence means. At this period, external objects have little identity, apart from the child's own actions: it is the action that creates a result:

> With a third level . . . . which begins with the coordination of vision and prehension (between 3 and 6 months, usually around 4½) new behavior appears which represents a transition between simple habit and intelligence. Let us imagine an infant in a cradle with a raised cover, from which hang a whole series of rattles and a loose string. The child grasps this and so shakes the whole arrangement without expecting to do so, or understanding any of the detailed spatial or causal relations. Surprised by the result, he reaches for the string and carries out the whole sequence several times over . . . . if the child is confronted with a completely new situation, such as the sight of something moving several yards from his cot, he responds by seeking and pulling the same string, as though he were trying to restart the interrupted spectacle . . . . (Piaget, 1960, pp. 101–102)

> Laurent at 7 months loses a cigarette box which he has just grasped and swung to and fro. Unintentionally he drops it outside the visual field. He then immediately brings his hand before his eyes and looks at it for a long time with an expression of surprise, disappointment, something like an expression of its disappearance. But far from considering its loss irremediable, he begins again to swing his hand, although it is empty. After this he looks at it once more! For anyone who has seen this act and the child's expression, it is impossible not to in-

> terpret such behavior as an attempt to make the object come back. Such an observation . . . . places in full light the true *nature of the object peculiar to this stage: a mere extension of action* [italics mine]. (Piaget, 1954, p. 22)

But what is the action? It is oriented; it has a sensory component. We are tempted to say that the child repeats a motor pattern, but it is not so—this is a sensorimotor pattern, although using cues that to the adult seem irrelevant.

Tame lemurs, reaching for a raisin, may drop the raisin, yet still bring the hand to their mouths and snuffle at it—so do baby rhesus. They may even reach for the raisin with one hand, stand on it, then bring the *other* to their mouths. It seems incredible that an adult primate should not realize which hand has the raisin, but this is not a fair statement of the problem. What the lemur does know is that reaching-to-people-results-in-raisins. Lemurs rewarded for reaching down into a bottle mouth began by learning to reach downward, although not oriented to the bottle: those learning to lift a box lid repeated their upward gesture, but on box or lid. And the result is very like the behavior of Lucienne and Laurent Piaget in their bassinets. The strategies of human baby, infant rhesus, and lemur are similar—to repeat an oriented reach with little attention to physical connection of objects (Jolly, 1964b).

Note that this is not a simple motor repetition. It has not only a perceptual, directional component but also even an emotional one—the lemur's own eagerness befuddles it.

4. Stage of finding hidden objects

The fourth stage of infancy, for Piaget, begins at about 8 to 10 months, when a child first uncovers hidden objects. Before this, the baby may retrieve an object when a small part is left visible but give up and stare or plead with the tester as soon as the object is gone completely:

> I offer Lucienne (9 mo.) a celluloid goose . . . . she grasps it at once and examines it all over. I place the goose beside her . . . . and cover it before her eyes, sometimes completely, sometimes revealing the head . . . . when the goose disappears completely, Lucienne immediately stops searching even when she is on the point of grasping it; she withdraws her hand and looks at me, laughing . . . . when the beak protrudes, not only does she grasp the visible part and draw the animal to her, but from the very first attempts she sometimes raises the coverlet beforehand in order to grasp the whole thing . . . . Never, even after having raised the coverlet several times on seeing the beak appear, has Lucienne tried to raise it when the goose was completely hidden . . . . (Piaget, 1954, p. 29)

Of course, there is a long build-up to actually uncovering a hidden object. Laurent, swinging his arm for the cigarette box, had some notion that the box was retrievable. In the visual sphere, this notion may come far earlier. Bower (1965) reports that if an object moves behind a screen and comes out changed, or if it is covered with a napkin and made to vanish through a trap door in the highchair tray, babies of 4 to 9 weeks old will show a startle response or a change in heart rate. However, the *reaching* for a totally hidden object comes later.

In stage 4 it is as though the child has just discovered that objects have a continuous existence in time. Now they no longer vanish to be retrieved, if at all, by a "superstitious," or inappropriately directed, repetition of the child's own act. Instead, things hide, and the child can manipulate the world to reveal them: lift the blanket, turn over the cup. The Loris is said not to uncover hidden objects, but on slight evidence (Jolly, 1964b; Subramoniam, 1957). This badly needs checking. There seem to be no primate developmental data on this stage!

Schaffer (Schaffer and Emerson, 1964; Schaffer, 1966) shows that this is also the period when children begin to protest at their mother's disappearance: if mere objects can be found, and continue to exist, the mother does as well.

However, in stage 4 the child is confused by a two-step hiding: if he finds his ball first in one place, then watches it being hidden in another, he goes back to look at the *first* place where he found it before. So Piaget describes:

> Lucienne (10 mo.) is seated with a coverlet on her lap and a cloth spread on the floor, at her left. I hide her rubber doll under the coverlet, in A; without hesitation Lucienne raises the coverlet and searches. She finds the doll and sucks it. I immediately place the doll under the cloth in B, taking care to have Lucienne see me. She looks at me until the doll is entirely covered up again, then without hesitation looks at A and raises the coverlet. She searches for a while . . . . same reaction with four sequential experiments . . . . [Then] once Lucienne has searched in A for the cloth hidden in B, I again raise the cloth at B in order to show her that the doll is still

Figure 148 An adult rhesus makes a simple object discrimination in the Wisconsin test apparatus. He displaces the object and picks his reward out of a small well. (Courtesy of Wisconsin Regional Primate Research Center.)

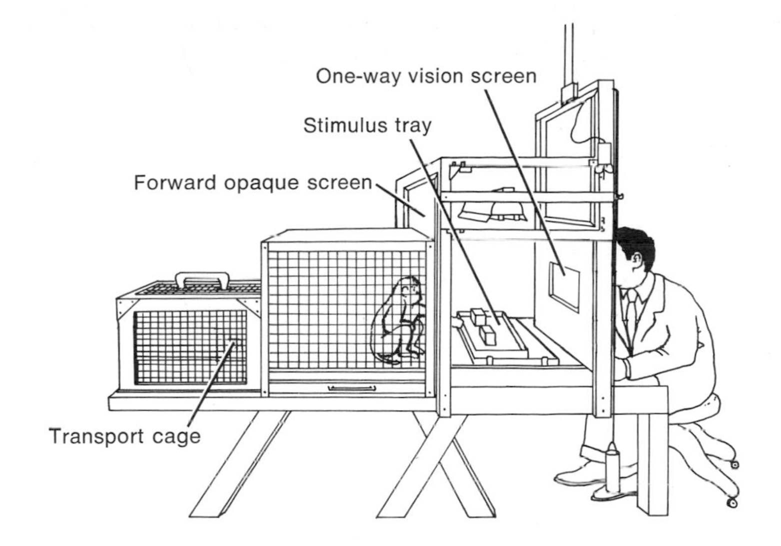

Figure 149 The Wisconsin general test apparatus. This apparatus, with its modifications, is by far the most widely used device for testing monkey learning. (After D. R. Meyer, F. R. Treichler, and P. M. Meyer, 1965, pp. 1–50; H. F. Harlow, 1951.)

> there, then I cover it up again; but Lucienne looks at the doll in B, and, as though moved by a new impetus, returns to A to pursue her search! (Piaget, 1954, p. 52)

This is a crucial experiment for Piaget. He argues that the object is now continuous in time but not in space: it can be found, but not necessarily where it disappeared. This is also a version of the classic "delayed-response" problem, which has been formulated in hundreds of other ways.

In the commonest form of delayed-response test, a primate is shown a stimulus tray with two food wells (Figure 149). The experimenter attracts the animal's attention, then, while it watches, puts a bit of food in one well. He covers both wells with two identical objects, then waits a definite time before pushing the tray forward, so that the animal can displace the right object and seize the food. An inanely simple task, at first sight—yet with delays of more than a few seconds between baiting and response it becomes difficult or impossible for many primates. Figure 150 indicates the phylogenetic differences one can find, and above all how steeply performance drops from 0- to 10-second delays. (The graph is approximate: the different species were tested with differing procedures, in different laboratories.)

Fletcher begins his review of primate delayed-response tests:

> With no close rival, past or present, the delayed-response problem remains the one behavioral test most sensitive to the widest range of experimental treatments. This powerful behav-

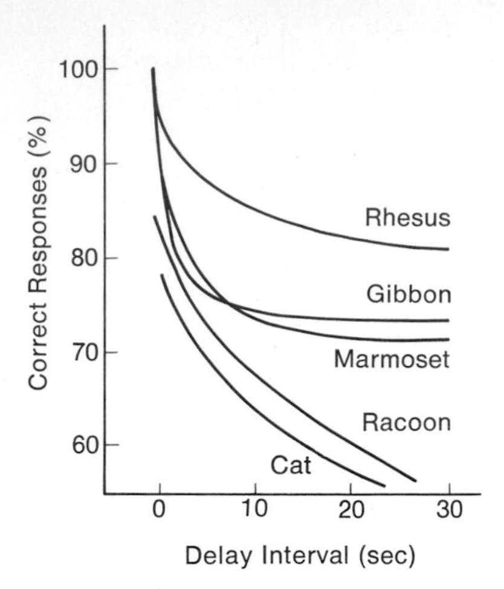

Figure 150 Species differences in a delayed-response test. (After H. J. Fletcher, 1965.)

> ioral assay reveals phylogenetic, ontogenetic and sex differences; it detects, where other tests fail to detect, the effects of brain lesions, drugs, radiation and deprivation . . . . Hunter (1913) originally presented the problem as one involving a response to a discriminative stimulus not physically present at the time of the response, and therefore requiring for its solution the capacity for symbolic, or representative processes. Considered at that time to be the first real test of "higher-order capacities" the delayed-response problem uniquely appealed to comparative psychologists. It is only natural that 50 years of research should produce a prodigious amount of data and many [other] analyses or interpretations . . . . (Fletcher, 1965, pp. 129–130)

Fletcher makes a good case that delayed-response success begins with the animal's orienting toward the correct object and, by obvious or covert means, maintaining the orientation through the delay period. Many factors that affect the animal's excitability or distractibility can thus be explained: drugs, irradiation, age, and even sex—the more placid rhesus females score consistently higher than the males.

Fletcher brings out two aspects of delayed-response testing that bear directly on the Piagetian version. In the first place, not surprisingly, if the two stimulus objects differ, like Lucienne's coverlet and cloth, animals perform better. However, if the *positions* of the two stimulus objects are switched, mammals from cat to chimpanzee tend to look in the baited *position*, not under the baited *object*. The strength of position preference, or what becomes with repeated testing "position habit," varies among species. Trained and sophisticated rhesus can carry a covert position habit that in no way interferes with rapid object discrimination learning (Riopelle and McChinn, 1961). Lemurs, and small babies, on the other hand, may respond to position overridingly, like Klüver's ringtailed lemur that pulled the right-hand box thirty-seven times out of fifty consecutive trials with the rewarded box to the left (Klüver, 1957). One senegal bushbaby showed the kind of possible conflict clearly: while orienting head and ears to the rewarded cup, right or left, he always actually reached to turn over the right-hand cup.

Perhaps, however, the 8- to 10-month-old baby's mistakes are not position responses but responses to a previously rewarded stimulus. This is supported, for instance, by the fact that if the interval between delayed-response trials for primates is increased, the animal is more likely to respond correctly. Piaget also agrees that "the object is still involved in a total situation characterized by the action that has just led to success" (Piaget, 1960, p. 110).

Young rhesus monkeys, like young human beings, do worse than older ones on delayed-response tests and tend toward strong position habits. Zimmermann and Torrey (1965) conclude that 5 months appears to be a minimal age for rhesus to perform efficiently on 0- to 5-second delays. They also conclude that age seems to be more important than experience in development of delayed-response performance. If rhesus babies and human babies were systematically tested under the same conditions, it might then turn out that a rhesus enters Piaget's stage 5 at about 5 months of age, whereas the human infant does not reach it until around 12 months. These of course are cognitive-manipulative stages—the rhesus monkey by this time has far outstripped the human baby in motor development.

5. Trial-and-error strategy stage

Piaget's fifth stage lasts from about 12 to 18 months of age in human babies. In this period, the baby can solve the delayed-response problem, so a hidden object seems to have continuous existence for the baby in space as well as time. The child is also developing many other means of controlling the world and many other modifications of its own actions. When it throws a mangled banana out of its highchair, the child now watches the banana fall and looks at the splodge on the floor, occasionally tipping itself out of the highchair in an effort to get at the banana and pick it up. This contrasts with earlier behavior of stage 4, when the child may look down as an object falls, but does not pursue the trajectory to the final resting place of the object thrown. Children in stage 5 will also pull in objects to them using a string or a stick or a pillow that the object is resting on. This behavior seems largely governed by deliberate trial and error, the child prodding or pulling bits of the set-up. Of course, between 12 and 18 months there is progressive development of deliberately varied strategies.

Here again the problems are classical ones in primate research: pulling in objects on strings or crossed strings or pseudocrossed strings, sweeping in food with sticks, and so forth. Zimmermann, reviewing the work of Mason and Harlow (1961), concludes that patterned string tests can only be solved by rhesus after several months of normal growth and that their solutions are not facilitated by extensive early training (Zimmermann and Torrey, 1965, p. 441).

Most adult primates pull in food on a single string without

hesitation. The only interest is to see how confused they are by complex visual patterns. However, lemurs often seem to need teaching to pull in the food. Klüver's (1957) description is typical. A female ringtailed lemur was offered a banana tied to a string. She first strained toward the banana for 20 minutes, then, apparently by chance, grabbed the string instead of the banana and so obtained the food. She then tried for another banana for 31 minutes, and at last grasped the string. "In the subsequent three tests she was somewhat less excited" and soon learned to pull in the food by means of the string. This illustrates some of the problems in describing this sort of thing. Was the lemur simply unable to see the connection, simply too much excited, or a bit of both? The results of a number of studies do seem to indicate that prosimians as a group may often respond to such a problem by trial-and-error approaches to the solution. They may then somewhat resemble the stage 5 child.

6. Deferred imitation and symbols

In stage 6, which starts about 15 to 18 months of age, the child begins representative imitation. It not only opens its mouth wider and wider while trying to understand how to open a matchbox, but it copies after a lapse of time. Jacqueline at 16 months, deeply impressed by a little boy of 18 months, later copied both his loud laugh and, detail for detail, his tantrum.

For Piaget, deferred imitation is a fundamental form of mental representation. This behavior shows that the child has some mental concepts apart from the immediate parameters of the situation. Therefore, the first words used spontaneously, not repeated directly after an adult, are the primary example of deferred imitation.

The same capacities underlie insight learning, such as shown by Köhler's chimpanzees, when this rudimentary representation leads to real understanding of a connection between objects in a new situation.

In stage 6, symbolic play begins as well. In symbolic play, the child's actions clearly represent a situation that, as clearly, is not real. Thus, the child may lie down and feign sleep or mouth a pebble instead of a sweet.

Piaget believed that symbolic play marks off child from animal, but then, among other examples, one turns to Washoe, the Gardners' (1969) chimpanzee. Washoe herself had been regularly bathed. Sometime between the ages of $1\frac{1}{2}$ to 2 years old, she picked up her doll, filled the bathtub with water, dumped the doll in the tub, and then took it out and dried it with a towel. Sometimes, in repetition, she has even soaped the doll. This is the same age at which human little girls begin such elaborate play. One child of 16 months, on first encountering a doll's crib, in a strange playroom, ran to find a doll and then a blanket to tuck in the doll, then whispered "Night, night."

It would be very interesting to know how much pretense goes on among wild primates. Carpenter (1964) offers one candidate in the unlikely species of the howler monkey. Howlers may sneak up on one another, sham feeding, and then pounce and play or attempt copulation. Sham feeding was even used by troop males approaching a solitary or approaching Carpenter. This is a very equivocal example, as feeding may become ritualized in all sorts of contexts. For instance, placing a leaf between the lips often occurs during gorillas' ritualized chest-beating display, perhaps functioning in part to reassure the other animals of the group. "Pretense" of feigned indifference is common in macaques. See, for instance, Bertrand's photograph (Figure 158, Chapter 19) of young stump-tailed macaques feeding near a teddy bear of which they are afraid, and elaborately ignoring the thing. In a sense, all social play is pretense, involving the metacommunications "This is not *real* fighting, this is not *real* mating or *real* hunting."

However, such metacommunication is a long way from representative pretense. Baby boys at least may enjoy rough-and-tumble play before the end of the first year (if it is not *too* rough). Clinging and rolling over with a sibling can develop straight from ventral clinging to the parent, with no hiatus. The same is true of chimpanzees. There is probably, as in so many other cases, a continuum from the pretense that is common to any kitten through the elaborate symbolic pretenses of the young Washoe or a second-generation Piaget.

Piaget thus sees Köhler's "insight behavior" as developing out of an earlier stage of trial-and-error behavior, pretense play out of physical play, and internal, mental, delayed representation out of simpler direct imitation. In stage 6, all this dawning symbolic behavior appears together—and this in turn leads into the symbols of language.

Thus end the six stages of infancy. The child has progressed from reflex grasp, to directed reach, to comprehension of objects' permanence in time and space, to trial-and-error combinations of objects, and finally to purposeful combinations worthy of Köhler's Sultan. The child of 2, then, has a manipulative approach to the world that would do credit to a chimpanzee. The child has laboriously created, out of the rudimentary perceptual structures he is given, a world of solid, permanent objects and the beginnings of symbolic relations among the objects.

CHILDHOOD AND THE CONCEPT OF CLASSES

However, an adult's mental world consists of far more than individual objects, haphazardly juxtaposed. We are accustomed to thinking in classes, and series, and invariances. It seems to us obvious that if apes are primates that lack tails, there must be more primates than there are tailed primates. If Margaretta is taller than Susan, and Susan taller than Morris, Margaretta must be taller than

Morris. If I tip a whole coffeepot over my cup, there is just as much coffee in the cup and on the saucer, table, and floor as there was in the original pot. These seem to us necessary truths (barring quibbles about the coffee evaporating or Morris jumping).

To the young child, these truths are far from obvious: he may flatly deny them, even when demonstrating with the objects themselves. Piaget calls the mental processes "operations." Not until early adolescence does a child think fully "operationally" in the sense that he can not only answer these questions but also explain his answers. From the ages of 2 to 11 or so, the child is gradually progressing from happy ignorance even of plurality, to the ability to cope with this sort of problem concretely by internalized action sequences on objects present for demonstration, to the formalized, mental operations explained in words.

Of course, Piaget was not the first to consider such logical processes. Braine (1968) writes: "It may be noted that the distinction between abstract and concrete thinking made by Goldstein and Sheerer (1941) appears to have much in common with Piaget's distinction between 'operational' and 'pre-operational' thinking and with Lashley's (1938) between first- and second-order generalizations. All these distinctions seem to follow that made by logicians between 'class' and 'class of classes'" (Braine, 1968, p. 194). The importance of Braine's putting together all these pairs of words is that Goldstein and Sheerer were working with psychotics and mental defectives, Piaget with children, Lashley thinking principally of animal studies, and the logicians in the farther pastures of philosophy and symbolic logic. Braine is thus making a sweeping generalization across many of the fields that concern themselves with the nature of thought.

Lashley gives, as an example of first-order generalization, discriminating "triangularity *per se*." Zimmermann has shown that rhesus infants can do this in the first weeks of life. A second-order generalization is the "oddity problem," in which the animal must choose the odd one of three objects, regardless of the particular perceptual characteristics of the two alike or the one odd. But one can go a bit further than saying that a first-order generalization is more directly linked to perception and a second-order generalization is more abstract. Second-order generalization means *consistently* applying some abstract criterion, that is, a mental concept, in the face of perceptual distraction by irrelevant factors.

Thus, Piaget gave children a set of shapes to sort into piles: "Put together the ones that go together" or "Put together the ones that are the same." Faced with this, a child often makes "graphic collections": he lays out a red triangle, then a red circle, then a blue circle, then a blue triangle. Each object is related to the next, but no overall criterion applies to the eventual groupings. The same child may be trained much earlier to always choose a triangular form in preference to a circle: the problem is not in distinguishing or generalizing "triangularity *per se*"; rather, it is in grasping the possibilities of the collection as a whole, then splitting it by consistent criteria.

As examples of such abstract thought we shall treat oddity and "learning set" problems, which have been extensively studied in primates and then the Piagetian problems of classification, seriation, and conservation.

1. Learning set

Harlow (1949) first codified primate "learning set," working with rhesus monkeys in standard test conditions, in the Wisconsin General Test Apparatus. Harlow presented rhesus with two different objects for "discrimination" learning, one of which covered a reward, for six trials. He then started again with two new objects, one of which was always rewarded. Gradually, the rhesus monkey became more and more proficient. When first given two new objects, he would pick up one. If that one had the reward underneath he would choose the same one again for the next five trials. If he had guessed wrong the first time, he then knew that the other object would be rewarded throughout the series.

This sort of second-order learning is a sensitive standardized indicator of differences among species and phylogenetic groups. The speed with which an animal will figure out the principle of a *series* of problems is grossly correlated with the phylogenetic scale. Rhesus monkeys are quicker than the New World squirrel monkey on this problem, and even the smaller New World monkeys in turn are quicker than the prosimians that have been tested. Many other mammals have subsequently been shown to form learning sets under laboratory conditions, but on the whole the rhesus monkeys are much quicker than cats and dogs to abstract the principle and dogs and cats are quicker than rats (Warren, 1965).

Second-order generalization improves with age. Groups of rhesus who began testing in the standard adult apparatus at 3 or 4 months of age were nearly unable to form learning sets, and even 1-year-olds performed well below adults. Children, as well, improve with age.

Harlow concluded that in fact learning sets account for an enormous amount of animals' normal behavior—any wild chimpanzee would have sticks about in its environment and would from early infancy be learning something about their properties. In a review of earlier work on "insight," particularly that of Köhler, Harlow (1951) pointed out how much of the manipulation of tools and objects, how many of the apparently sudden flashes that led to the solution, depended as well on a slow build-up of previous experience.

On the other hand, experience may not play a direct role in rhesus' ability to *form* learning sets. Although there are differences in learning between animals from rich or poor object environments, between socially isolated or mother-reared animals (Harlow *et al.*, 1969; Menzel *et al.*, 1963a; Menzel, 1963), and between even forest- and town-living rhesus (Singh, 1965, 1966a), these can in large part be attributed to calm or overfearful approach to the testing situations. The emotional influences on learning will be discussed in Chapter 19.

2. Oddity problems

In oddity problems (Lashley's original example of second-order generalization) the primate is offered three or five stimuli and has to choose the one that does not resemble the others. Rhesus and chimpanzees can even learn Weigl-type oddity problems, in which if the stimulus tray is one color they should choose the odd stimulus, or if it is the other color they should choose one of the two matching stimuli that is on the end of the row of three stimuli.

Davis *et al.* (1967) (Figure 152) have tested lemurs and seven species of monkeys on identical oddity problems, one of the few comparative studies done in a single laboratory. Surprisingly, they found the New World woolly monkey far and away the most efficient, followed closely by the cebus and three species of macaques, with the lemur and the spotnosed guenon and the little New World squirrel monkey trailing behind the rest. Of the fifty-one individuals tested, the performance of forty-nine improved during the test. However, one spotnose and one squirrel monkey did not improve at all. At the other extreme, the ten best individuals, whose accuracy ranged above 90 per cent, included three of five woolly monkeys, three of nine cebus, two of eleven rhesus, one of five stumptails, and one of eight pigtails. If performance on this oddity test can be taken as typical, this measure of cognitive development reinforces the feeling one gets from anatomical and

Figure 151 A juvenile rhesus solves an oddity problem by displacing the odd one of three objects from the food well. (Courtesy of Wisconsin Regional Primate Center.)

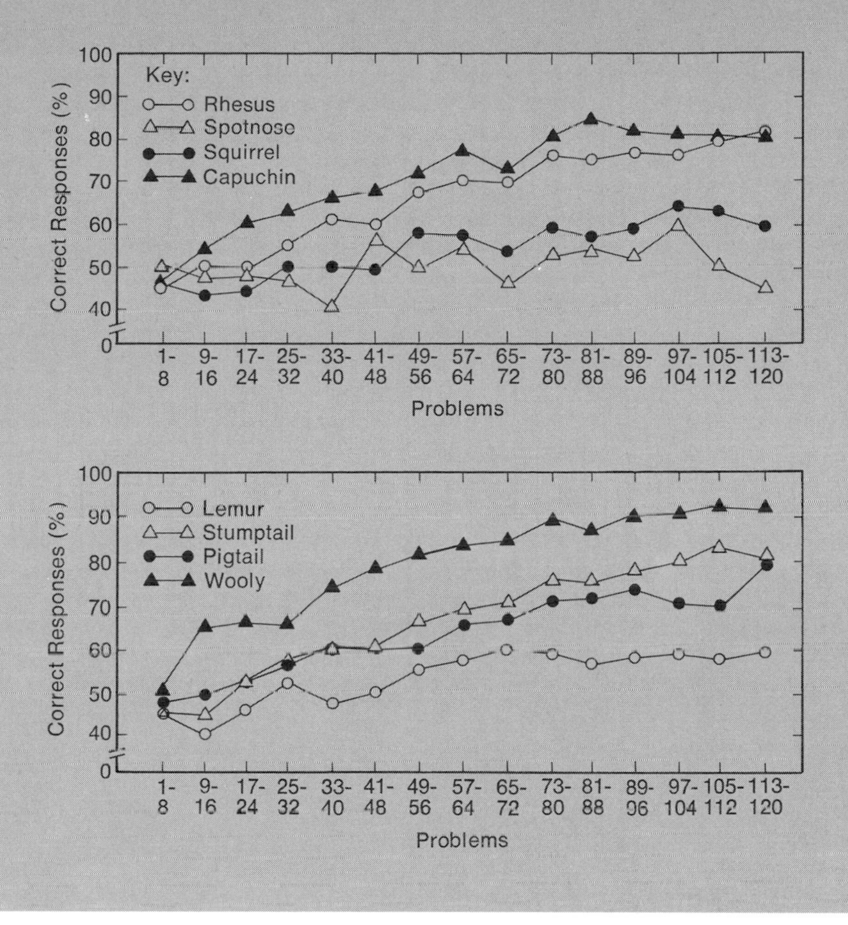

Figure 152 Species differences on an oddity test. All species improved with practice, "advanced species" in each phylogenetic line improved more than smaller, "duller" species in each line. (After R. T. Davis *et al.*, 1967.)

social studies that the Old World and New World monkeys have a parallel evolution from the simplest and perhaps stupidest forms to complex and intelligent species and individuals in each phylogenetic line.

Brown and Lloyd (1971) assess some oddity test criteria in children: verbal as against nonverbal responses and color stimuli as against geometric forms or silhouettes of familiar objects, with groups of children all of IQ approximately 100. They make the important point that nonverbal solution comes earlier than the verbal formulation (*cf.* below). However, Brown and Lloyd conclude that the verbal formulation indicates a more stable acquisition—children who reached the verbal criterion were more likely to improve on the second day's testing.

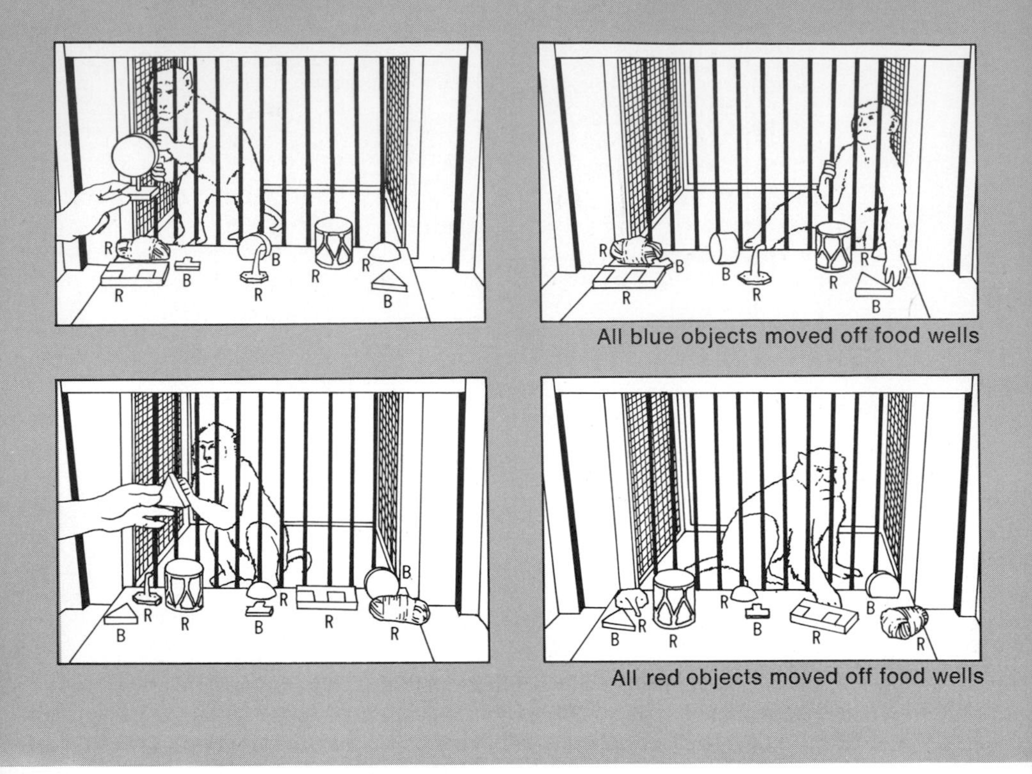

Figure 153 Matching to sample. The rhesus, Corrie, learned that the circle meant she should move blue (B) objects and the triangle that she should move red (R) objects. (After B. Weinstein, 1945.)

3. Matching to sample

What relation do the abstractions necessary for learning set, oddity problems, and so forth have with Piagetian classifications? First, there is an empirical set of questions. At what age do primates solve such problems? Or is there a leap in rate of solution corresponding with any Piagetial level?

Second, there is a logical connection, which is most clearly shown in yet another primate test, "matching to sample." In simplest form the primate is shown a sample, say, a triangle, and required to choose for reward between another triangle and a circle. This is a rudimentary step of classification: the triangle class as against the nontriangle, with the flexibility to choose the circle class if the sample is a circle. Weinstein (1945) took the process further. He taught two rhesus, Corry and Zo, to choose red objects when shown a red triangle and blue objects when shown a blue ellipse. As the number and variety of choice objects increased, Zo "became disturbed" and dropped out, but Corry eventually could choose all the red objects from a collection and none of the blue ones if he was shown an *unpainted* triangle, whereas if shown an unpainted ellipse he chose all the blue (Figure 153). (Lehr, 1967, has similarly shown that primates can choose insect and flower classes.)

This is unequivocal sorting into consistent, mutually exclusive classes. Furthermore, it is sorting to a symbolic cue, as detached perceptually as a verbal instruction to "Pick out the blue ones." It is thus the last step before the crucial transition to Piaget's sorting tests, when the child is told to "Pick out the ones that are *alike,*" while the psychologist waits to see if the child himself chooses some criterion such as "the blue ones."

Figure 154 Graphic collections made by small children. The objects are related by "edge-matching," with one leading to the next, or by geometric arrangement and not by sorting into exclusive categories on consistent criteria. (After A. L. Baldwin, 1967.)

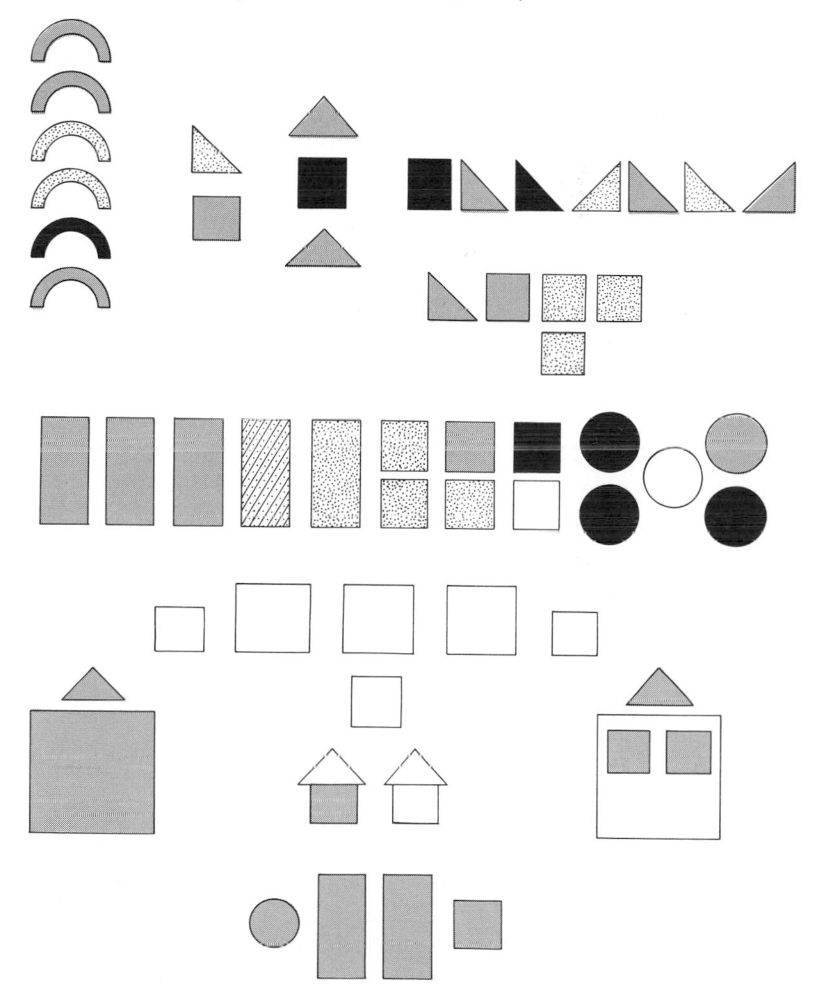

4. Classification

But children do not so choose—not until the age of 7 or so. Nor did Goldstein and Sheerer's (1941) schizophrenics. In one test Goldstein and Sheerer gave out skeins of wool, to sort into "those that are alike." A conventional adult casually groups the reddish hues together; schizophrenics might start so, then add a bright yellow because it looks nice with red. Figure 154 (page 313) shows some "graphic collections" resulting from Piaget's groups of sortable shapes. Olver and Hornsby (1966) gave children pictures of objects to sort. Children explained their groupings: "some are red, some are gold, and some are yellow." "Candle and clock are on a table and this lamp is round and this clock is." There is a logic—not the logic of classes, but one that relates anything in turn to anything else.

Viki, the Hayes' chimpanzee, spontaneously sorted objects into exclusive classes: forks against spoons, or buttons against screws. She could change her basis of sorting, dividing the same set of objects by form, size, color, or material. She sorted photographs of animals vs. people, classing her father in his cage as an animal, and herself (unclad, but in the Hayes' living room) unhesitatingly as a person (Hayes and Nissen, 1971).

5. Class inclusion

When a "preoperational" child is shown a box of brown and white beads all made out of wood and asked if there are more brown beads or more wooden ones, the child may answer "There are more brown ones, because, look, there are only two white." Piaget takes this sort of answer as showing that the child does not understand classes including or overlapping with other classes, the fact that the class of brown ones is a part of the class of wooden ones. The experiment can of course be complicated with two sets of overlapping classes, the blue and red squares and circles, for instance. The children get confused about the meaning of "all" and "some" or even "more." One child aged 5, when shown three red squares, two blue squares, and two blue circles and asked if all the circles were blue, said "No, there are only two." As the relations of classes form the basis of abstract logical thinking, these tests are of great philosophical importance, and they could easily be tried by nonverbal methods with the lower primates as well as with children, whose confusion may be in part semantic.

6. Seriation

Young children also have difficulty in placing objects in a series. They may take a row of sticks of various lengths and pair off one as longer and another as shorter, but to put a whole lot in a row with any consistent ordering mechanism is far more difficult. Even worse, when asked to insert another stick into their final arrangement, they generally begin by taking the whole thing apart and laboriously rematching pairs of sticks together. The child must be able to cope with the transitive relation "If A is longer than B, and B is longer than C, then A is longer than C" to be able to perform such problems efficiently. The same sort of relation underlies the use of measuring sticks to determine which of two separated objects is taller. Object A must be related to measuring stick B and the stick to object C, the child retaining some notion of the transitive relation among the three things, if he is to compare separated objects by measurement. Braine (1968) did *nonverbal* experiments on measuring and seriation. He concluded that these operations appear around 5 years of age, a good 2 years earlier than Piaget found them using verbal methods. However, Braine agreed that a whole complex of abilities seems to appear together at about the same time, which is very satisfying, because they could all be analyzed in the single logical form of the transitive relationship.

Primates can of course distinguish larger pieces of food from smaller pieces of food. They can also be trained to choose signs for larger or smaller pieces of food, such as different-colored rings (Menzel, 1969b). Kapune (1966) taught a rhesus monkey to select from among six different levels of food reward, with different-colored rings representing each level. It could be argued that Kapune's rhesus was very close to true seriation in the Piagetian sense. The monkey, when given a board containing twelve rings, some of each color, would first choose all those of the color highest rewarded, then those of the next highest color, and so on. This monkey is at a parallel stage to Corry, or even more advanced: both could *choose* a category of objects or a series of objects, but perhaps neither could have *arranged* diverse objects by series or by category.

7. Conservation

Piaget's most frequently quoted experiment is conservation of quantity, in which two glasses of identical size and shape are used. The experimenter or the child himself fills up the glasses to the same level. The child is then asked if there is the same amount of water. He says (one hopes) yes. The experimenter then pours the water from one glass into another markedly taller and thinner or wider and squatter. The young child says there is now a different quantity of water.

Bruner *et al.* (1966) have refined the experimental technique in order to identify the effects of different instructions, different training, different heights of the top of the glass compared with the top of the water, and even the marked differences among children of various cultures. This experiment need not be done with water: it can be colored beads poured from one container to another or even a ball of clay first made into a sphere and then pounded flat or rolled to a snake. Here, culture and experience play a major role—the sons of Mexican potters know all about clay snakes but are baffled like the rest of their village by pouring water (Price-Williams *et al.*, 1968).

Piaget and Bruner characterize the children's difficulties as perceptual. That is, the children center on a single perceptual aspect of the situation—tallness of the column of water or thinness of the snake of clay—and cannot take account of the other aspects of the situation, also perceptual, of course, or the experiential aspect that pouring water does not change it. To become a truly operational thinker, the child must be able to keep in mind more than one aspect of the situation and know that changing the apparent shape does not change the quantity.

A form of the conservation problem more amenable to use with primates is the simpler one of presenting a certain number of objects, clay pellets or, more usefully, candies, in two rows. One of the rows is then expanded or shoved together. The child is asked whether there are more or less or the same number of objects in the manipulated row. Nonverbally he is allowed to take one row of candies and eat it. It is well known that not only primates but also ravens and parrots have some conception of number, although matching in a one-to-one series does not come reliably until perhaps 7 years of age in children. As Piagetian conservation is proving an extremely fruitful tool for studying the mentality of children of different ages and different cultures, so also the way is open to study the mentality of infant chimpanzees.

So far I have only discussed Piagetian stages up to the 6- or 7-year-old levels, when the child becomes capable of conservation and coping with classes. However, these are still concrete operations. The child still fumbles verbally up to early adolescence, when the Swiss children studied by Piaget achieved full mental control over logical operations. Naturally, no one expects nonhuman primates to cope on this level. The important question is not even how far up the Piagetian scale of responses any given primate can go, but whether it goes through the same stages in the same developmental order and whether its mind seems to move from one logical level to the next in the same fashion.

EQUILIBRATION

Psychologists and philosophers have always wondered about levels of thought. Plato and Aristotle and Whitehead and Russell have all debated the nature and significance of classes. Is the class of all cats a construct of the mind or does it have some mystic reality, is there some ideal CAT whose nature all imperfect toms and tabbies partake of? How does the baby come to associate blackness and movement and hurrying into an object called the cat, or how does the baby dissociate our cat into a single exemplar of the intersecting classes of black things and quadrupeds? The genius of Piaget has been to translate the puzzles of the logician into the practical problems solved by the growing infant. Piaget shows how the infant at first does not react as though objects had a continuous coherent existence in space and time, then masters the concept of objects but cannot deal with overlapping classes of objects, and finally achieves the logical power to cope with the concept of classes of classes. This is not the place to go into the full scope of Piaget's theory of how one level progressively unfolds and gives rise to another. But one must at least say that in this theory there is great emphasis on the action of the child himself, either physical or mental.

As an old system is being outgrown, the child first centers his attention on one aspect, perhaps one perceptual aspect such as the height of water in a cylinder. Progressively increasing the height of the test cylinder and narrowing it finally make the child shift his attention to another dimension, the narrowness, and he may even reverse his previous judgment of whether there is more or less water in the new cylinder without guessing that it is the same quantity. As the child grows older, nearer to the new level of thought that allows him to realize that the quantity is the same, he will shift with ever-increasing frequency and at less exaggerated shapes of the cylinder, centering first upon one aspect and then on another.

At last he is able to combine the two sets of perceptual data. He combines perception of disappearance and perception of reappearance and the fact that he himself can move objects, like the screen or napkin covering his toy, into a new discovery "Why, the toy is there all along!" He combines the height and width of the cylinder with his own previous experience of pouring water here and there and on himself into a new realization: "If you do not add or subtract anything, no matter how it looks the quantity is the same." Piaget's own description of his view of this ancient

Figure 155 Internalizing action. By 21 months the toddler uses its mouth to explore only particularly irresistible objects, though small infants reach toward any object with the mouth rather than a hand. However, the toddler's working mouth still aids intense thought. (A. Jolly.)

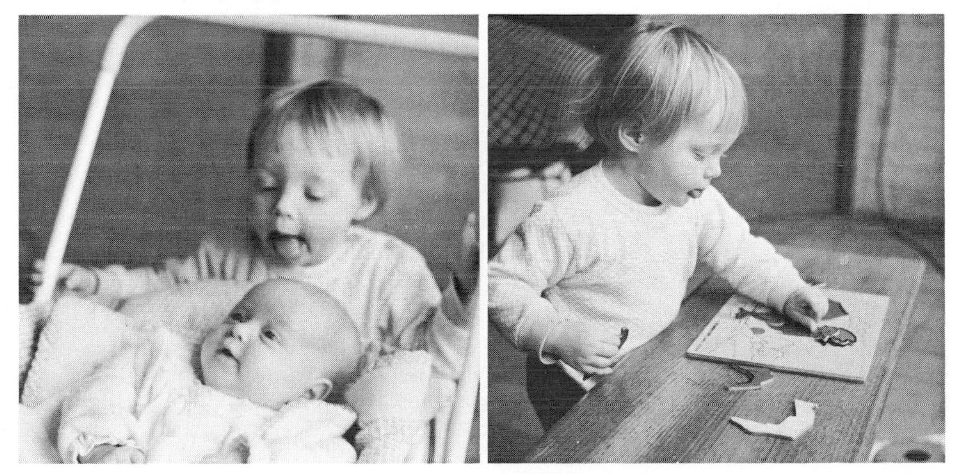

problem can perhaps do to close. It is at the moment untestable, probably with children and certainly with primates:

> The crucial turning point . . . . shows itself in a kind of equilibration . . . . which affects the complex of ideas forming a single system . . . . in this there is something comparable to the abrupt complex restructuring described in the gestalt theory, except that, when it appears, there arises the very opposite of crystallization embracing all relations in a single static network; *operations, on the contrary, are formed by a kind of thawing out of intuitive structure, by the sudden mobility which animates and coordinates the configurations that were hitherto more or less rigid* [italics mine] despite their progressive articulation . . . . after trial and error imagination there follows, sometimes abruptly, a feeling of coherence and, of necessity, the satisfaction of arriving at a system which is both complete in itself and indefinitely extensible. (Piaget, 1960, p. 139)

SUMMARY

Phylogeny does not recapitulate ontogeny. However, Piaget offers a natural ordering of cognitive levels, that is, the order in which they are attained by a growing human child. This may be the best available standard for describing cognition in other primates. Different modes of response give very different answers. Problems that seem logically similar may be "understood" at different ages if tested by visual fixation as against manual reaching, or by manual as against verbal replies. This may be an illuminating area for comparative research, because the primates develop motor control relatively more rapidly than people, and a human infant's helplessness ensures a long period of purer "perceptual" learning. Stages of recognition and social attachment to the species and Piagetian stages of object manipulation and motor development surely have different rates of growth in primates.

Many of the classic primate experiments, of both the early "insight" and the later "learning" schools, are relevant to Piagetian stages of growth, but, given the differences of viewpoints, technique, and vocabulary, it would take a theoretically argued monograph to do more than sketch in the correspondences as is done here. Visual cues, of color, size, or form, can be discriminated by humans or rhesus monkeys in the first days of life. The baby then learns to recognize the permanence of particular objects, smiling at his mother or habituating to experimental stimulus objects. Later, the child reaches for objects, although he repeats an oriented reach with little attention to physical connection of objects. This has some parallels in the behavior of adult prosimians. Still later, a baby begins to uncover hidden objects, but only after several more months can he solve "delayed-response tests," which are extensively studied in primates as well. After this, children solve the classic primate pulling-in and raking experiments. All these stages involve a gradual mastery of the "idea of an object"—its permanence in time, and in space, and its connections with the physical world. Then, in the final stage of infancy, a child begins to symbolize objects: in pretense play, in "insightful" combinations of objects, and in the symbols of language. This stage is reached by human-tutored apes, although not, so far, by any monkey. The child then gradually progresses to abstract, "operational" thought—the capacity to deal not with objects but with classes of objects, and classes of classes. Primate studies that bear on these higher levels of abstraction include tests of "learning set," oddity problems, classification, and seriation.

Study of the growth of logic takes one from the earliest manipulations into the realm of symbol and language, the tools of the mystic, scientist, and poet. Although present cognitive theories are still inadequate, they trace some path from the feeding of the ape to the mysteries of man.

18 Language

Men have suggested one distinction after another to separate themselves from the brute beasts, ranging from an immortal soul to the humbler but nearly as indestructible hand axe. One by one each of these distinctions has crumbled, having been by-passed by science or clear transitions discovered among primates, as in the tool-making behavior of apes.

Language is the current Rubicon: "The more that is known about [communication in monkeys and apes], the less these systems seem to help in the understanding of human language" (Lancaster, 1968a). An ancient tradition says that man is the only creature to use symbols; a newer tradition says that man has an ordained grammatical competence. And yet there are signs that even this latest bastion of humanity is breached. The signs are mostly embodied in the person of two juvenile chimpanzees. One, named Washoe, lived in a house trailer in Nevada and conversed in a childish version of the American Sign Language for the Deaf. The other, Sarah, embarked on symbolic logic, using plastic "words" on a magnetic board.

Of course, no experiments that reveal transitions to rudimentary human language will diminish the importance of language in our own lives. A human being develops supported and directed by language from his second year of life. Language underlies emotional and cognitive growth, as well as historically transmitted culture. A search for transitions cannot explain the total importance of language to human beings any more than the chimpanzee's termite stick can explain the hydrogen bomb. But if we believe that we evolved from some protohominid, our language as well must have had its beginnings in a mammalian signal system.

The search for transitions has been long. The Kelloggs and Nadia Kots, who first raised chimpanzees in their homes, were convinced that their charges understood perhaps fifty or sixty phrases of English or Russian (Kellogg, 1968). Viki, the Hayeses' chimpanzee, could actually pronounce three words: mama, papa, and cup (Hayes, 1951). However, she had to strain to produce any voluntary vocalization. Her words were usually whispered by forcing the air out, rather than being an even flow like our speech.

R. A. and B. T. Gardner (1969), of the University of Nevada, concluded that if a chimpanzee were to learn to "speak," it would be much more appropriate for the animal's natural capacities to learn a language of gesture. Everyone who has kept chimpanzees, from Yerkes onward, has remarked on their capacity to imitate gestures and their vivid miming. Van Lawick-Goodall reports a huge variety of communicative gestures in her wild populations, patting and touching and begging and even sending off. It might be that these gestures of chimpanzees in the wild are as rigidly fixed as their vocalizations, but the Gardners reasoned that there was a hope that the animal would be flexible enough in this medium to learn a new "language." They acquired a ½ to 1 year old wild-born chimpanzee, named her Washoe, and installed her in a house trailer and play yard with a succession of sympathetic caretakers. The caretakers talked to each other and to her in the American Sign Language for the Deaf, where different positions of the hands, called "signs," stand for different words. In 5 years of training Washoe learned some one hundred thirty word signs and combined them in two- to three-word phrases in a fashion very like children's first grammar.

What is this language we are so proud of? It can be discussed in at least three aspects: design features, symbols, and grammar.

DESIGN FEATURES AND PHONETICS

Human beings have a vast range of nonlinguistic communication (*cf.* Chapter 9). In fact, most of our personal relations, the expression of our emotions and our feelings for each other, are communicated nonverbally. That is, we have language as a second system for talking about things or refining our concepts, alongside the first

TABLE 19 DESIGN FEATURES OF LANGUAGE

DF 1	Vocal–auditory channel
DF 2	Broadcast transmission and directional reception
DF 3	Rapid fading (the sound of speech does not hover in the air)
DF 4	Interchangeability (adult members of any speech community are interchangeably transmitters and receivers of linguistic signals)
DF 5	Complete feedback (the speaker hears everything relevant of what he says)
DF 6	Specialization (the direct-energetic consequences of linguistic signals are biologically unimportant; only the triggering consequences are important)
DF 7	Semanticity (linguistic signals function to correlate and organize the life of a community because there are associative ties between signal elements and features in the world; in short, some linguistic forms have denotations)
DF 8	Arbitrariness (the relation between a meaningful element in a language and its denotation is independent of any physical or geometrical resemblance between the two)
DF 9	Discreteness (the possible messages in any language constitute a discrete repertoire rather than a continuous one)
DF 10	Displacement (we can talk about things that are remote in time, space, or both from the site of the communicative transaction)
DF 11	Openness (new linguistic messages are coined freely and easily, and, in context, are usually understood)
DF 12	Tradition (the conventions of any one human language are passed down by teaching and learning, not through the germ plasm)
DF 13	Duality of patterning (every language has a patterning in terms of arbitrary but stable meaningless signal-elements and also a patterning in terms of minimum meaningful arrangements of those elements)
DF 14	Prevarication (we can say things that are false or meaningless)
DF 15	Reflexiveness (in a language, we can communicate about the very system in which we are communicating)
DF 16	Learnability (a speaker of a language can learn another language)

After Hockett and Altmann (1968) and Marler (1969b).

system of communication that is so homologous to that of the chimpanzee.

Charles Hockett (Hockett, 1963; Hockett and Ascher, 1964; Hockett and Altmann, 1968) gives a list (Table 19) of the "design features," as he calls them, of language. Note that the first item does not necessarily apply to language: language may be written or even, among the deaf, gestural. However, human language as it evolved was vocal–auditory.

Design features 2 through 6 are shared with much animal communication, and there are a few animal parallels with features 7 through 10 (see Altmann, 1967; Hockett and Altmann, 1968; Marler, 1969b).

Hockett and Ascher (1964) discuss several of the attributes of human language that seem to differ from primate call systems or human nonverbal communication.

1. Openness

Language is an *open* system, call systems are *closed*. With language a speaker can say new things, utterances that have probably never been said before and certainly that have not been said before by that speaker. This is true of grammar (see below). It is even true of words. However, with most call systems one is limited to a predetermined set of expressions or vocalizations. The best one can do is mix these vocalizations. For instance, in a situation where food and danger are both represented, some intermediate call might indicate some intermediate situation. Hockett and Ascher suggest that "The constant rubbing together of whole utterances by [this] blending mechanism . . . . generated an increasingly large stock of minimum meaningful signal elements—the premorphemes of prelanguage."

Chimpanzee vocalizations are "open" in the sense of grading into each other through intermediates. Marler (1969a) shows that chimpanzee vocalizations *all* grade into each other, so in a sense there is only one group of calls. This is the extreme case of the graded noises first discussed by Rowell and Hinde (1962) for the rhesus monkey. However, until the variations are shown to be significant to other chimpanzees or rhesus, it may be premature to regard this as a case of openness. Neither do Hockett and Ascher explain how these signals could be divided into their component parts to establish duality of patterning or discreteness.

2. Discreteness

A graded series of calls, even if it were "opened" somewhat by the use of intermediate calls, would rapidly become overloaded. Such a graded series would be an analogue system, where the intensity of the call might correspond with the intensity of the situation, or the shading from aggressive to fearful call indicate the degree of aggressiveness or timidity of the animal. This representation, in which the continuous variation of some parameter of the call is equivalent to the continuous variation of what is to be expressed, simply could not attain the complexity of true language, unless there were a separate parameter for every single thing that varies in the world around. Language instead is digital. Discrete words represent discrete ranges of experience.

Not only words but also sounds are divided into discrete quantities. We actually produce a huge variety of sounds and many more could be made that do not exist in any given language. However, in objectively recorded speech itself, and in large part through the mind of the hearer, the continuum of sound is unconsciously classified into a limited number of permitted single sounds called "phonemes" that join in a limited number of permitted combinations called "morphemes." We can thus process discrete bits of acoustic information, without being swamped by the infinite continuum.

3. Duality of patterning

The two levels—of sounds (phonemes or morphemes) and of words—thus give language a *duality of patterning.* Both levels are discrete: neither operates as a graded continuum. However, the phoneme and morpheme levels are closed, finite. We do not suddenly invent a new sound in our language except by conscious or snob mimicking of foreign words. (The pleb uses foreign words with his familiar morphemes: "Gay Paree.") We can then combine the finite number of meaningless morphemes into an open system with an infinite number of new but meaningful words: blitzkrieg, Post Toasties, Behaviorism.

Hockett and Ascher (1964) believe that at some point after the development of openness "Articulatory motions came to be directed not toward the generation of a suitable acoustic gestalt, but toward the sufficiently precise production of the relevant smaller features of sound that identified one premorpheme as over against the others. With this change, premorphemes became true morphemes, the features of sound involved became phonological components [phonemes], and pre-language had become true language."

Openness, in the sense of continuously graded calls that probably have a continuous range of meaning, is likely in chimpanzee vocalizations. However, duality of patterning has scarcely been considered in nonhuman primates. Only now are playback experiments being made with primates (Hellmann, 1967) and with birds to determine just what the parts of a single call mean. Neither has chimpanzee gestural communication really been analyzed in these terms. Sarles (1969) makes the point that "The history of phonetic listening in language description is long, well-documented and exactly what we try to teach out and unlearn in introductory courses in linguistics . . . . the idea of discreteness, as is well known to those who have any acquaintance with psycho-acoustics, is in the mind of the perceivers, not in the nature of language. Thus the different operations which are performed on animal and human language yield entirely different and non-comparable kinds of units; phonemic for human language, phonetic for animal language." As Hockett and Ascher say, "If we could hear the pre-language of our fore-runners, it would probably not sound like human speech. It would sound much more like animal calls, and only very careful analysis would reveal its language-like properties."

4. Displacement

A fourth characteristic of language is displacement. An animal gives a call in the situation appropriate to the call, presumably when the appropriate emotion is evoked. Words, on the other hand, can be used at a distance in time and space from their referents. This is the difference between Strusaker's (1967c) vervets giving different alarm calls for eagle, snake, or lion, the baboons barking "Baboo," even for an hour after the leopard has disappeared into his thicket, and the primatologist writing down "Barked at leopard" in his notebook. We will have much more to say on displacement in the next section, on symbols, for the major distinction between sign and symbol is that the sign is still tied to the situation and its accompanying emotion, whereas the symbol is divorced and independent.

However, it must be said here that, ontogenetically, infants' speech begins to develop from their babbling and comfort noises rather than from the higher-intensity distress calls that demand instant response from the mother. Marler (1969a) says that of all the chimpanzee calls, their "rough grunts" are most closely related to the phonetic characteristics of human speech. Rough grunts include food barks, greeting grunts, and the laughter of play. In all these situations the chimpanzees are fairly relaxed, and all these noises may have a rewarding quality to other chimpanzees.

It could be then that (making the leap to supposing that protohominid calls were something like those of chimpanzees) in fact such grunts were the raw material for the development of speech. This would at least be consistent with the fact that we have retained a full set of nonverbal emotional communications while speech has evolved alongside.

Chimpanzee grunts resemble the pulsed structure of speech but lack the formants we then impress on the basic grunt. Andrew (1963a) suggests a primate parallel for our consonants and our resonances of different parts of the upper respiratory tract. Baboon grunts, like human speech, have a low fundamental and many overtones, which resonate differently with movements of the mouth and thus with facial expression. Baboons have a stylized "greeting" grunt, where lip smacking and/or tongue protrusion modifies the sound of the greeting. Andrew argues that baboons in a large, cohesive social group, under continual pressure to know each other's state of mind because of aggression within and predators round about the troop, may have evolved this refined means of signaling facial expression by sound. His arguments need not be confined to aggressive, large-group savanna animals, although the protohominids may have been such. What the signaling does imply is a need to keep in accurate touch at a distance or when the other animals backs are turned. Thus, the subtleties that can be signaled in chimpanzees by actual touch, such as reassurance, may be shown in baboons as well as men by vowels!

One common factor in both Marler's and Andrew's derivations is the greeting grunt. This may be coincidence: or it might be a real clue to the earliest social functions of speech.

5. Arbitrariness

Finally, language is *arbitrary,* learned, traditional. This is a necessary corollary of the point that language is open in the sense that an infinite number of new statements are possible. Even if the structure of grammar turns out to be innate, and integral with the structure of the brain, the actual forms of language must be learned if it is to be a system of infinite capacity. A genetic program is indeed a program and not an inexhaustible store. Thus, a call system that contains only a few types of calls, or that has the calls grading analogically into each other through only a few parameters, may be biologically fixed in its content, and so might the deep structure of a grammar, but the Shorter Oxford English Dictionary is unlikely to be.

Oddly, we again do not know how much of nonverbal communication is learned. Bruner (1968), for instance, points out that children's crying may be conventionalized after the first week or so of life. They can use only a part to indicate the whole, being fairly sure that a whimper will bring mother running. We know that looking at another person directly establishes an intensity of relationship and may often serve as a threat, if only by analogy with all the rest of the mammals. This probably is innately determined in us as well, but the frequency of glancing at other people in conversation and the distance at which we may stand to catch their eye is a highly cultural phenomenon. In England a man who looks you straight in the eye is honest and true; in Madagascar he is simply impolite. Not only the form of gestures may be learned but also contexts or responses. But even though troops of Japanese macaques differ in some of their communication (S. Green, personal communication), and chimpanzees very likely do, this is a long way from the sheer quantity of arbitrary learning accomplished by a baby who learns to speak.

To sum up, many of the crucial aspects of true language might appear in rudimentary form in the vocal or gestural communication of primates or the nonverbal communication of human beings. The rudiments have hardly been looked for, and when found they are a far cry from highly evolved language. It is only the logical analyses of Hockett that show how in fact the protohominids probably went through such a fumbling stage and how these particular attributes of a few sounds could have been gradually refined from mere sound into morpheme. On phonetic grounds two types of primate sounds may somewhat resemble speech: the formants of savanna baboon grunts and the food, greeting, and play grunts of chimpanzees.

SIGNS AND SYMBOLS

Symbols are at a distance from the things they represent. They may be at a physical distance in space or time; they are also at an emotional distance. They may contain the pleasure of control or intellectual satisfaction with naming an object; they do not form part of an immediate appeal to deal with the situation they describe. Signs, on the other hand, are tied to the situation in space, time, and emotional relevance. If a person hits his finger with a hammer and yells, his yell is a sign. If he remarks later "I banged my finger horribly today," he is using symbolic speech. But is this definition absolute? No, there are intermediates between signs and symbols. There is a gradation from the uninhibited yell through the whimper through a culturally conditioned stiff upper lip through saying "Ouch" in various tones of voice to the symbolic report "I banged my finger."

The distinction between sign and symbol has again been a major philosophical concern. In fact, it is a major concern of thought. The symbolic formulation and control of visual art, mathematics, sense perception, are fundamental. A study in depth of any field tends to lead back to the nature of abstraction or symbolization itself. This section will take a dangerously narrow path and discuss the development of words in human babies and in the two verbal chimpanzees. I shall use the words "sign" and "symbol" as the learning of language seems relevant to them, but leave aside vast realms where the same concepts should and must be used.

1. Displacement and emotionality

In the first place, the transition from sign to symbol must be considered in its emotional aspect. It is probably true that all symbols have some emotional overtone: for those who really speak the language of mathematics a feeling of beauty and purity can arise out of an equation on a blackboard. But some words more than others seem incompletely separated, almost not distant enough from their referents: for instance, the magical names of God and the unmagical names for sexual intercourse and excrement. Eric Heller (1959) in *The disinherited mind* bewails the decline of Europe from the moment that the bread and wine became "symbolic" of the blood and body of Christ instead of magically continuous with their referents. Although this book is avoiding all reference to underlying neurophysiology, one cannot resist mentioning the patients of Nielson (Orr and Cappannari, 1967) who had suffered damage to the "speech area" of the brain and could say no more than a few words but still cursed and cried Hallelujah!

Lewis (1963) convincingly describes the first intermediate sign-symbol in a child's learning to speak. A baby between the ages of 1 year and $1\frac{1}{2}$ years could only say "Mummy" when actually wanting or communicating with his mother or, in one case, when surprised by a poster of a smiling woman. When asked just to make a declarative statement in answer to "Where's Aunty?" he answered "Ahtie"; to "Where's Dumpy?" he answered "Dede"; to "Where's Mummy?" he did not say "Mummy" but merely pointed in the appropriate direction. The evidence Lewis quotes is slender, but probably highly significant. I have also seen in the growth of one child how the word "Mummy" may be so loaded that it is not used in indifferent situations, while the child happily chatters or plays with more neutral words like "shoe," "duck," and "bath." Lewis (1951) excludes "Mummy" from his lists of children's first words, even though it is very commonly the first "word." One reason is that it develops so directly from the baby babble "ma-ma" that the mother probably "recognizes" it before the child is actually directing it to her. The other reason is that for so long after it becomes attached to her it is not so much a word, in the adult sense, as an invocation.

2. Washoe and Sarah

The two chimpanzees that are learning "language" have done so by different systems, which are intended to reveal rather different aspects of language. Premack (1970) taught a young female chimpanzee named Sarah to place variously shaped pieces of plastic on a magnetized board. Each plastic chip represented a word, whereas a string of chips was a phrase. Sarah's phrases were thus in part controlled by the experimenter: she could choose wrong words but not make ill-formed words. She could only choose from the limited supply of words given her to answer any one question; so she could be right or wrong but not wholly irrelevant.

Within these limits, Sarah clearly used symbols. She had about forty words: "same" and "different"; "yes" and "no"; "on," "under," and "insert"; and a number of nouns and adjectives. As Premack said, he was not concerned in ascertaining the possible size of a chimpanzee's vocabulary, but its possible grammatical complexity. He tested Sarah to see if she was really using the words as symbols by asking "Apple same-as . . .?" and then offering a number of choices: red or green, round or square, and so forth. Sarah's "word" for apple was a blue triangle, but she described it as red and round, as with a stem, and as less desirable than grapes.

It may seem obvious that a chimpanzee could solve such a test. We have seen in the previous chapter that chimps can do oddity problems, and even Weigl-type oddity problems, where the tray of one color is the command "choose the *different* stimulus" and the tray of another color is "choose one of the *similar* stimuli." In other words, the Weigl tray, like Sarah's plastic chip, is a symbol for same or different. We have also seen that primates can learn to use poker chips as tokens for food, or rings of different color as tokens for different sizes of food. Small wonder that Sarah could efficiently use tokens as symbols for apple, banana, grape! Premack's brilliance, then, is in translating the criteria of the linguists into the terms of experimental psychology—not in teaching Sarah, but in convincing the professors.

Washoe, on the other hand, learned a far more open system, which raises all the ambiguities and questions that surround language-learning by human children. The Gardners taught Washoe the American Sign Language for the Deaf (ASL) (Gardner and Gardner, in press). ASL is not finger spelling. Each position of the hands corresponds to a separate word. The Gardners call her words "signs," which would be confusing in the present context; so, except in direct quotes, I shall call them words. ASL, as the Gard-

Figure 156 Washoe signing "drink." (Courtesy of R. A. and B. T. Gardner.)

ners say, "is a language by the most widely used criterion that we have: that it is used as such by a community of people."

This language has the duality of patterning discussed in the preceding section:

> As words can be analyzed into phonemes, so signs can be analyzed into what have been called cheremes. There are fifty-five cheremes, nineteen of which identify the configuration of the hand or hands making the sign; twelve, the place where the sign is made; twenty-four the action of the hand or hands. Thus the pointing hand configuration yields one sign near the forehead, another near the cheek, another near the chin, still another sign near the shoulder, and so on. At any given place, the pointing hand yields one sign if moved toward the signer, another if moved away, another if moved vertically . . . . and so on, but, if a tapered hand is used instead of a pointing hand, then a whole new family of signs is generated. (Gardner and Gardner, in press)

Thus ASL is an arbitrary language, not a set of pictorial or "natural" gestures, although there are stylized pictorial (iconic) ones. There is no international sign language for the deaf. The language is a formal set of symbols that must be learned like a spoken language.

The transition from nonsymbolic to symbolic communication is particularly interesting in Washoe, not only because she is a chimpanzee but also because her "natural" signs and her learned symbols are in the same medium—that of gesture. This would also be true of deaf human children. However, in hearing human babies much of the emotionally based communication is also done by gesture or by noises quite unlike their speaking voices. Thus, they may go on signaling or signing "More, more" or "Pick me up" by stretching their arms in the appropriate direction for long after they have acquired words for less loaded situations. Or, they may almost always accompany the word with the sign. Because the gesture or the howl of distress is clearly in a different medium from spoken speech in the hearing child, we are apt to emphasize the dichotomy between them, and if we are studying the development of language we usually consider conventionalization of gesture as a different province entirely. However, it is quite possible that a child's symbol for "Pick me up" becomes a stereotyped lifting of the arms related to its original anguished reach for its mother, but almost as culturally conventional as the phrase "Pick me up." Here then, there is a transition in form itself between sign and symbol. One might say that the drawing of a pig on a blackboard is worlds away from the letters PIG written down. Only when one deals with a hieroglyphic language does this transition blur. How is the accurately drawn lotus flower of the early Egyptian dynasties *qualitatively* different from the stylized scratches that indicate "lotus" in the later eras? Thus gestural language learning in a nonspeaking chimpanzee or a deaf human child shows us clearly the sort of intermediates that can exist between sign and symbol.

Washoe was taught words in several different ways. One of the ways, although not the most common one, was by shaping, by rewarding to an increasingly narrow standard, a gesture that she made anyway. Thus the chimpanzee's begging gesture of open palm and reaching hand, which in fact is common to most of the primates, was shaped into the conventional ASL word for "Give me" or "Come" with a beckoning hand. This is one of the clearest transitional words.

Washoe was also taught by guidance. The instructors actually placed her hands in the appropriate position. This is a fruitful way of teaching children and proved to be so with Washoe.

She was also rewarded with food and sweets and love when she made correct words or, in the course of shaping, approximations to correct words. The Gardners also tried rewarding "babbling." Babbling, for Washoe, was movements of the hands that resembled cheremic behavior. However, only one of the words in her vocabulary seemed to rise directly out of this babbling: touching the side of her nose or her friends' noses with her index finger to mean "funny." The incidence of babbling was highest in the period after Washoe had learned her first few words and then gradually declined. She at length learned so many words, a total of eighty-five or more, that she usually had a moderately appropriate word for what she wanted and did not need to make random gesticulations. "As she learned more signs, she was more likely to attempt some sample of the signs she had. Thus when offered a tempting bit of food she might try a string of related words such as food, fruit, berry, banana, sweet, cheese."

Finally, Washoe acquired a number of her words through observational learning:

> A part of the daily routine had been to brush her teeth after every meal. When this routine was first introduced, Washoe generally resisted. She gradually came to submit with less and less fuss, and after many months she would even help or sometimes brush her teeth herself. Usually, having finished her meal, Washoe would try to leave her highchair; we would restrain her, signing "First, tooth brushing, then you can go." One day, in the tenth month of the project, Washoe was visiting the Gardner home and found her way into the bathroom. She climbed up on the counter, looked at our mug full of tooth-brushes, and signed "tooth-brush." (Gardner and Gardner, 1969)

The Gardners continue that Washoe was most unlikely to be asking for her teeth to be brushed; it seemed in fact to be just a remark.

Children play with words, repeating over and over again variants of their minute vocabulary, and at a later stage even grammatical constructions (Weir, 1962). Washoe as well did a little talking to herself. Occasionally she sat up a tree conducting a long babbled monologue and stopped when she noticed she was being observed. She sometimes signed in a mirror, named pictures to herself out of a picture book, and even, on the way to the potty chair, signed "Hurry." However, this spontaneous talk seemed far less frequent in Washoe than in any human child.

Washoe, on occasion, invented a word. The most dramatic was "bib." The Gardners could not find the ASL word for bib in their manuals and so adopted the iconic or stylized pictorial sign for napkin or wiper, made by touching the mouth region with an open hand and wiping movement.

> Washoe had begun to use this sign appropriately for bibs, but it was still unreliable. One evening at dinner time, a human companion was holding up a bib and asking her to name it. Washoe tried "come-gimme" and "Please," but did not seem to be able to remember the bib sign we had taught her. Then, with the index finger of both hands, she drew an outline of a bib on her chest—starting from behind her neck where a bib should be tied, moving her index fingers down along the outer edge of her chest, and bringing them together again just above her navel.
>
> We could see that Washoe's sign for bib was at least as good as ours, and both were inventions. At the next meeting of the human participants in the project, we discussed the possibility of adopting Washoe's invention as an alternative to ours, but decided against it. The purpose of the project was, after all, to see if Washoe could learn a human system of

two-way communication, and not to see if human beings could learn a system devised by an infant chimpanzee. We continued to insist on the napkin/wiper sign for bib, until this became a reliable item in Washoe's repertoire. Five months later, when we were presenting films on Washoe's signing to fluent signers at the California School for the Deaf in Berkeley, we learned that drawing an outline of a bib on the chest with both index fingers is the correct sign for bib. (Gardner and Gardner, 1969)

The Gardners go on to point out that, although this "bib" is an iconic or pictorial representation not completely abstract from the nature of bibs themselves, it does illustrate some very important points about this kind of representation, mainly that there are many iconic ways of representing any one object. It is the linguistic community that chooses, arbitrarily, which way is correct.

To sum up the preceding sections on symbols: the symbol is divorced in a real sense from the immediate emotion and the immediate situation that evokes an emotional "sign." Symbols are also arbitrary, are learned, and have a duality of patterning in that each meaningful utterance is built up from meaningless components, either phonemes or cheremes. Washoe's "words" satisfy all these criteria.

3. Categories

But how does a word come to mean a *particular* object or class of objects or relation? Even assuming that the baby, or the baby chimpanzee, has some capacity for symbolization, for representing one thing by another, how do the symbols come to correspond with the classes of the outside world or of its linguistic community?

Infants seem to generalize their earliest words in many ways, not simply the ways an adult would accept as logical. The Gardners point out that this generalization is common in all sorts of spheres. For instance, Washoe learned to use keys to open the padlocked doors of the cupboards in her house trailer. She soon transferred this skill to other locks and keys, including ignition keys. Similarly, she learned the word or sign for key using the original padlock keys as a reference and promptly generalized to using the sign for other keys and to ask for keys for various locks when no key was in sight. The Gardners say that they can see no reason why these two forms of generalization should be separated.

But this generalization need not follow adult lines at all: "Charles Darwin's boy, when just beginning to speak, said 'Quack,' with reference to a duck and then applied the word to water; then to birds and insects on the one hand and to liquids on the other. Later, having seen a representation of an eagle on a French coin, he named other coins quack" (Lewis, 1963, p. 49). A similar example is a child, Margaretta, one of whose words was "doggie," applied to all small animals including dogs. One prized book displayed pictures of a doggie, a teddy bear, and daffodils. She called them all "doggie" and proceeded to generalize to include real flowers and

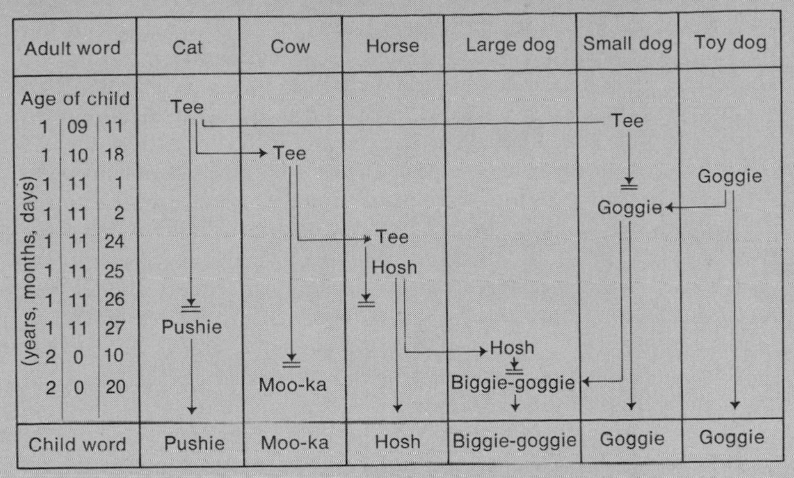

Figure 157 An infant's words for animals. Expansion and contraction of categories. (After M. M. Lewis, 1951.)

circular geometric patterns. Either category of fuzzy animals or flower patterns makes sense to us, but it apparently was no problem for a child to use the one word for the lot.

Figure 157 shows Lewis's detailed analysis of his child's learning animal names. The child progresses from "tee," the contraction of Timothy, their cat's name, through "goggie," "hosh," and so forth. Lewis points out that, as well as the obvious generalization from one animal to another, some of the child's choices are perfectly logical. After all, the St. Bernard is clearly more like a hosh than like a toy goggie. However, as each distinct adult word was offered, the child dutifully incorporated it into his vocabulary, even accepting the compromise "biggie-goggie" for the St. Bernard.

Roger Brown (1958) discusses naming and how much the adult dictates and the child accepts. Partly, he points out, *apparent* generalization appears because adults offer only words that occur frequently in their own vocabularies, or that they think suitable for a child. Thus Lewis's child had in fact referred to the category of mammals or quadrupeds, but neither word was going to be told him if "goggie" or "dog" could be offered instead. Brown agrees that the referents of children's words are at first very large, almost undifferentiated categories and then more concrete ones comparable with adults' objects. As the child matures, his vocabulary enlarges to include adult abstractions and groupings of classes. Thus Lewis's child with his group of all quadrupeds or Margaretta with her very unadult grouping of animals and flower patterns had formed infantile categories. The only requirement for membership seemed to be that one member shared *any* quality with an adjacent member, just like Bruner's series of objects or Piaget's graphic collections.

Each member relates to an adjacent one, but no overall criterion that an adult would recognize applies to every member uniting the whole. As Brown points out, the fact that these collections take on simple names, such as "dog," with simple object meanings to an adult tells us very little about the nature of the collection, merely that adults are likely to converse with their children about doggies.

The infant then rapidly learns to confine his more concrete nouns to the categories used by the adults around him. Thus, by the time he is 2 or 2½, he is probably using "dog" for dogs, and only as a schoolboy will he progress to grouping four-legged animals on the adult abstract criterion as quadrupeds. There is thus an exact linguistic parallel to the Piagetian progression from recognizing relations of objects, to recognizing the permanence of objects in space and time as individual things, to being able to group or class categories of objects. However, the linguistic progression comes at a different age from the same progression measured manually by hiding or arranging physical objects, or even still later than that measured visually by the infant's startled response to a disappearing toy. It is exciting in that if the stages are indeed logically analogous and follow each in the same order, then there is a basis for a whole theory of mental growth.

GRAMMAR

The works of Chomsky have brought a revolution in the concept of the nature of language. Current research has deserted study of the symbolic or naming capacity of the child and turned to deciphering fundamental grammatical structures. Chomsky (1957), Lenneberg (1967), and McNeill (1966), among others, have suggested that the universals of grammar, the deep structures that underlie all the various surface transformations of observed grammar, may be innate to some extent in the human being. These suggestions range from a simple statement that we must have a very strong biological tendency toward the learning of language, which Lenneberg has argued (and which in fact to anyone who has studied innate tendencies in other animals seems obviously true) through McNeill's suggestion that even the detailed categories of parts of speech are to some extent given to the child. However, the newer mystique of grammar has also become the new shibboleth, the qualitative dividing line offered between man and beast. Thus Premack and Schwartz (1966), in discussing designs for another experiment to teach language to chimpanzees, say that naming behavior, the association of sounds with objects, would indicate communication but not language and would be neither particularly surprising nor particularly useful. Nothing less than grammatical construction will satisfy them.

One great challenge to the grammarians comes from B. F. Skinner

(1957). Skinner points out that an appropriately adjusted schedule of rewards for action can teach almost any animal almost anything. Skinner can teach pigeons to play ping-pong or to guide guided missiles or simply to peck at a lighted spot in a sequence totally incomprehensible to the uninitiated layman who does not know the schedule of response and reward that has shaped the pigeon's performance. Skinner argues that if he can do this with a pigeon in a Skinner box, surely the subtle, many-times-a-day rewards offered to the growing baby could shape verbal behavior in that child to any complexity. Skinner sees no need to postulate universals of grammar on the logical grounds of linguistic "openness." On the contrary, the child's verbal behavior is just a bafflingly complex response schedule that we could easily understand if we had the child's cumulative response-reward record. Furthermore, the child's responses are *wholly* determined by his response-reward history—this is an inverted Calvinism, with learning in the role of predestination.

Chomsky, instead, writes:

> The study of language . . . . [is] a branch of theoretical human psychology. Its goal is to exhibit and clarify the mental capacities that make it possible for a human to learn and use a language. As far as we know, these capacities are unique to man, and have no significant analogue in any other organism. If the conclusions of this research are anywhere near correct, then humans must be endowed with a very rich and explicit set of mental attributes that determine a specific form of language on the basis of very slight and degenerate data. Furthermore, they make use of the mentally represented language in a highly creative way, constrained by its rules but free to express new thoughts . . . . If this is correct, there is no hope in the study of the control of human behavior . . . . (Chomsky, 1969, p. 84)

In part, the argument can be settled by logic and observation: Skinner says there are enough data in the child's environment to arrive at grammatical thought; Chomsky says there are not enough. But the argument could also rapidly become as sterile as any other instinct-learning controversy. No one has been able to record a child's environment in sufficient detail to tell. The deprivation experiments that would show conclusively which bits of language come from where would be very difficult to do if not thoroughly unethical. Deaf children can tell us much, but deafness is too global a deficit for easy analysis. One might try raising some children with adults speaking a nonlanguage—but first the experimenter would have to decide how the adults were to reach this criterion and then he would have to decide if he would actually go through with it.

Oddly, people often generalize as though there is only one important way that children learn language. Imitation of the mother, innately given grammar, social reinforcement, each have had their champions. Even the three Jolly siblings joined rival theoretical camps in the cradle. The first was an imitator, with a good ear for sound and an average rate of development in words and grammar. At $1\frac{1}{2}$ years she would babble to herself an English monologue, complete with the intonations of declarative and interrogative sentences, commas, and clauses. Rarely a real word intruded into these "sentences." Because she imitated sound rather than either meaning or grammar, and because no one is likely to argue the universality of Americanized English, she would have provided ample ammunition for the imitation school. However, the second child was a Chomskyite. She began to speak, on her first birthday, which is average, but promptly dropped all meaningless babbling in favor of a vocabulary of ten and then twenty words. At 23 months she made remarks like "Mummy, can I take my apple all-the-way home?" She was not simply precocious in grammar, but seemed conscious of her grammatical advances, as when at 23 months on being asked "Would you like this?" she fixed her mother with two blue eyes and deliberately announced "I would!" The social psychologist might have seen her desperate to organize her world, but a linguist would have delightedly turned to studying the grammar rather than any other aspect of her speech. The third Jolly is still preverbal, but it is clear already that he is a highly social creature—he has to be, born a teddy bear to two young sisters. Thus his declarative babblings, like much of the rest of his behavior, are aimed at other people and are frequently rewarded with an answer from one of the family. This baby would provide enough material to confirm the views of a hardened Skinnerian.

Obviously, none of these three children are learning through only one method, nor do they bear at all on the logical distinctions. However, it seems worth pointing out that three siblings can differ enough in their apparent *emphasis* to "confirm" any theory in its own sense of importance.

With this background, what is the earliest form of grammar or combining of words, and how does this compare in young children and Washoe the chimpanzee? Several people have studied the first two-word grammar, among them Braine (1963). A few words, which Braine called "pivots" occur very frequently, and often in the same position in the two-word phrase. The rest are members of a residual "open" class that contain everything else. McNeill (1966) goes on to speculate how these classes could be progressively subdifferentiated into noun phrase, verb phrase, and familiar parts of speech. It may seem that if one is going to begin with two-word phrases, almost any two words may take on the character of verbish and nounish, but the crucial aspect to the grammarian is the frequencies of each type of phrase with relation to the other phrases.

Washoe, like human children, had a category of frequently used pivot words and less frequently used open words (Tables 20 and 21). Not only were her pivots statistically more frequent but they were also the same kinds of words and often the very same words that appear as children's pivots. "Come-gimme," "want," "more,"

TABLE 20 WASHOE'S "PIVOT WORDS"
Words preferred as components of combinations in a sample of 294 different two-word combinations

Number of Different Words	Combined with
43	Come-gimme
31	Please
30	You
27	Go
25	Me
24	Hurry
22	More
22	Up
20	Open
19	Out
17	In
17	Food-eat

From Gardner and Gardner (in press).

"up," "open," "out," and "eat" are all pivots used by various children studied. Table 21 shows two schemes of classifying these two-word phrases. About 70 to 85 per cent of children's two-word phrases (in published studies) fit into Brown's proposed grammatical classes, whereas 78 per cent of Washoe's fitted the Gardners'. There would be little point in analyzing the categories in detail here, but the table shows how children's early phrases can be glossed into adult structures of speech and how similar were Washoe's phrases.

Washoe made longer remarks of three or four words as well. Some of these were just made by adding signs for demand or emphasis, like "Please tickle more" or "Come Roger tickle" or "Open out, please hurry." Some, however, specified subject and object, such as "You me in" or "Peekaboo me." The Gardners caution that these could perfectly well be learned globally or semantically—that, for an immature primate of any species "I tickle you" and "You tickle me" may be different in the same way as "out" and "in." Others have taken regularities in sequence as representing real grammatical rules, as in the regularities of the pivot-open classes. Again the Gardners caution that although regularities in position appeared in Washoe's speech, there are simpler explanations, notably that Washoe's preferred sign orders were the same as those preferred by her tutors.

TABLE 21 PARALLEL DESCRIPTIVE SCHEMES FOR THE EARLIEST COMBINATIONS OF CHILDREN AND WASHOE

Brown's (1970) Scheme for Children			Gardners' Scheme for Washoe	
Types		Examples	Types	Examples
Attributive:	Ad + N	*Big train, Red book*	Object–attribute[a]	*Drink red, Comb black*
			Agent–attribute	*Washoe sorry, Naomi good*
Possessive:	N + N	*Adam checker, Mommy lunch*	Agent–object	*Clothes Mrs. G., You hat*
			Object–attribute[a]	*Baby mine, Clothes yours*
Locative	N + V	*Walk street, Go store*	Action–location	*Go in, Look out*
			Action–object[b]	*Go flower, Pants tickle*
			Object–location	*Baby down, In hat*
	N + N	*Sweater chair, Book table*	(not applicable)	
Agent–action:	N + V	*Adam put, Eve read*	Agent–action	*Roger tickle, You drink*
Action–object:	V + N	*Put book, Hit ball*	Action–object[b]	*Tickle Washoe, Open blanket*
Agent–object:	N + N	*Mommy sock, Mommy lunch*	(not applicable)	
	(not applicable)		Appeal–action	*Please tickle, Hug hurry*
			Appeal–object	*Gimme flower, More fruit*

[a,b]Superscripts indicate types classified two ways in Brown's scheme and only one way in Gardners' scheme.

From Gardner and Gardner (in press).

Lenneberg (1969) stipulates the series of tests that would lead him to believe that Washoe had language. The last and most crucial of the tests is that she understand productive language: that is, she could answer *any* question or perform *any* command within a limited vocabulary. The commands must be sentences, combining verb, preposition, adjective, and noun, such as "Take [the] big shoe and put [it] under the bed." Washoe does not say anything so complex (as yet), and the Gardners have not reported whether she responds to such commands. Again, however, the argument will be complicated by how much is grammatical and how much "just" semantic. Bronowski and Bellugi (1970) argue that Washoe lacked even the rudiments of predication, although they complicate the story by comparing her to human 3-year-olds when she seems more at the level of a human 2-year-old. The variety of her appropriate phrases can be indicated on a simpler level by Washoe's responses to Susan, a research assistant, experimentally stepping on her rubber doll: "Up Susan, Susan up, mine please up, gimme baby, please shoe, more mine, up please, please up, more up, baby down, shoe up, baby up, please more up" and "you up." Whether such openness of response does or does not correspond to the openness of language is a problem of definition.

Premack (1970), on the other hand, has deliberately set out to answer just this challenge. Sarah (unlike some psychotic children) could respond appropriately to compound-sentence commands, such as "Sarah insert banana pail, apple dish." A simple understanding of the words was not enough to make sure the right object went into the right container: neither was the common-sense rule that fruits go into containers but not vice versa. Premack points out that chimpanzees' rules may not be fully hierarchical as yet. Perhaps Sarah will become confused by variants like "Sarah insert banana pail, banana apple dish" or "Sarah insert banana dish, dish pail." However, he has at least the means to test Sarah's grammatical competence.

The Gardners conclude their article with, to my mind, a wholly justified polemic against those who would try to separate animal communication from human language too didactically on any bases. Neither Washoe nor Sarah may be embarking on syntax quite as human children do, and one would expect them in any case to stop at some point in their linguistic progress. Perhaps it is even more important that they do not play with, practice, and delight in language. However, some ability to combine symbols into an organized whole is surely the least we can allow an animal capable of adequately bathing her doll.

LANGUAGE AND THOUGHT

The growing human child actively constructs his mental world, at least according to the schools of philosophy and psychology drawn from in this book. The child himself analyzes the world into its attributes and constructs from them objects and organizations of objects. The analysis stems in part from physical action, and much of the child's thought can be considered as "internalized actions" following the same laws: "The human practice of naming parts of the environment presupposes and rests on a more fundamental activity, namely, that of analyzing the environment into distinct parts and treating these as separate objects. That is, there is implied in the structure of cognitive sentences a view of the outside world as separable into things which maintain their identity and which can be manipulated in the mind, so that even actions and properties are reified in words. In this philosophical sense predication is not merely putting together words in syntactical patterns, nor even the manipulation in the mind of ready-made objects and categories. Rather, predication in the first place is a way of analyzing the environment into parts, and only after that can they be regrouped into new arrangements and new sentences" (Bronowski and Bellugi, 1970).

This active analysis and synthesis take place at many levels, and many thinkers describe *hierarchies* of mental (and physical) syntheses, in which an object or idea at any level is both a unit in its own right and a part of the next synthetic level—what Koestler (1967) calls the Janus principle. Piaget, Bruner, Chomsky, and Koestler have in common the postulation of this hierarchical form, although each makes his own description of how the mind moves from one level to synthesize the next.

At the least, this discussion has shown what some of the possible syntheses are and what the sequences of syntheses are in the growing human child, both in the realm of handling objects (that is, grasping, finding, sorting) and in the linguistic realm (that is, naming, predication, classification). Although most of the experimental primate work has been formulated in a different vocabulary, it is clear that both the achievements of nonhuman primates and the mistakes they make are relevant or sometimes identical to the manipulation, language, and, presumably, thinking of children.

SUMMARY

Language is currently treated as a Rubicon that divides man from beast. Language has design features that include openness (the ability to say new things), discreteness (chopping the continuum of sound into a limited number of phonemes and the continuum of meanings into a number of words), duality of patterning (sound against meaning), displacement from the immediate emotional context, and an arbitrary assignment of sound to meaning. At some stage the protohominids must have evolved these design features out of a less-structured call system.

Symbols are divorced from the immediate emotion and immediate situation that evoke an emotional sign. However, there are transitions between sign and symbol. Sarah, who used plastic words, and Washoe, who conversed in the American Sign Language for the Deaf, are chimpanzees who learned linguistic symbols.

The categories that one symbol represents for the very young child may not resemble adult categories. One word may be used for a "graphic collection" or "edge-matched" series of objects. Then, words are narrowed to concrete meanings. Later, the child achieves abstract, adult classification. This is a linguistic parallel to Piagetian stages of object recognition and classification.

Grammar is the core of modern language study. Skinner believes that a child learns the grammatical structure of speech (and all the rest of his behavior) by chaining responses to data given in the environment. Chomsky believes that (1) grammar is a hierarchical structure, (2) the basis of grammar is innately given, (3) *because* the structure is given, not learned, the human mind is capable of creating an infinite number of new ideas, and (4) grammar is unique to man. Although Chomsky may be right about the structure of grammar, we will probably find evolutionary origins for this as for everything else. Washoe's two word combinations resembled children's earliest phrases, while Sarah comprehended simple hierarchical sentences.

Social Learning

Most primate learning is social learning. Psychologists may analyze the complexity of learning in strictly controlled and nonsocial situations, but higher primates as a rule live in social situations from birth to death. As we have seen, they learn many of their relations with each other. They learn from their mothers and about their mothers, from and about their siblings, and about the structure of their troop. They may learn to modify even the details of their communication: we ourselves certainly have culturally modified our nonverbal signals.

Primates not only learn much of their social behavior, they also learn about the world in a social context. They learn the trails and the boundaries of their home range, they learn food sources and water sources, they learn what to approach and what to fear. Few primates learn by themselves to flee the leopard; few would survive the learning. Instead, they see the alarm of older members of their group and in turn pass on the tradition. (Do the terrors *in vacuo* of our 3- to 4-year-olds date from the era when they really needed to learn to identify the bogeyman and never stray too far lest he "get them"?)

K. R. L. Hall (1968) sums up this view in his article on social learning in primates. He points out that the studies of psychologists in the laboratory are rarely relevant to primates in the field. Washburn and Hamburg (1965) as well emphasize the all-important role of not only learning but of social learning in the life of primates. Fifty years ago Eugene Marais, a South African who had the chance and the idiosyncratic desire to observe a troop of wild baboons just after the Boer War, came to the same conclusions (Marais, 1969). His manuscript *The Soul of the Ape,* which was apparently lost or hidden after his death in the 1930s, describes his observations as well as some of his experiments with hand-raised baboons. One baboon could not tell nourishing from poisonous food, a distinction that even the youngsters of the wild troop knew. Wild baboons in the area turn over stones to catch insects and scorpions:

> The scorpion is rapidly beaten about with the hand until half dazed, and is then turned on its back with a flick of the finger and seized by the legs. In this position it cannot sting. The tail containing the sting and poison sac is carefully removed before eating. I have never seen a wild baboon stung by a scorpion during this process . . . . to this, its natural environment, our captive baboon was suddenly introduced for the first time when it was full grown . . . . although it was in the midst of unturned stones covering innumerable insects, it had no idea of turning them over . . . . when a stone was turned exposing a number of scuttling beetles and scorpions, it leaped away in terror. (Marais, 1969, pp. 98–99)

Marais quotes as well differences in social behavior among troops of baboons and among individuals as proof of the influence of learning in all these spheres of the baboon's existence. He is thus totally contemporary in his emphasis that not only do primates learn a great deal (which everyone who has worked with primates has recognized) but that social learning is essential to many infrahuman primates even to survive or to produce offspring.

FACILITATION, OBSERVATION, IMITATION

Hall and Goswell (1964) say "The essential learning-how-to-learn socially is a fundamental adaptation of the monkey and ape, derived from the mother/infant relationship, and then transferring readily to other kinds of relationship within the group as the animal develops. This is so obviously the way of life of these animals that it has so far defied a realistic experimental analysis, partly because it is so obvious" (p. 61). They themselves suggest three categories of social learning: following, facilitation, and observational learning.

The three categories are distinguished by the times at which the performer and observer undertake the action. An infant monkey following its mother may be led into many behaviors resembling its mother's, and the actions may overlap broadly in time. However, the baby then must stop itself, when its mother changes activities. Another example of following would be the synchronized movements of birds in a flock. Facilitation, on the other hand, occurs when the observing animal's attention is directed toward something that the initiator is doing, and the observer may then continue after the initiator has stopped. The commonest example is of course when one animal picks up a piece of food and another animal begins to feed as well, sometimes in fact taking away the original piece of food. New food habits can be passed around the troop by this means. In the third category, observational learning, the initiator does something and stops, and only later does the observer imitate the performance or do something similar in a different situation. Of course, the categories grade into each other, and Hall points out that they are intentionally simply stated so as not to imply any "higher" or "lower" mental capacities necessary for the different kinds. In the older psychological literature, there was a great deal of emphasis on the process of imitation. It was reasoned that imitation of one animal by another involved some sort of concept of the bodily or mental similarity between the two. This was compared with recognizing one's own image in a mirror. But, as Hall says, the equating of such intellectual comprehension with the capacity to learn by imitation seems to be taking things a great deal too far. Social synchrony of movements in a bird flock and social facilitation of feeding are examples of a very general phenomenon not confined to the primates. One can also see an obvious adaptive advantage, not only for finding food but especially in flight responses. A flock of birds or of lemurs feeding on the ground either takes flight or startles up into the trees. Such an occurrence often originates with no more than a sudden movement by one of the members of the flock; however, all the animals respond to this suddenness by fleeing to a safer place.

Learning by observation can be and has been tested in the laboratory. Even kittens may be quicker to solve a lever-pressing problem when they have the chance of watching their mother or, to a lesser extent, another female cat solving the problem before they themselves try it (Cabe, 1968). Hall and Goswell (1964) found that young patas monkeys avoided a box after seeing their mother startle when she opened the lid. (They arranged for the startle by putting a live snake inside the box.) This sort of social learning is not confined to alarm or feeding situations. One of Hall's patas monkeys began one day to pull at some aluminum sheeting that formed a part of the ceiling of the cage. Others of the group then took her place, one by one. Eventually the adult male moved to the spot and was strong enough to effectively break away the aluminum.

Hall points out that "this learning is of the most elementary kind, involving only a transfer of exploratory, manipulatory behavior patterns, such as most [monkeys] use most days on other objects, to a new location" (Hall and Goswell, 1964, p. 68). However, it is the cumulative effect of such observational learning that makes such a vast qualitative difference between the monkey mind and that of other mammals. When a significantly large part of one's behavior is learned in this fashion it can lead to the final complexities of the social life of a monkey troop.

It is possible, at least for a chimpanzee, to achieve a second-order learning about imitation learning. Both the Hayeses' Viki and Washoe learned to imitate on command whatever gesture is demonstrated. The Hayeses occasionally wished Viki would not. They would themselves demonstrate things like striking matches that Viki learned all too readily how to imitate, but a great many of the Hayeses' psychological tests were carried out through the medium of asking Viki to "do this like me" (Hayes, 1951).

TEACHING

Although observational learning of various sorts is so ubiquitous and important in the primates, there seems to be no evidence that primates actually teach each other. But here again it is a matter of definition. Teaching in this case would mean guiding another animal by leading it to a food source or placing its hand on a termite stick (Barnett, 1968). Even this is hinted at in the behavior of, for instance, Crawford's (1937) young chimpanzees who could cooperate to pull in a box of food too heavy for them both. When one of the chimpanzees was not helping to pull, the other would go over and touch its hand or otherwise indicate that it wanted help (Miller *et al.*, 1966). But this begging, as in the begging for meat by wild chimpanzees, is only a request for action and not a demonstration of how to do an action. Miyadi (1967), discussing the transmission of learned behavior among Japanese macaques, makes it one of his fundamental points that although the observing animals pay great attention to a new action and seem to be going through a process of very active learning, the performing animals have done nothing that one could call teaching. Van Lawick-Goodall concurs that, among wild chimpanzees, there is no active teaching.

However, Ewer (1969) points out that this is hardly the whole story. Many animals, although not actually teaching in the human sense, place their young in a situation conducive to the young's learning. Thus, a mother cat brings prey for her kittens. First she brings killed food, enough for them to eat, then live prey, which she and the family "play" with. Then she may lead her kittens in stalking and half catch the prey for them or catch it if it gets away from their fumbling. Schaller (1967) describes the same sort of behavior in tigers and lions. He watched a mother tiger throw down a buffalo repeatedly while her young leaped on it. She never used the suffocating, killing throat grip, but simply dragged the creature over by its hindquarters while her 2-year-old offspring did their best to dispatch it. This presupposes no foresight on the part of the mother animal. She may have not even the dimmest idea of why she is going about with a live mouse in her mouth or wrestling with a live buffalo. However, the effect is one of teaching. In a more flexible way, we could say that the dominant macaque mother teaches her young son her own dominant status simply by her actions toward other members of the group. Even more accurately we could say that the subordinates of a group are doing the teaching by grimacing and deferring to the infant when he himself is still a baby in the shadow of his mother. We thus should expect to find transitions between a chimpanzee pulling back her young one from messing about with the dominant male to the human mother warning "Don't spill your milk on Grandpop" and from the chimpanzee mother termiting in front of her fascinated child to Rensch and Döhl teaching Julia to open fourteen kinds of locks.

SOCIAL DEPRIVATION AND LEARNING

In spite of the fact that most of a normal monkey's learning occurs in social situations, prolonged social deprivation does not seem to affect the monkey's final capacity for learning set formation, discrimination problems, or some match-to-sample tasks (Harlow *et al.*, 1969; Angermeier *et al.*, 1967). Animals reared for 6 to 9 months under conditions of strict social isolation may reach as high a criterion as "normal" cage-reared animals. Thus, even drastic deprivation may not affect formal reasoning or learning capacities for simple tasks.

However, the animals perform very badly at the *beginning* of tasks, usually because they seem hyperexcited in the test situation. This may even be true of animals tested at 3 years old or more, although they were isolated only for the first 6 to 9 months of life. Menzel (Menzel, 1963; Menzel *et al.*, 1963*a,b*) explains this as a hyperstimulation. The deprived chimpanzees that he tested reacted to mild stimuli as if they were strong ones, with fear and cowering or with hyperexcitement. With repeated testing after they had come out of isolation, they adjusted better to the situation. Harlow, similarly, attributes the poor early performance of his isolated rhesus monkeys to their difficulty in adapting to the test situation itself. Chimpanzees may in fact compensate better than rhesus for early isolation. Chimpanzees seem more flexible, both in learning about objects and in learning such basic social behaviors as mating with the opposite sex (Davenport and Rogers, 1968; Davenport *et al.*, 1969). Of course, in the natural situation where a young monkey must learn about life socially, where it must be able to approach strange objects to an appropriate degree, the emotional hyper-excitement in learning situations would be just as much of a handicap in its final performance as would "purely intellectual" difficulties (Walters, 1968).

A still more disturbing test is the recent experiment of Menzel *et al.* (1970) on tool using in wild-born and restriction-reared chimpanzees. He gave eighteen near-adult chimpanzees Köhler's classic test of raking in a bit of banana with a stick. At every level of manipulation, beyond simple play with the sticks, wild-born chimpanzees were more efficient and skillful in solving the problem. The frightening part is that the chimpanzees differed *only* in their experience during the first 2 or 3 years of life, that is, their early infancy and childhood, before even wild-born chimpanzees use tools well. After this, the chimpanzees were all caged similarly, or together, with comparable manipulative and social experience for 4 to 6 years. The early isolates had long since outgrown their hyperexcitement and seemed no less interested in the bananas than their wild-born counterparts. Thus, Menzel shows that for such relatively complex dealing with the world early experience may be crucial. Human babies in different places or of different social classes (Goldberg, 1970) may begin to learn *not* to play with objects even at 6 months old! If the effects of such early training are as long lasting as with chimpanzees, and apply less to simple discrimination tests than to complex manipulation of the outside world, the implications for human skills are enormous.

NOVELTY AND THE TROOP

In the section of Chapter 2 on manipulation and tools we have already seen that wild primates rarely play with or manipulate objects, whereas caged primates in their boredom may do so far more. Menzel (1966) put out small plastic toys where a troop of wild Japanese macaques would find them and observed the response. Often the monkeys responded with studied avoidance that was clear to the observer but hard to define. Occasionally, a mother apparently ignored the object herself but then actively pulled her infant away from it. The testing conditions mattered a great deal. Menzel placed a collection of nine innocuous toys on top of a favorite sitting rock, in the position usually taken by the most dominant animal present. After 4 days of intermittent testing the troop began to avoid the rock and area altogether. However, Menzel left about twenty of his toys, including the same objects, under an overturned crate in the woods all night. The next morning they had all been stolen except for two rubber snakes, and juveniles or infants appeared periodically through the morning with one in hand. Similarly, a rope stretched across a monkey path would be

Figure 158 The group as a whole decides to "ignore" an object. With feigned indifference, the young stumptails pick up scattered rice around a frightening teddy bear. However, if one began to play with the teddy bear, all would try to snatch it. (From M. Bertrand, 1969.)

avoided, but if it was left bunched up in the woods it might well become a plaything.

Social facilitation counts for a great deal in the wild troop. If one animal picks up or plays with an object, others are very likely to join in, even if it is only a stick like all other sticks lying about the woods.

Menzel's study confirms the general impression that age is all important in manipulating new objects or learning to cope with new situations. It is the playful infants and juveniles of any species who approach a new object and who are most expendable if it turns out to be dangerous. Conversely, the older the animal the less likely it is to involve itself in an unknown situation, like the Japanese macaque leader who would not let his troop go into a trap.

However, this bounciness and quickness of approach are not the same as speed in formal learning. The only attempt at testing learning capacity in the wild that I know is that of Tsumori (Tsumori *et al.*, 1965; Tsumori, 1966, 1967). He did a variant of the delayed-response test by the "sand-digging" technique. He buried peanuts in the beach sand on the island of Koshima, with great patience arranging the situation so that each member of the troop in turn had a chance to find the buried peanuts without too much interference from its colleagues. Tsumori then measured success and latency to success in each of the individuals. He found that it was the late adolescents who were quickest and most proficient at the delayed-response technique. This would agree with the laboratory tests that indicate that learning speed and complexity increase with age to near adulthood. Menzel (1969a), studying the exploratory behavior of various-age chimpanzees in a new enclosure, suggests

Figure 159 A chimpanzee child plays with a stick. (Courtesy of H. van Lawick.)

that the lesser amount of apparent exploration in the adults derives from the fact that the adults can simply glance around and accumulate a great amount of information or explore their environment once and remember it, whereas the youngsters must bounce up and down every tree several times to gain the same amount of knowledge.

And in turn quickness of formal learning is not the same as total amount of stored knowledge. For instance, Thelma Rowell (1969) points out that disastrous droughts occur about every 20 years in the Queen Elizabeth Park where she worked. Only the oldest baboons of the troop would be able to remember where the last waterholes and the last food sources are to be found in a drought. In less dramatic circumstances it may be the older troop members who integrate the various information of the day to steer the troop around its more accustomed paths.

Whole troops as well as individuals and age classes vary in their approach to objects. Miyadi notes that some troops of Japanese macaques are very easy to provisionize, whereas others remain wild in spite of the most appealing efforts of the scientists. Some species seem more adaptable than others—macaques and baboons range in and out of human settlements throughout Africa and India, whereas leaf eaters are more usually confined to their leaves. As always, this is not a hard-and-fast rule. Manley (personal communication) tells of a troop of purplefaced langurs, one of the more specialized leaf-eating species, ordinarily confined to the tops of the forest, scavenging about seaside rocks in an area where the high trees had been cut down and they had only low beach scrub to sleep in. They seemed as adept in this odd environment as any South African seaside baboon.

The most revealing set of experiments has been those of S. T. Singh (1965, 1966a). He compared Indian rhesus caught in the forest, their original habitat, with those caught in the city, where they live by thieving from the bazaars and sleeping on roof tops. As with socially deprived monkeys, the two habitat groups were equally efficient in learning discrimination problems and in tests of "pure" cognition. However, the urban monkeys were far more active, and manipulated and contacted objects readily and frequently. Again, there is a difference in willingness to approach objects that does not correlate with an actual measure of learning speed but is clearly highly correlated with the environment and upbringing of the individuals.

In short, one can conclude that the innovation of behavior and particularly of new behavior toward objects in wild troops depends as much on their initial interest in and approach to objects as on their learning capacities. Some species are more adaptable, playful, and innovative than other ones, and quite probably individuals brought up in a rich and demanding environment, such as an Indian city, will be more adaptable than their country cousins. As for cognitive ability itself, it certainly increases with age, at least up to adulthood. Environmental conditions, at least gross laboratory deprivation, may particularly affect higher levels of skill, such as tool use.

CULTURE

A great deal of the behavior of the primates can be called cultural, in the sense that it is transmitted by learning from generation to generation. This is true not only of social behavior but of behavior toward the environment, as simple a thing as the traditional home range of a troop.

Culture has been most thoroughly studied in Japanese macaques. Here, the Japanese have looked at new behaviors that have begun since provisionization of the wild macaques and seen how they spread from individual to individual of the troop. One of the first studies was by Itani (1958) of the Takasakiyama troop learning to eat caramels. They not only accepted this odd tourist bait but learned one by one to unwrap the candies before eating. Many other behaviors have been discovered or invented since: washing off the grit from sweet potatoes, taking a handful of wheat into water and washing the sand out of it, and even swimming. In every case it is very young juveniles or even not quite independent infants

Figure 160 Brothers. Social learning may occur through direct imitation, often in family lines—the subordinate commonly observes and copies the dominant. (Courtesy of J. Thompson.)

who begin a behavior pattern. The monkeys most closely associated with the infants observe them and often copy the pattern, or take away the food. Thus, new behavior flows from the infant to its mother and siblings. They, in turn, pass on the behavior to associated female friends, male consorts, or play-group peers. Very often a new pattern will spread first through a single kin group, such as siblings and their real, related aunts, who associate with each other.

Miyadi (1967) has codified the rules of cultural transmission, most of which we have seen already. The patterns are transmitted by observation, not by teaching. They tend to go up the dominance hierarchy only when animals are, for some other reason, closely observing each other, as the mother or aunt will observe the infant. They go down the dominance hierarchy more rapidly. When a dominant male or female has acquired a pattern, the other animals are watching him and so will copy him. As the infants normally initiate behavior, it is thus at first slow to spread, but if the ruling hierarchy takes it up it becomes more standard practice through the troop. In several cases, the older males of the troop have never copied a new behavior from their subordinates; they eat the new-fangled sweet potatoes but will not wash them and are far too stuffy to swim.

Marais, like many later primatologists, turned to the differences in behavior among troops of baboons as evidence for their learned traditions. He cites, for example, two troops who had unique feeding patterns. Members of one troop picked the hard fruit of the baobab tree and carried the fruits to the foot of the hills, where the nearest stones were. They then smashed them, using the stones as hammers. This is the only example we have, besides a population of West African chimpanzees that Struhsaker has recently discovered, of a wild primate using stones for hammering. Another troop had been left with only one safe drinking spot, which was a thermal spring:

> The water in the spring itself and for some distance downstream was too hot to drink, and a farmhouse, toward which the water flowed, made it dangerous for the baboons to go further downstream .... On the occasion we observed their behavior about a third of the troop lined up along the watercourse below the spring and each one scooped a furrow through the mud. When these furrows were filled with water they moved farther up the hillside to wait for it to cool .... those that took part in the operation of making the furrows consisted of about equal numbers of adults and young ones, and the difference in their respective behavior was interesting. The adults went about their work quietly, methodically, and phlegmatically, after the Chacma manner, but the youngsters were greatly excited, jerking out the mud erratically, and frequently, when the water came in contact with their hands uttering cries of rage .... the mud was generally so soft that many furrows were obliterated and only those dug in the firmer area lasted long enough to cool the water. But even the majority of these could not be used because they were made the wrong way. Whenever the furrow was dragged in a more or less downstream direction, the continued entrance of hot water prevented cooling. A small proportion were scooped up more or less upstream or at right angles to the current and in these the water cooled more quickly. Whether the correct method was adopted by accident or design it was impossible for us to establish, since we had no opportunity of ascertaining whether the same individual always adopted the same method of construction (Marais, 1969, pp. 74–76)

SUMMARY

Most primate learning takes place in a social context. Choice of food, feeding methods, identification of predators, and home range use come not through individual discovery but through social learning. Primates may simply follow or be facilitated by the sight of another primate fleeing or feeding; they may also actively imitate. There is apparently no deliberate teaching.

Social deprivation early in life leads to hyperexcitement and hyperreactivity, which interfere with formal learning. There may also be long-term impairment of complex skills such as tool use.

Figure 161 Social learning. Fifi watches Flo fishing for termites. (Courtesy of H. van Lawick.)

A wild troop may ostentatiously ignore strange objects or compete to play with them—as among humans, the group, not just the individual, encourage or block innovation. Juvenile or infant animals make most behavioral innovations in the wild, although wild adolescents may be quickest at formal learning (delayed-response) tests. Older troop members impose restraint and probably carry long-term memory for the troop. New behavior is passed around a Japanese macaque troop through kinship lines or among other close associates such as consort pairs. It is far more easily passed from dominant to subordinate, so leading males may never learn a new fashion. Troop differences, in both feeding and social behavior, attest to the existence of cultural transmission in primates. Not just the individual but also the group or the lineage accumulate knowledge.

The Evolution of Intelligence

SELECTION FOR LEARNING

We have seen the primate's behavior as a fabric of ever more complex, learned responses. We have progressed from a basic description of four-handed arboreal animals through a description of the evolutionary pressures that permit, or force, most higher primates to live as social animals. We have seen how the various species divide the environment and how within each species individuals form troops of limited size in limited home ranges. Within this ecological framework we have seen how individual acts of aggression, reproduction, and friendship merge into a social whole, and how the society shapes an infant to eventually play his role within it. We have then seen how the mind of the growing infant, at least of the human infant, creates logical operations out of the shifting data of his senses that allow him to master and organize his world.

Therefore, the unifying theme is the emergence of society within primate ecology and the emergence of intelligence as the warp and woof of society.

There are two obvious evolutionary pressures toward greater intelligence that do *not* stem from society. One is adaptability to changed environments. Most primates can adapt to changed foodstuffs, and different populations of almost any species eat different fruits and insects in different forests. A few, such as savanna baboons, macaques, and men, are outstandingly adaptable, colonizing cliff and forest and field and urban complex with almost equal vigor. The adaptable animal is buffered against adverse circumstances.

A second evolutionary pressure is that mammals as a whole have been growing brighter, to judge by the increase in relative brain size. Thus, as prey grew more intelligent, predators did so too. The packs of wolves and wild dogs and the prides of lions may be as complex in social roles or learned hunting skills as the troops of many primates. Primates prey on each other; surely our ancestors did as well. Primates compete with each other for food more closely than they compete with other animals. Thus, there are pressures of competition and predation from outside each species, and if the advantage is to the clever, each competitor will evolve to be ever cleverer (Andrew, 1962).

Finally, there is the pressure to adapt to society itself. Even if the original selective pressures for intelligence may have come from outside the species, the individual social roles themselves demand great dependence on learning in primates, as opposed to the highly articulated groups of social insects where individuals of a caste are interchangeable.

But to depend on learning one must be social. There must be simple physical time to learn about the world and time for the appropriate learning situations to arise. There must be at least one adult with the growing young to teach it the identity of food and predators. There is no point in learning if one has to learn everything oneself: a more restricted, but quicker, instinctive recognition would be much more efficient.

Thus, there is a spiral of dependency and intelligence: ever greater learning necessitates ever greater dependency, and longer dependency allows further learning.

I have argued (Jolly, 1966b) that social life evolved at the prosimian level before the appearance of simian intelligence. This still seems likely, at least in the sense that modern prosimians, and many other mammals, form permanent groups, with each individual having its own role in the troop, whereas manipulative and learning capacity appear only in the higher primates. Thus, "man's social emotions are older than all his general ingenuity, and the first complexities of his mind grew with his social dependence" (Jolly, 1966a, p. 167).

Learning about the environment from within society and learning about society itself are thus the primate way of life. And society itself learns, even at the primate level. The older generation guards the traditions, useful or useless, that will be passed to the young. This was surely true of the human ancestor as well—he was bound by and in his culture for millions of years before we would credit him with humanity.

COLLECTIVE LEARNING

Eugene Marais contrasted the soul of the baboon with the soul of the white ant. He studied the termite hills of South Africa and the termites that lived within, governed by instinct but in a social organization of many more individuals, more tightly knit, than those of any primate but man. He came to the conclusion that the termite hill was a single organism. The workers were expendable members of the community, sloughed off like the cells of our skin. (The same idea had been proposed before by W. M. Wheeler (1911) about communities of social ants.) Marais deliberately contrasted this social organism, where the busy individuals lived out their lives governed by instinct or "phyletic memory," blindly bound to the higher interest of the whole, with the baboon troop, where each individual developed its own individual "causal" memories and incorporated into its own store of knowledge the traditional ways of its tribe.

But man, like the termite, is reaching the point where at least his cognitive processes are becoming collective, not individual, for we can make progress using each other's ideas. We have been a long time reaching this stage. The baboon and the chimpanzee already live in a nexus of social tradition, and our protohominid ancestors presumably did so as well. However, for millennia after the invention of the hand axe, human technology progressed at no quicker pace than a biological appendage might evolve. Then when Acheulean man began to make tools according to local tradition there came a sudden spurt, for those days, in the rate of progress. Men began to get a somewhat clearer idea of the process of learning from each other. And so we have accelerated. Writing and libraries provided a common memory store. The scientific revolution provided a still more conscious idea that it is possible to observe the world and synthesize ever more powerful hypotheses, testing them on an ever wider range of data. Post-Rennaissance science became a collective learning set for new learning. At last, with computers not only to store the data but also selectively to retrieve it, there seem to be no limits to the power of human creativity. We have been called prosthetic creatures, unable to exist without the hand axe as an artificial extension of our limbs. We are approaching worldwide science with computers as synthetic extensions of our minds.

As T. S. Kuhn shows, our theories have not become more "scientific" in the sense of becoming more impeccably logical over the years. However, we have surely made progress, if only in the sense that a Ptolemaic astronomical theory would not have sufficed to send men to the moon. We make progress from synthesis to synthesis, like Piagetian children. At first, we simply do not see the data that contradict our theory. We stare at a model of water in a tilted glass and draw the water level parallel to the bottom of the glass because we have not yet discovered gravity. We see that our mother's hair hangs down and yet draw her with hair radiating outward because hair obviously sticks out of people's heads. Then uncertainty arises, we change our answer from demonstration to demonstration, creating part theories to deal with partial facts. At last, we arrive at a new synthesis, leap to a conclusion that gives us the power and flexibility to deal with the observed world in a new way. The observations are collectively made, and as more and more people go into science, more and more of the theories are created independently in different minds. The work of Piaget is continuous with the work of Kuhn, as both are concerned with the creation of reality, not its discovery. They are talking about the creation of means of organizing truth in the mind of any child confronted with the data of its senses or of any genius confronted with the overwhelming complexity of the growth of his science.

We are primates, by our loves and fears and hatreds, by the cock of our thumbs, and by the size of our big toes. Our thumbs have been modified to hold precision tools; our big toes have flattened to walk upon the ground; our loves and hatreds are shaped to the needs of human groups. But, above all, we are *Homo sapiens.* Our primate ancestors took the path of learning, buffering themselves against the vagaries of their environment by the complexities of their society and their intelligence. We exchanged instinctive certainty for adaptive complexity, and in our myth bought knowledge at the price of innocence.

Our panspecific mind and our worldwide society are only the logical outcome. As we cannot reverse evolution, we have no choice but to continue using our knowledge to accept the responsibilities for our society. We can only evolve on our chosen path to an ever more powerful community of knowledge, or else use that knowledge to destroy ourselves.

Bibliography

Index

Bibliography

Ainsworth, M. D. S., 1967, *Infancy in Uganda: Infant care and the growth of love,* Johns Hopkins Press, Baltimore, 471 pp.

Aldrich-Blake, P., 1970, Problems of social structure in forest monkeys, IN Social behavior in birds and mammals, ed. J. H. Crook, Academic, New York, pp. 79–102.

Alexander, B. K., and Bowers, J., 1967, The social structure of the Oregon troop of Japanese macaques, *Primates,* 8, 333–340.

Altmann, S. A., 1962, A field study of the sociobiology of rhesus monkeys, *Macaca mulatta, Ann. N.Y. Acad. Sci.,* 102, 338–435.

Altmann, S. A., 1965, Sociobiology of rhesus monkeys II: Stochastics of communication, *J. Theoret. Biol.,* 8, 490–522.

Altmann, S. A., 1967, The structure of primate social communication, IN *Social communication among primates,* ed. S. A. Altmann, Chicago U. P., Chicago, pp. 325–362.

Altmann, S. A., 1968a, Sociobiology of rhesus monkeys III; The basic communication network, *Behavior,* 32, 17–32.

Altman, S. A., 1968b, Sociobiology of rhesus monkeys IV; Testing Mason's hypothesis of sex differences in affective behavior, *Behavior,* 32, 49–69.

Altmann, S. A., and Altmann, J., 1970, *Baboon ecology, Biblioteca Primatologia,* No. 12, Chicago U. P., Chicago and S. Karger, Basel, 220 pp.

Ambrose, J. A., 1963, The concept of a critical period for the development of social responsiveness, IN *Determinants of infant behavior II,* ed. B. M. Foss, Methuen, London, pp. 201–226.

Andrew, R. J., 1962, Evolution of intelligence and vocal mimicking, *Science,* 137, 585–589.

Andrew, R. J., 1963a, Trends apparent in the evolution of vocalization in the Old World monkeys and apes, *Symp. Zool. Soc. Lond.,* 10, 89–101.

Andrew, R. J., 1963b, The origins and evolution of the calls and facial expressions of the primates, *Behavior,* 20, 1–109.

Angermeier, W. F., Phelps, J. B., and Reynolds, H. H., 1967, The effects of differential early rearing upon discrimination learning in monkeys, *Psychon. Sci.,* 8, 379–381.

Anthoney, T. R., 1968, The ontogeny of greeting, grooming, and sexual motor patterns in captive baboons (supersp. *Papio cynocephalus*), *Behavior,* 31, 358–372.

Ardrey, R., 1967, *The territorial imperative,* Anthony Blond, London.

Argyle, M., 1967, *The psychology of interpersonal behavior,* Penguin, Harmonsworth, 223 pp.

Ashley Montagu, M. F., 1968, *Man and aggression,* Oxford U. P., London, 178 pp.

Ashton, E. H., and Oxnard, C. E., 1964, Functional adaptations in the primate shoulder girdle, *Proc. Zool. Soc. Lond.,* 142, 49–66.

Avis, V., 1962, Brachiation: The crucial issue for man's ancestry, *Southwest. J. Anth.,* 18, 119–148.

Baenniger, L. P., 1968, Dominance hierarchies: The problem of undimensionality, *Amer. Zool.,* 8, 698.

Baldwin, A. L., 1967, *Theories of child development,* Wiley, New York, 618 pp.

Baldwin, J. D., 1968, The social behavior of adult male squirrel monkeys (*Saimiri sciureus*) in a semi-natural environment, *Folia Primat.,* 9, 281–314.

Baldwin, J. D., 1969, The ontogeny of social behavior of squirrel monkeys (*Saimiri sciureus*) in a semi-natural environment, *Folia Primat.,* 11, 35–79.

Barnett, S. A., 1968, The "instinct to teach," *Nature,* 220, 747–749.

Beach, F. A., 1967, Maternal behavior in males of various species, *Science,* 157, 1591.

Beck, B. B., 1967, A study of problem solving by gibbons, *Behavior,* 28, 95–109.

Bellugi, U., and Brown, R., 1964, The acquisition of language, *Monogr. Soc. Res. Child Develop.,* No. 29.

Benchley, B., 1942, *My friends the apes,* Little, Boston.

Bernstein, I. S., 1962, Response to nesting materials of wild-born and captive chimpanzees, *Animal Behav.,* 10, 1–6.

Bernstein, I. S., 1964, Role of the dominant male rhesus monkey in response to external challenges to the group, *J. Comp. Physiol. Psychol.,* 57, 404–406.

Bernstein, I. S., 1965, Activity patterns in a cebus monkey group, *Folia Primat.,* 3, 211–224.

Bernstein, I. S., 1966a, Analysis of a key role in a capuchin (*Cebus albifrons*) group, *Tulane Studies Zool.,* 13, 49–54.

Bernstein, I. S., 1966b, An investigation into the organization of pigtail monkey groups through the use of challenges, *Primates,* 7, 471–480.

Bernstein, I. S., 1967a, Intertaxa interaction in a Malayan primate community, *Folia Primat.,* 7, 198–207.

Bernstein, I. S., 1967b, A field study of the pigtail monkey (*Macaca nemestrina*), *Primates,* 8, 217–228.

Bernstein, I. S., 1968a, The lutong of Kuala Selangor, *Behavior,* 32, 1–16.

Bernstein, I. S. 1968b, Primate status hierarchies, *Amer. Zool.,* 8, 741 (abst.).

Bernstein, I. S., 1969a, Spontaneous reorganization of a pigtail monkey group, IN *Proceedings of the Second International Congress of Primatology I: Behavior,* ed. C. R. Carpenter, Karger, Basel, pp. 48–51.

Bernstein, I. S., 1969b, Stability of the status hierarchy in a pigtail monkey group (*Macaca nemestrina*), *Animal Behav.,* 17, 452–458.

Bernstein, I. S., and Sharpe, L. G., 1966, Social roles in a rhesus monkey group, *Behavior,* 26, 91–104.

Bertrand, M., 1969, *The behavioral repertoire of the stumptail macaque, Biblioteca Primatologia,* No. 11, Karger, Basel/New York, 273 pp.

Bingham, H. C., 1932, Gorillas in a native habitat, *Carnegie Inst. Wash. Publ.,* 426, 1–66.

Birch, H. G., 1945, The relation of previous experience to insightful problem solving, *J. Comp. Psychol.,* 38, 367–383.

Bishop, A., 1962, Control of the hand in lower primates, *Ann. N.Y. Acad. Sci.,* 102, 316–337.

Bishop, A., 1964, Use of the hand in lower primates, IN *Evolutionary and genetic biology of primates II,* ed. J. Buettner-Janusch, Academic, New York, pp. 133–226.

Blurton-Jones, N. G., 1967, An ethological study of some aspects of social behavior of children in nursery school, IN *Primate ethology,* ed. D. Morris, Weidenfield and Nicholson, London, pp. 347–368.

Blurton-Jones, N. G., Criteria used in describing facial expressions, in prep.

Blurton-Jones, N. G., and Trollope, J., 1968, Social behavior of stumptailed macaques in captivity, *Primates,* 9, 365–394.

Bobbitt, R. A., Jensen, G. D., and Gordon, B. N., 1964, Behavioral elements (taxonomy) for observing mother–infant–peer interactions in *Macaca nemestrina, Primates,* 5, 71–80.

Bolwig, N., 1959, A study of the behavior of the chacma baboon, *Papio ursinus, Behavior,* 14, 136–163.

Booth, A. H., 1957, Observations on the natural history of the olive colobus monkey *Procolobus verus* (van Boneden), *Proc. Zool. Soc. Lond.,* 129, 421.

Booth, C., 1962, Some observations on the

behavior of *Cercopithecus* monkeys, *Ann. N.Y. Acad. Sci.*, 102, 477–486.

Bourlière, F., 1964, *The natural history of mammals,* 3rd ed., Knopf, New York, 387 pp.

Bourlière, F., Bertrand, M., and Hunkeler, C., 1969, L'écologie de la mone de lowe (*Cercopithecus campbelli lowei*) en Côte d'Ivoire, *La Terre et la Vie,* 2, 135–163.

Bourlière, F., Bertrand, M., and Hunkeler, C., 1970, Ecology and behavior of Lowe's guenon (*Cercopithecus campbelli lowei*) in the Ivory Coast, IN *Systematics and behavior of the Old World monkeys,* ed. J. R. Napier, Academic Press, New York, pp. 297–350.

Bowden, D., Winter, P., and Ploog, D., 1967, Pregnancy and delivery behavior in the squirrel monkey (*Saimiri sciureus*) and other primates, *Folia Primat.*, 5, 1–42.

Bower, T. G. R., 1965, Perception in infancy, Paper read at Center for Cognitive Studies Colloquium, Harvard University, Cambridge, Mass.

Bowlby, J., 1969, *Attachment and loss I: Attachment,* Internat. Psychol. Library, No. 79, Hogarth, London, 428 pp.

Braine, C., 1970, New finds on the Swartkraans australopithecine site, *Nature,* 225, 112–119.

Braine, M. D. S., 1963, The ontogeny of English phrase structure: The first phrase, *Language,* 39, 1–13. Reprinted in Anderson, R. C., and Asubel, D. P., eds., 1966, *Readings in the psychology of cognition,* Holt, New York, pp. 303–320.

Braine, M. D. S., 1968(1959), The ontogeny of certain logical operations: Piaget's formulation examined by nonverbal methods, *Psychol. Monogr.*, No. 475, 1959. Reprinted abridged in Sigel, I. E., and Hooper, F. H., eds., 1968, *Logical thinking in children,* Holt, New York, pp. 164–206.

Bronowski, J., and Bellugi, V., 1970, Language, name, and concept, *Science,* 168, 669–673.

Brown, A. L., and Lloyd, B. B., Criteria of success: a developmental study of oddity learning, *Brit. J. Psychol.*, 61, 21–26.

Brown, R., 1958, How shall a thing be called? *Psychol. Rev.*, 65, 14–21.

Bruner, J. S., 1968, *Process of cognitive growth: Infancy,* Clark U. P., Williamstown, 75 pp.

Bruner, J. S., Olver, R. R., Greenfield, P. M., *et al.*, 1966, Studies in cognitive growth, Wiley, New York, 380 pp.

Buettner-Janusch, J., and Andrew, R. J., 1962, Use of the incisors by primates in grooming, *Amer. J. Phys. Anth.*, 20, 129–132.

Burt, W. H., 1943, Territoriality and home range concepts as applied to mammals, *J. Mammal.*, 24, 346–352.

Butler, H., 1964, The reproductive biology of a strepsirhine (*Galago senegalensis senegalensis*), *Internat. Rev. Gen. Exp. Zool.*, 1, 241–296.

Butler, H., 1967, The estrus cycle of the Senegal bushbaby (*Galago senegalensis senegalensis*) in the Sudan, *Proc. Zool. Soc. Lond.*, 151, 143–162.

Cabe, P. A., 1968, Observation learning in cats, *Science,* 159, 1489–1491.

Carpenter, C. R., 1964, *Naturalistic behavior of nonhuman primates,* Pennsylvania State U. P., University Park, Pa., 454 pp.

Carpenter, C. R., 1965, The howlers of Barro Colorado Island, IN *Primate behavior,* ed. I. DeVore, Holt, New York, pp. 250–291.

Carpenter, C. R., and Nishimura, A., 1969, The Takasakiyama colony of Japanese macaques (*Macaca fuscata*), IN *Proceedings of the Second International Congress of Primatology I: Behavior,* ed. C. R. Carpenter, Karger, Basel, pp. 16–30.

Castell, R., and Maurus, M., 1967, Das sogenannte Urinmarkieren von Totenkopfaffen (*Saimiri sciureus*) in Abhängigkeit von umweltbedingten und emotionalen Faktoren, *Folia Primat.*, 7, 170–176.

Chalmers, N. R., 1968a, Group composition ecology, and daily activities of free living mangabeys in Uganda, *Folia Primat.*, 8, 247–262.

Chalmers, N. R., 1968b, The social behavior of free-living mangabeys in Uganda, *Folia Primat.*, 8, 263–281.

Chalmers, N. R., 1968c, The visual and vocal communication of free-living mangabeys in Uganda, *Folia Primat.*, 9, 258–280.

Chance, M. R. A., and Jolly, C. J., 1970, *Social groups of monkeys, apes, and men,* Thames and Hudson, London, 224 pp.

Charles-Dominique, P., 1966a, Naissance et croissance *d'Arctocebus calabarensis* en captivité, *Biol. Gabon.*, 2, 331–345.

Charles-Dominique, P., 1966b, Analyse de contenus stomacaux *d'Arctocebus calabarensis, Perodicticus potto, Galago alleni, Galago elegantulus,* et *Galago demidovii, Biol. Gabon.*, 2, 347–353.

Charles-Dominique, P., 1968, Réproduction

des lorisides africains, IN *Cycles genitaux saisonniers de mammifères sauvages,* ed. Canivenc, R. Masson, Paris, pp. 2–9.

Chiang, M., 1967, Use of tools by wild macaque monkeys in Singapore, *Nature,* 214, 1258–1259.

Chivers, D., 1969, On the daily behavior and spacing of free-ranging howler monkey groups, *Folia Primat.,* 10, 48–103.

Chomsky, N., 1957, *Syntactic structures,* Mouton, The Hague, 118 pp.

Chomsky, N., 1969, Form and Meaning in natural language, IN *Communication,* ed. J. D. Roslansky, North Holland, Amsterdam, pp. 63–86.

Conaway, C. H., and Koford, C. B., 1965, Estrous cycles and mating behavior in a free-ranging band of rhesus monkeys, *J. Mammal.,* 45, 577–588.

Conaway, C. H., and Sade, D. S., 1965, The seasonal spermatogenic cycle in free-ranging rhesus monkeys, *Folia Primat.,* 3, 1–12.

Cowgill, U. M., 1964, Visiting in *Perodicticus, Science,* 146, 1183–1184.

Cowgill, U. M., 1966, Season of birth in man, *Ecology,* 47, 614–623.

Crawford, M. P., 1937, The cooperative solving of problems by young chimpanzees, *Comp. Psychol. Monogr.,* 14, 1–88.

Crook, J. H., 1965, The adaptive significance of avian social organizations, *Symp. Zool. Soc. Lond.,* 14, 181–218.

Crook, J. H., 1966, Gelada baboon herd structure and movement: A comparative report, *Symp. Zool. Soc. Lond.,* 18, 237–258.

Crook, J. H., and Aldrich-Blake, P., 1968, Ecological and behavioral contrasts between sympatric ground-dwelling primates in Ethiopia, *Folia Primat.,* 8, 180–191.

Crook, J. H., and Gartlan, J. S., 1966, On the evolution of primate societies, *Nature,* 210, 1200–1203.

Darwin, C., 1871, *The descent of man, and selection in relation to sex,* Murray, London, 692 pp.

Darwin, C., 1872, *Expression of the emotions in man and animals,* Murray, London, 372 pp.

Davenport, R. K., and Rogers, C. M., 1968, Intellectual performance of differentially reared chimpanzees I: Delayed response, *Amer. J. Mental Deficiency,* 72, 674–680.

Davenport, R. K., Rogers, C. M., Menzel, E. W., 1969, Intellectual performance of differentially reared chimpanzees II: Discrimination-learning set, *Amer. J. Mental Deficiency,* 73, 963.

Davis, R. T., and Leary, R. W., 1968, Learning of detour problems by lemurs and seven species of monkeys, *Percept. Mot. Skills,* 27, 1031–1034.

Davis, R. T., Leary, R. W., Casebeer Smith, M. D., and Thompson, R. F., 1968, Species differences in the gross behavior of nonhuman primates, *Behavior,* 31, 326–339.

Davis, R. T., Leary, R. W., Stevens, D. A., and Thompson, R. F., 1967, Learning and perception of oddity problems by lemur and seven species of monkey, *Primates,* 8, 311–323.

Deag, J., and Crook, J. H., 1970, Social behavior and agonistic buffering in the wild Barbary macaque, *Macaca sylvana L., Folia Primat.,* in press.

DeVore, I., 1965, Changes in the population structure of Nairobi Park baboons 1959–1963, IN *The baboon in medical research I,* ed. H. Vagteborg, Texas U. P., Austin, pp. 17–28.

DeVore, I., and Hall, K. R. L., 1965, Baboon ecology, IN *Primate behavior,* ed. I. DeVore, Holt, New York, pp. 20–52.

DeVore, I., and Washburn, S. L., 1960, Baboon behavior (16 mm sound color film), University Extension, University of California, Berkeley.

Döhl, J., 1966, Manipulier Fähigkeit und "einsichtiges" Verhalten eines Schimpansen bei komplizierten Handlungsketten, *Z. Tierpsychol.,* 23, 77–113.

Döhl, J., 1968, Über die Fähigkeit einer Schimpansen, umweg mit selbständigen Zwischenzielen zu überblicken, *Z. Tierpsychol.,* 25, 89–103.

Doyle, G. A., Pelletier, A., and Bekker, T., 1967, Courtship, mating, and parturition in the lesser bushbaby *Galago senegalensis moholi* under semi-natural conditions, *Folia Primat.,* 7, 169–197.

Doyle, G. A., Anderson, A., and Bearder, S. K., 1969, Maternal behavior in the lesser bushbaby *Galago senegalensis moholi* under semi-natural conditions, *Folia Primat.,* 11, 215–238.

DuMond, F. V., 1968, The squirrel monkey in a semi-natural environment, IN *The squirrel monkey,* eds. L. A. Rosenblum and R. W. Cooper, Academic Press, New York, pp. 88–146.

Eibl-Eibesfeldt, I., 1968, Ethological perspectives on primate studies, IN *Primates: Studies in adaptability and variability,* ed. P. C. Jay, Holt, New York, pp. 479–486.

Eimerl, S., and DeVore, I., 1966, *The primates,* Life Nature Library, 198 pp.

Eisenberg, J. F., 1966, The social organization of mammals, *Handbuch Zool.,* 8, 39, 1–92.

Eisenberg, J. F., and Kuehn, R. E., 1966, The behavior of *Ateles geoffroyi* and related species, *Smithson. Misc. Coll.,* 151, 1–63.

Ellefson, J. O., 1967, A natural history of gibbons in the Malay Peninsula, Ph.D. thesis, University of California, Berkeley.

Ellefson, J. O., 1968, Territorial behavior in the common white-handed gibbon, *Hylobates lar* Linn., IN *Primates: Studies in adaptation and variability,* ed. P. C. Jay, Holt, New York, pp. 180–199.

Epple, G., 1967, Vergleichende Untersuchungen über Sexual- und Sozialverhalten der Krallenaffen (Hapalidae), *Folia Primat.,* 7, 37–65.

Epple, G., 1968, Comparative studies on vocalization in marmoset monkeys (Hapalidae), *Folia Primat.,* 8, 1–40.

Epple, G., and Lorenz, R., 1967, Vorkommen, Morphologie, und Funktion der Sternaldrüse bei den Platyrrhini, *Folia Primat.,* 7, 98–126.

Ervin, S. M., 1967, Imitation and structural change in children's language, IN *New directions in the study of language,* ed. E. Lenneberg, MIT Press, Cambridge, Mass.

Evans, C. S., and Goy, R. W., 1968, Social behavior and reproductive cycles in captive ringtailed lemurs (*Lemur catta* L.), *J. Zool. Lond.,* 156, 181–197.

Ewer, R. F., 1968, *Ethology of mammals,* Logos Press, London, 418 pp.

Ewer, R. F., 1969, The "instinct to teach," *Nature,* 223, 698.

Fantz, R. L., 1964, Visual experience in infants: Decreased attention to familiar patterns relative to novel ones, *Science,* 146, 668–670.

Fantz, R. L., 1968, Visual discrimination in a neonate chimpanzee, *Percept. Mot. Skills,* 8, 59–66.

Fletcher, H. J., 1965, The delayed response problem, IN *Behavior of nonhuman primates,* eds. A. M. Schrier, H. F. Harlow, and F. Stollnitz, Academic Press, New York, pp. 129–166.

Fossey, D., 1970, Making friends with mountain gorillas, *Nat. Geog.,* 137, 1, 48–68.

Furuya, Y., 1965, Social organization of the crabeating monkey, *Primates,* 6, 285–336.

Furuya, Y., 1968, On the fission of troops of Japanese monkeys I: Five fissions and social changes between 1955 and 1966 in the Gagyusan troop, *Primates,* 9, 323–350.

Furuya, Y., 1969, On the fission of troops of Japanese monkeys II: General view of the troop fission of Japanese monkeys, *Primates,* 10, 47–70.

Gardner, R. A., and Gardner, B. T., 1969, Teaching sign language to a chimpanzee, *Science,* 165, 664–672.

Gardner, B. T., and Gardner, R. A., in press, Two-way communication with a chimpanzee, IN *Behavior of nonhuman primates III,* eds. A. Schrier and F. Stollnitz, Academic Press, New York.

Gardner, B. T., and Wallach, L., 1965, Shapes of figures identified as a baby's head, *Percept. Mot. Skills,* 20, 135–142.

Gartlan, J. S., 1968a, Ecology and behavior of an isolated population of vervet monkeys on Lolui Island, Lake Victoria, *Hum. Biol.,* 40, 122.

Gartlan, J. S., 1968b, Structure and function in primate society, *Folia Primat.,* 8, 89–120.

Gartlan, J. S., and Brain, C. K., 1968, Ecology and social variability in *Cercopithecus aethiops* and *Cercopithecus mitis,* IN *Primates: Studies in adaptation and variability,* ed. P. C. Jay, Holt, New York, pp. 253–292.

Gautier, J. P., 1967, Émissions sonores liées à la cohésion du groupe, et aux manifestations d'alarmes dans les bandes de talapoins (*Miopithecus talapoin*), *Biol. Gabon.,* 3, 18–30.

Gautier, J. P., 1969, Émissions sonores d'espacement et de ralliement par deux cercophithèques arboricoles, *Biol. Gabon.,* 5, 118–145.

Gautier, J. P., and Gautier-Hion, A., 1969, Les associations polyspecifiques chez les cercopithecidae du Gabon, *La Terre et la Vie,* 2, 164–201.

Gautier-Hion, A., 1966, L'écologie et l'éthologie du talapoin *Miopithecus talapoin talapoin, Biol. Gabon.,* 2, 311–329.

Gautier-Hion, A., 1968, Étude du cycle annuel de réproduction du talapoin (*Miopithecus talapoin*) vivant dans son milieu naturel, *Biol. Gabon.,* 4, 163–173.

Gautier-Hion, A., 1970, L'organization sociale d'une bande de talapoins (*Miopithecus talapoin*) dans le Nord-Est du Gabon, *Folia Primat.,* 12, 116–141.

Goldberg, S., 1970, Infant care, stimulation, and sensory motor development in a high density urban area of Zambia, Human Development Research Unit Report 15, University of Zambia, Lusaka.

Goldstein, K., and Scheerer, M., 1941, Abstract and concrete behavior: An experimental study with special tests, *Psychol. Mongr.,* 53, 1–151.

Goodall, J. (van Lawick-), 1963, Feeding behavior of wild chimpanzees: A preliminary report, *Symp. Zool. Soc. Lond.,* 10, 39–47.

Goodall, J. (van Lawick-), 1965, Chimpanzees of the Gombe Stream Reserve, IN *Primate behavior,* ed. I. DeVore, Holt, New York, pp. 425–473.

Goodhart, C. B., 1960, The evolutionary significance of human hair patterns and skin coloring, *Adv. Sci.,* 17, 53–59.

Gorer, G., 1968, Man has no "killer" instinct, IN *Man and Aggression,* ed. M. F. Ashley Montagu, Oxford U. P., London, pp. 27–36.

Grand, T. I., 1968, The functional anatomy of the howler monkey, *Allouata caraya, Amer. J. Phys. Anth.,* 28, 163–182.

Grant, E. C., 1969, Human facial expression, *Man,* 4, 525–536.

Grimm, R. J., 1967, Catalogue of sounds of the pigtailed macaque, *J. Zool. Lond.,* 152, 361–373.

Haddow, A. J., and Ellice, J. M., 1964, Studies on bushbabies (*Galago spp.*) with special reference to the epidemiology of yellow fever, *Trans. Roy. Soc. Trop. Med. Hyg.,* 58, 521–538.

Hall, K. R. L., 1962a, Numerical data, maintenance activities, and locomotion of the wild chacma baboon (*Papio ursinus*), *Proc. Zool. Soc. Lond.,* 139, 181–220.

Hall, K. R. L., 1962b, The sexual, agonistic, and derived social behavior patterns of the wild chacma baboon (*Papio ursinus*), *Proc. Zool. Soc. Lond.,* 139, 283–328.

Hall, K. R. L., 1963a, Observational learning in monkeys and apes, *Brit. J. Psychol.,* 54, 201–226.

Hall, K. R. L., 1963b, Tool-using performances as indications of behavioral adaptability, *Curr. Anth.,* 4, 479–494.

Hall, K. R. L., 1965a, Ecology and behavior of baboons, patas, and vervet monkeys in Uganda, IN *The baboon in medical research,* ed. H. Vagteborg, Texas U. P., Austin, pp. 43–61.

Hall, K. R. L., 1965b, Behavior and ecology of the wild patas monkey, *Erythrocebus patas,* in Uganda, *J. Zool.,* 148, 15–87.

Hall, K. R. L., 1968, Social learning in monkeys, IN *Primates: Studies in adaptation and variability,* ed. P. C. Jay, Holt, New York, pp. 383–397.

Hall, K. R. L., and DeVore, I., 1965, Baboon social behavior, IN *Primate behavior,* ed. I. DeVore, Holt, New York, pp. 53–110.

Hall, K. R. L., and Gartlan, J. S., 1965, Ecology and behavior of the vervet monkey (*Cercopithecus aethiops*), Lolui Island, Lake Victoria, *Proc. Zool. Soc. Lond.,* 145, 37–56.

Hall, K. R. L., and Goswell, M. J., 1964, Aspects of social learning in captive patas monkeys, *Primates,* 5, 59–70.

Hall-Craggs, E. C. B., 1965, An analysis of the jump of the lesser galago (*Galago senegalensis*), *J. Zool. Lond.,* 147, 20–29.

Hansen, E. W., 1966, The development of maternal and infant behavior in the rhesus monkey, *Behavior,* 27, 107–149.

Harlow, H. F., 1949, The formation of learning sets, *Psychol. Rev.,* 56, 51–56.

Harlow, H. F., 1951, Primate learning, IN *Comparative psychology,* ed. C. P. Stone, 3rd ed., Prentice-Hall, New York, pp. 183–238.

Harlow, H. F., and Harlow, M. K., 1965, The affectional systems, IN *Behavior of nonhuman primates,* eds. A. M. Schrier, H. F. Harlow, and F. Stollnitz, Academic Press, New York.

Harlow, H. F., Schitz, K. A., and Harlow, M. K., 1969, Effects of social isolation on learning performance of rhesus monkeys, IN *Proceedings of the Second International Congress of Primatology I: Behavior,* ed. C. R. Carpenter, Karger, Basel, pp. 178–185.

Harrison, B., 1963, *Orangutan,* Doubleday, Garden City, N.Y., 190 pp.

Hayes, C., 1951, *The ape in our house,* Harper, New York.

Hayes, K. J., and Nissen, C. H., 1971, Higher mental functions of a home-raised chimpanzee, IN *Behavior of nonhuman primates,* ed. A. M. Schreier and F. Stollnitz, Academic, New York, pp. 4, 60–116.

Hediger, H., 1950, *Wild animals in captivity,* Butterworth, London.

Heller, E., 1959, *The disinherited mind,* Meridian, New York, 306 pp.

Hellmann, C. S., 1967, Vocal simulation in *Lemur, Amer. Zool.,* 7, 803 (abst.).

Herbert, J., 1968, Sexual preference in the rhesus monkey *Macaca mulatta* in the laboratory, *Animal Behav.,* 16, 120–128.

Hershkovitz, P., 1969, The evolution of mammals on southern continents VI: The recent mammals of the neotropical region, a zoogeographic and ecological review, *Quart. Rev. Biol.,* 44, 1–70.

Hilegarda, Sta., Abbatissa, col. 1329, Physica, Book 7, *De animalium,* 1385 pp.

Hill, W. C. O., 1953, *et seq.,* *Primates: Comparative anatomy and taxonomy,* Vols. 1–6, Edinburgh U. P., Edinburgh.

Hinde, R. A., 1966a, Ritualization and social communication in rhesus monkeys, *Phil. Trans. Roy. Soc. B,* 251, 285–294.
Hinde, R. A., 1966b, *Animal behavior: A synthesis of ethology and comparative psychology,* McGraw-Hill, New York, 544 pp.
Hinde, R. A., and Rowell, T. E., 1962, Communication by postures and facial expressions in the rhesus monkey (*Macaca mulatta*), *Proc. Zool. Soc. Lond.,* 138, 1–21.
Hinde, R. A., and Spencer-Booth, Y., 1967a, The effect of social companions on mother–infant relations in rhesus monkeys, IN *Primate ethology,* ed. D. Morris, Weidenfield and Nicolson, London, pp. 267–286.
Hinde, R. A., and Spencer-Booth, Y., 1967b, Behavior of socially living rhesus monkeys in their first 2½ years, *Animal Behav.,* 15, 169–198.
Hinde, R. A., Rowell, T. E., and Spencer-Booth, Y., 1964, Behavior of socially living rhesus monkeys in their first 6 months, *Proc. Zool. Soc. Lond.,* 143, 609–649.
Hladik, A., and Hladik, C. M., 1969, Rapports trophiques entre végétation et primates dans la forêt de Barro Colorado (Panama), *La Terre et la Vie,* 1, 25–117.
Hladik, C. M., and Hladik, A., 1967, Observations sur le rôle des primates dans la dissémination des végétaux de la forêt Gabonaise, *Biol. Gabon.,* 3, 43–58.
Hockett, C. F., 1963, The problem of universals in language, IN *Universals of language,* ed. Joseph H. Greenberg, MIT Press, Cambridge, Mass.
Hockett, C. F., and Altmann, S. A., 1968, A note on design features, IN *Animal communication,* ed. T. A. Sebeok, Indiana U. P., Bloomington, pp. 61–72.
Hockett, C. F., and Ascher, R., 1964, The human revolution, *Curr. Anth.,* 5, 135–168.
Hooff, J. A. R. A. M. van, 1967, The facial displays of the catarrhine monkeys and apes, IN *Primate ethology,* ed. D. Morris, Weidenfield and Nicolson, London, pp. 7–68.
Hooff, J. A. R. A. M. van, 1970, A component analysis of the social behavior of a captive chimpanzee group, *Experientia,* 26, 549.
Hutchinson, G. E., 1965, *The ecological theater and the evolutionary play.* Yale U. P., New Haven, 139 pp.
Huxley, A., 1939, *After many a summer,* Chatto, London, 314 pp.
Huxley, J. S., 1914, The courtship habits of the great crested grebe (*Podiceps cristatus*) with an addition to the theory of sexual selection, *Proc. Zool. Soc. Lond.,* 35, 491–562.
Huxley, T. H., 1863, Man's place in nature, Macmillan and Co., London, 328 pp.
Imanishi, K., 1965, The origin of the human family: A primatological approach, IN *Japanese monkeys,* ed. and publ. S. A. Altmann, Alberta, Canada.
Itani, J., 1958, On the acquisition and propagation of a new food habit in the troop of Japanese monkeys at Takasakiyama, *Primates,* 1, 131–148.
Itani, J., 1959, Paternal care in the wild Japanese monkey, *Macaca fuscata fuscata, Primates,* 2, 61–93.
Itani, J., 1963a, Vocal communication in the wild Japanese monkey, *Primates,* 4, 2, 11–66.
Itani, J., 1963b, The social construction of national troops of Japanese monkeys in Takasakiyama, *Primates,* 4, 3, 1–42.
Itani, J., and Suzuki, A., 1967, The social unit of chimpanzees, *Primates,* 8, 355–382.
Izawa, K., and Nishida, T., 1963, Monkeys living in the northern limit of their distribution, *Primates,* 4, 67–88.
Jackson, G., and Gartlan, J. S., 1965, The flora and fauna of Lolui Island, Lake Victoria, *J. Ecol.,* 53, 573–597.
Janson, H. W., 1952, *Apes and ape lore in the Middle Ages and the Renaissance,* Warburg Inst. Studies, London, 20, 384 pp.
Jay, P., 1965, The common langur of North India, IN *Primate Behavior,* ed. I. DeVore, Holt, New York, pp. 197–249.
Jensen, G. D., 1965, Mother–infant relationship in the monkey *Macaca nemestrina:* Development of specificity of maternal response to own infant, *J. Comp. Physiol. Psychol.,* 59, 305–308.
Jensen, G. D., 1968, Reaction of monkey mothers to long-term separation from their infants, *Psychon. Sci.,* 11, 171–172.
Jensen, G. D., and Tolman, C. W., 1962, Mother–infant relation in the monkey, *Macaca nemestrina:* The effect of brief separation and mother–infant specificity, *J. Comp. Physiol. Psychol.,* 55, 131–136.
Jensen, G. D., Bobbitt, R. A., and Gordon, B. N., 1967, The development of mutual independence in mother–infant relations in pigtail monkeys, *Macaca nemestrina,* IN *Social communication among primates,* ed. S. A. Altmann, Chicago U. P., Chicago, pp. 43–54.
Jensen, G. D., Bobbitt, R. A., and Gordon, B. N., 1968a, Sex differences in the de-

velopment of independence of infant monkeys, *Behavior,* 30, 1–14.

Jensen, G. D., Bobbitt, R. A., and Gordon, B. N., 1968b, Effects of environment and the relationship between mother and infant pigtailed monkeys (*Macaca nemestrina*), *J. Comp. Physiol. Psychol.,* 66, 259–263.

Jewell, P. A., 1966, The concept of home range in mammals, *Symp. Zool. Soc. Lond.,* 18, 85–110.

Jewell, P. A., and Oates, J. F., 1969a, Breeding activity in prosimians and small rodents in West Africa, *J. Reprod. Fert. Suppl.,* 6, 23–38.

Jewell, P. A., and Oates, J. F., 1969b, Ecological observations on the lorisoid primates of African lowland forest, *Zool. Afr.,* 4, 231–248.

Johnson, J. I., and Michels, K. M., 1958, Discrimination of small intervals and objects by raccoons, *Animal Behav.,* 6, 164–170.

Jolly, A., 1964a, Prosimians' manipulation of simple object problems, *Animal Behav.,* 12, 560–570.

Jolly, A., 1964b, Choice of cue in prosimian learning, *Animal Behav.,* 12, 571–577.

Jolly, A., 1966a, *Lemur behavior,* Chicago U. P., Chicago, 187 pp.

Jolly, A., 1966b, Lemur social behavior and primate intelligence, *Science,* 153, 501–506.

Jolly, C. J., 1963, A suggested case of evolution by sexual selection in primates, *Man,* 63, 177–178.

Jolly, C. J., 1970, The seed-eaters: a new model of hominid differentiation based on a baboon analogy, *Man,* n.s. 5, 5–26. 5–26.

Jones, C., and Sabater Pi, J., 1968, Comparative ecology of *Cercocebus albigena* (Gray) and *Cercocebus torquatus* (Ker) in Rio Muñi, West Africa, *Folia Primat.,* 9, 99–113.

Jones, C., and Sabater Pi, J., 1969, Sticks used by chimpanzees in Rio Muñi, West Africa, *Nature,* 223, 100–101.

Kagan, J., 1968, On cultural deprivation, IN *Environmental influences,* ed. D. C. Glass, Rockefeller U. P., New York, pp. 211–250.

Kaiser, I. H., and Halberg, F., 1962, Circadian periodic aspects of birth, *Ann. N.Y. Acad. Sci.,* 98, 1056–1068.

Kapune, T., 1966, Untersuchungen zur Bildung eines "Wertbegriffs" bei neideren Primaten, *Z. Tierpsychol.,* 23, 324–363.

Kaufman, I. C., and Rosenblum, L. A., 1966, A behavioral taxonomy for *Macaca nemestrina* and *Macaca radiata* based on longitudinal observation of family groups in the laboratory, *Primates,* 7, 205–258.

Kaufman, I. C., and Rosenblum, L. A., 1967, Depression in infant monkeys separated from their mothers, *Science,* 155, 1030–1031.

Kaufmann, J. H., 1962, Ecology and social behavior of the coati, *Nasua narica,* on Barro Colorado Island, Panama, *Univ. Calif. Publ. Zool.,* 60, 95–222.

Kaufmann, J. H., 1965, A 3-year study of mating behavior in a free-ranging band of rhesus monkeys, *Ecology,* 40, 500–512.

Kaufmann, J. H., 1967, Social relations of adult males in a free-ranging band of rhesus monkeys, IN *Social Communication among primates,* ed. S. A. Altmann, Chicago U. P., Chicago, pp. 73–98.

Kawabe, M., 1966, One observed case of hunting behavior among wild chimpanzees living in the savanna woodland of Western Tanzania, *Primates,* 7, 393–396.

Kawai, M., 1958a, On the system of social ranks in a natural troop of Japanese monkeys I: Basic rank and dependent rank, *Primates,* 1, 111–130.

Kawai, M., 1958b, On the system of social ranks in a natural troop of Japanese monkeys II: Ranking order as observed among the monkeys on and near the test box, *Primates,* 1, 131–148.

Kawai, M., 1965, Newly acquired precultural behavior of the natural troop of Japanese monkeys on Koshima Island, *Primates,* 6, 1–30.

Kawai, M., Azuma, S., and Yoshiba, K., 1967, Ecological studies of reproduction in Japanese monkeys (*Macaca fuscata*) I: Problems of the birth season, *Primates,* 8, 35–74.

Kawamura, S., 1958, Matriarchal social ranks in the Minoo-B troop: A study of the rank system of Japanese monkeys. *Primates,* 1, 148–156.

Kawamura, S., 1967, Aggression as studied in troops of Japanese monkeys, *UCLA Forum Med. Sci.,* 7, 195–223.

Kellogg, W. N., and Kellogg, L. A., 1933, *The ape and the child,* McGraw-Hill, New York, 341 pp.

Kellogg, W. N., 1968, Communication and language in the home-raised chimpanzee, *Science,* 162, 423–427.

Kern, J., 1964, Observations on the habits of the proboscis monkey, *Nasalis larvatus Wurmb,* made in the Brunei Bay area, Borneo, *Zoologica,* 49, 183–192.

Kessen, W., 1967, Sucking and looking: Two organized congenital patterns of behavior in the human newborn, IN *Early behavior,* eds. H. W. Stevenson, E. H.

Hess, and H. L. Rheingold, Wiley, New York, pp. 147–180.

Klopfer, P., 1967, Behavioral stereotypy in birds, *Wilson Bull.,* 79, 290–300.

Klüver, H., 1957 (1st ed. 1933), *Behavioral mechanisms in monkeys,* Chicago U. P., Chicago, 387 pp.

Knoblock, H., and Pasamanick, B., 1959, The development of adaptive behavior in an infant gorilla, *J. Comp. Physiol. Psychol.,* 52, 699–704.

Koestler, A., 1967, *The ghost in the machine,* Hutchinson, London, 407 pp.

Koford, C. B., 1963, Rank of mothers and sons in bands of rhesus monkeys, *Science,* 141, 356–357.

Koford, C. B., 1965, Population dynamics of rhesus monkeys on Cayo Santiago, IN *Primate behavior,* ed. I. DeVore, Holt, New York, pp. 160–174.

Köhler, W., 1927, *The mentality of apes,* 2nd ed., Routledge & Kegan Paul, London.

Kohts, N., 1923, *Untersuchungen über die erkenntnis Fähigkeiten des Schimpansen aus dem zoopsychologischen Laboratorium des Museum Darwinianum in Moskau,* Moscow.

Kollar, E. J., Edgerton, R. B., and Beckwith, W. G., 1968, An evaluation of the behavior of ARL colony chimpanzees, *Arch. Gen. Psychiat.,* 19, 580–594.

Kortlandt, A., 1967, Experimentation with chimpanzees in the wild, IN *Neue Ergebnisse der Primatologie,* eds. D. Starck, R. Schneider, and H.-J. Kuhn, Fischer, Stuttgart, pp. 208–224.

Kortlandt, A., and Kooij, M., 1963, Protohominid behavior in primates, *Symp. Zool. Soc. Lond.,* 10, 61–88.

Kortlandt, A., and van Zon, J. C. J., 1969, The present state of research on the dehumanization hypothesis of African ape evolution, IN *Proceedings of the Second International Congress of Primatology III,* Karger, Basel, pp. 14–16.

Koyama, N., 1967, On dominance rank and kinship of a wild Japanese monkey troop in Arashiyama, *Primates,* 8, 189–216.

Kühme, W., 1965, Freilandstudien zur Soziologie des Hyänenhundes (*Lycaon pictus lupinus* Thomas, 1902), *Z. Tierpsychol.,* 22, 495–541.

Kuhn, T. S., 1962, *The structure of scientific revolutions,* Chicago U. P., Chicago, 172 pp.

Kummer, H., 1967, Tripartite relations in hamadryas baboons, IN *Social communication among primates,* ed. S. A. Altmann, Chicago U. P., Chicago, pp. 63–72.

Kummer, H., 1968, Social organization of hamadryas baboons, A field study, *Bibliotheca Primatologica,* No. 6, S. Karger Basel/New York, 189 pp.

Kummer, H., and Kurt, F., 1965, A comparison of social behavior in captive and wild hamadryas baboons, IN *The baboon in medical research,* ed. H. Vagteborg, Texas U. P., Austin, pp. 65–80.

Lahiri, R. K., and Southwick, C. H., 1966, Parental care in *Macaca sylvana, Folia Primat.,* 4, 257–264.

Lancaster, J. B., 1968a, On the evolution of speech, IN *Primates: Studies in adaptation and variability,* ed. P. C. Jay, Holt, New York, pp. 439–457.

Lancaster, J. B., 1968b, On the evolution of tool-using behavior, *Amer. Anth.,* 70, 56–70.

Lancaster, J. B., and Lee, R. B., 1965, The annual reproductive cycle in monkeys and apes, IN *Primate behavior,* ed. I. DeVore, Holt, New York, pp. 486–513.

Lawick-Goodall, J. van, 1967a, Mother–offspring relationship in wild chimpanzees, IN *Primate ethology,* ed. D. Morris, Weidenfield and Nicolson, London.

Lawick-Goodall, J. van, 1967b, *My friends the wild chimpanzees,* National Geographic, Washington, 204 pp.

Lawick-Goodall, J. van, 1968a, A preliminary report on expressive movements and communication in the Gombe Stream chimpanzees, IN *Primates: Studies in adaptation and variability,* ed. P. C. Jay, Holt, New York, pp. 313–382.

Lawick-Goodall, J. van, 1968b, The behavior of free-living chimpanzees in the Gombe Stream Reserve, *Animal Behav. Monogr.,* 1, 165–311.

Lee, R. B. and I. DeVore, eds., 1968, *Man the hunter,* Aldine, Chicago.

Le Gros Clark, W. E., 1962, *The antecedents of man,* 2nd ed., Edinburgh U. P., Edinburgh, 374 pp.

Lehr, E., 1967, Experimentelle Untersuchen an Affen und Halbaffen über Generalisation von Insekten- und Blütenabbildungen, *Z. Tierpsychol.,* 24, 208–244.

Lenneberg, E. H., 1967, *Biological foundations of language,* Wiley, New York, 507 pp.

Lenneberg, E. H., 1969, A word between us, IN *Communication,* ed. J. D. Roslansky, North Holland, Amsterdam, pp. 107–131.

Lewis, M. M., 1951, *Infant speech,* Routledge, London.

Lewis, M. M., 1963, *Language, thought, and personality,* Harrap, London.

Lewis, M. M., 1968, *Language and personality in deaf children,* National Foundation for Educational Research in England and Wales, Slough, U.K., 239 pp.

Lieberman, P. H., Klatt, D. H., and Wilson, W. H., 1969, Vocal tract limitations on the vowel repertoires of rhesus monkey and other nonhuman primates, *Science,* 164, 1185–1187.

Lindburg, D. G., 1967, Patterns of reproduction in wild rhesus monkeys, *Amer. Zool.,* 7, 802 (abst.).

Lipsitt, L., 1967, Learning in the human infant, IN *Early Behavior,* eds. H. W. Stephenson, E. H. Hess, and H. L. Rheingold, Wiley, New York, pp. 225–248.

Loizos, C., 1967, Play behavior in higher primates: A review, IN *Primate ethology,* ed. D. Morris, Weidenfield and Nicolson, London, pp. 176–219.

Loizos, C., 1969, An ethological study of chimpanzee play, IN *Proceedings of the Second International Congress of Primatology I: Behavior,* ed. C. R. Carpenter, Karger, Basel, pp. 87–93.

Lorenz, K., 1952, *King Solomon's ring,* Crowell, New York, 202 pp.

Lorenz, K., 1965, *Evolution and modification of behavior,* Chicago U. P., Chicago, 125 pp.

Lorenz, K., 1966, *On aggression,* Methuen, London, 273 pp.

Lorenz, K., and R. D. Martin (trans.), 1970, *Studies in animal and human behavior,* Methuen, London, 1, 403 pp.

Lorenz, K., and R. D. Martin (trans.), in press, *Studies in animal and human behavior,* London, Methuen, 2.

Lowther, F. de L., 1939, The feeding and grooming habits of the galago, *Zoologica,* 24, 477–480.

Loy, J., 1970, Behavioral responses of free-ranging rhesus monkeys to food shortage, *Amer. J. Phys. Anth.,* 33, 263–272.

MacArthur, R., and Levins, R., 1964, Competition, habitat selection, and character displacement in a patchy environment, *Proc. Nat. Acad. Sci.,* 51, 1207–1210.

MacRoberts, M. H., and MacRoberts, B. R., 1966, The annual reproductive cycle of the barbary ape (*Macaca sylvana*), *Amer. J. Phys. Anth.,* NS25, 299–304.

Manley, G. H., 1966, Reproduction in lorisoid primates, *Symp. Zool. Soc. Lond.,* 15, 69–88.

Marais, E., 1969, *The soul of the ape,* Anthony Blond, London, 226 pp.

Marler, P., 1965, Communication in monkeys and apes, IN *Primate behavior,* ed. I. DeVore, Holt, New York, pp. 544–584.

Marler, P., 1968, *Aggregation and dispersal: Two functions of primate communication,* IN *Primates: Studies in adaptation and variability,* ed. P. C. Jay, Holt, New York, pp. 420–438.

Marler, P., 1969a, Vocalizations of wild chimpanzees, IN *Proceedings of the Second International Congress of Primatology I: Behavior,* ed. C. R. Carpenter, Karger, Basel, pp. 94–100.

Marler, P., 1969b, Animals and man: Communication and its development, IN *Communication,* ed. J. D. Roslansky, North Holland, Amsterdam, pp. 23–62.

Marler, P., 1969c, *Colobus guereza:* Territoriality and group composition, *Science,* 163, 93–95.

Marler, P., and Hamilton, W. J., III, 1966, *Mechanisms of animal behavior,* Wiley, New York, 771 pp.

Martin, P. S., and Wright, H. E., eds., 1967, *Pleistocene extinctions,* Yale U. P., New Haven.

Martin, R. D., 1968a, Reproduction and ontogeny in tree shrews (*Tupia belangeri*) with reference to their general behavior and taxonomic relationships, *Z. Tierpsychol.,* 25, 409–495, 505–532.

Martin R. D., 1968b, Toward a new definition of primates, *Man,* 3, 377–401.

Martin, R. D., 1969, The evolution of reproductive mechanisms in primates, *J. Reprod. Fert., Suppl.* 6, 49–66.

Maslow, A. H., 1936, The role of dominance in the social and sexual behavior of infrahuman primates III: A theory of the sexual behavior of infrahuman primates, *J. Genet. Psychol.,* 48, 310–338.

Mason, W. A., 1966, Social organization of the South American monkey *Callicebus moloch:* A preliminary report, *Tulane Studies Zool.,* 13, 23–28.

Mason, W. A., 1968a, Early social deprivation in the nonhuman primates: Implications for human behavior, IN *Environmental influences,* ed. D. C. Glass, Rockefeller U. P., New York, pp. 70–100.

Mason, W. A., 1968b, Use of space by *Callicebus* groups, IN *Primates: Studies in adaptation and variability,* ed. P. C. Jay, Holt, New York, pp. 200–216.

Mason, W. A., and Harlow, H. F., 1961, The effects of age and previous training on patterned-strings performance of rhesus monkeys, *J. Comp. Physiol. Psychol.,* 54, 704–707.

Mason, W. A., Davenport, R. K., Jr., and Menzel, E. W., Jr., 1968, Early experience and the social development of rhesus monkeys and chimpanzees, IN *Early experience and behavior: The psychobiology of development,* Thomas, Springfield, Ill., pp. 440–480.

McBride, G., Parker, I. P., and Foenander, F.,

1969, The social organization and behavior of the feral domestic fowl, *Animal Behav. Monogr.*, 2, 127–181.

McCall, R. B., and Kagan, J., 1967, Stimulus–schema discrepancy and attention in the infant, *J. Exp. Child Psychol.*, 5, 381–390.

McNeill, D., 1966, Developmental psycholinguistics, IN *The genesis of language,* eds. F. Smith and G. A. Miller, MIT Press, Cambridge, Mass., pp. 15–84.

Mejer, G. W., 1965, Other data on the effects of social isolation during rearing upon adult reproductive behavior in the rhesus monkey (*Macaca mulatta*), *Animal Behav.*, 13, 228–231.

Menzel, E. W., 1963, The effects of cumulative experience on responses to novel objects in young isolation-reared chimps, *Behavior,* 21, 1–12.

Menzel, E. W., 1966, Responsiveness to objects in free-ranging Japanese monkeys, *Behavior,* 26, 130–150.

Menzel, E. W., 1969a, Chimpanzee utilization of space and responsiveness to objects: Age differences and comparison with macaques, IN *Proceedings of the Second International Congress of Primatology I: Behavior,* ed. C. R. Carpenter, Karger, Basel pp. 72–80.

Menzel, E. W., 1969b, Responsiveness to food and signs of food in chimpanzee discrimination learning, *J. Comp. Physiol. Psychol.*, 68, 484–489.

Menzel, E. W., 1969c, Experimental studies of leadership in a group of young chimpanzees, *Amer. Zool.*, 9, 1070.

Menzel, E. W., Davenport, R. K., and Rogers, C. M., 1963a, The effects of environmental restrictions on the chimpanzee's responsiveness to objects, *J. Comp. Physiol. Psychol.*, 56, 78–85.

Menzel, E. W., Davenport, R. K., and Rogers, C. M., 1963b, Effects of environmental restriction upon the chimpanzee's responsiveness in novel situations, *J. Comp. Physiol. Psychol.*, 56, 329–334.

Menzel, E. W., Davenport, R. K., and Rogers, C. M., 1970, The development of tool-using in wild-born and restriction-reared chimpanzees, *Folia Primat.*, 12, 273–283.

Meyer, D. R., Treichler, F. R., and Meyer, P. M., 1965, Discrete training techniques and stimulus variables, IN *Behavior of nonhuman primates,* eds. A. M. Schreier, H. F. Harlow, and F. Stollnitz, Academic Press, New York, pp. 1–50.

Michael, R. P., 1968, Gonadal hormones and the control of primate behavior, IN *Endocrinology and human behaviour,* ed. R. P. Michael, Oxford U. P., London, pp. 69–93.

Michael, R. P., and Herbert, J., 1963, Menstrual cycle influences grooming behavior and sexual activity in the rhesus monkey, *Science,* 140, 500–501.

Michael, R. P., and Keverne, E. B., 1968, Pheromones in the communication of sexual status in primates, *Nature,* 218, 746–749.

Michael, R. P., and Saayman, G. S., 1967, Individual differences in the sexual behavior of male rhesus monkeys (*Macaca mulatta*) under laboratory conditions, *Animal Behav.*, 15, 460–466.

Miles, W. R., 1963, Chimpanzee behavior: Removal of foreign body from companion's eye, *Proc. Nat. Acad. Sci.*, 49, 840–843.

Miller, R. E., Banks, J. H., Jr., and Kuwahara, H., 1966, The communication of affect in monkeys: Cooperative reward conditioning, *J. Gen. Psychol.*, 108, 121–134.

Miller, R. E., Caul, W. F., and Mirsky, I. A., 1967, Communication of affect between feral and socially isolated monkeys, *J. Pers. Soc. Psychol.*, 7, 231–239.

Mitchell, G. D., 1968a, Intercorrelations of maternal and infant behaviors in *Macaca mulatta, Primates,* 9, 85–92.

Mitchell, G. D., 1968b, Persistent behavior pathology in rhesus monkeys following early social isolation, *Folia Primat.*, 8, 132–147.

Mitchell, G. D., 1968c, Attachment differences in male and female infant monkeys, *Child Develop.*, 39, 611–620.

Mitchell, G. D., 1969, Paternalistic behavior in primates, *Psychol. Bull.*, 71, 399–416.

Mitchell, G. D., and Stevens, C. W., 1969, Primiparous and multiparous monkey mothers in a mildly stressful social situation: The first 3 months, *Develop. Psychobiol.*, 1, 280–286.

Mitchell, G. D., Arling, G. L., and Møller, G. W., 1967, Long-term effects of maternal punishment on the behavior of monkeys, *Psychon. Sci.*, 8, 209–210.

Mitchell, G. D., Harlow, H., Griffin, G., and Møller, G., 1967, Repeated maternal separation in the monkey, *Psychon. Sci.*, 8, 197–198.

Miyadi, D., 1967, Differences in social behavior among Japanese macaque troops, IN *Neue Ergebnisse der Primatologie,* eds. D. Starck, R. Schneider, and H. J. Kuhn, Fisher, Stuttgart.

Mizuhara, H., 1964, Social changes of Japanese monkey troops in Takasakiyama, *Primates,* 4, 27–52.

Møller, G. W., Harlow, H. F., and Mitchell, G. D., 1968, Factors affecting agonistic communication in rhesus monkeys (*Macaca mulatta*), *Behavior,* 31, 339–357.
Moreau, R. E., 1966, *The bird faunas of Africa and its islands,* Academic Press, New York, 406 pp.
Morris, D., 1957, "Typical intensity" and its relation to the problem of ritualization, *Behavior,* 11, 1–12.
Morris, D., 1962, *The biology of art: A study of the picture-making behavior of the great apes and its relationship to human art,* Methuen, London, 176 pp.
Morris, D., 1967, *The naked ape,* Cape, London, 252 pp.
Morris, D., 1969, *The human zoo,* Cape, London, 256 pp.
Mowbray, J. B., and Cadell, T. E., 1962, Early behavior patterns in rhesus monkeys, *J. Comp. Physiol. Psychol.,* 55, 350–357.
Moynihan, M., 1960, Some adaptations which help to promote gregariousness, IN *Proceedings of the Twelfth International Ornithology Congress,* pp. 523–541.
Moynihan, M., 1964, Some behavior patterns of platyrrhine monkeys I: The night monkey (*Aotes trivirgatus*), *Smithson. Misc. Coll.,* 146(5), 1–84.
Moynihan, M., 1966, Communication in the titi monkey, *Callicebus, J. Zool. Lond.,* 150, 77–127.
Moynihan, M., 1967, Comparative aspects of communication in New World primates, IN *Primate ethology,* ed. D. Morris, Weidenfield and Nicolson, London, pp. 236–266.
Müller-Scwharze, D., 1969, Complexity and relative specificity in a mammalian pheromone, *Nature,* 223, 525–526.
Napier, J. R., 1960, Studies of the hands of living primates, *Proc. Zool. Soc. Lond.,* 134, 647–657.
Napier, J. R., 1961, Prehensility and opposability in the hands of primates, *Symp. Zool. Soc. Lond.,* 5, 115–132.
Napier, J. R., and Napier, P. H., 1967, *A handbook of living primates,* Academic Press, London, 456 pp.
Napier, J. R., and Walker, A. C., 1967, Vertical clinging and leaping: A newly recognized category of locomotor behavior of primates, *Folia Primat.,* 7, 204–219.
Neville, M. K., 1968a, Ecology and activity of himalayan foothill rhesus monkeys (*Macaca mulatta*), *Ecology,* 49, 110–122.
Neville, M. K., 1968b, A free-ranging rhesus troop lacking adult males, *J. Mammal.,* 49, 771–773.
Neville, M. K., 1968c, Male leadership change in a free-ranging troop of Indian rhesus monkeys (*Macaca mulatta*), *Primates,* 9, 13–28.
Nishida, T., 1966, A sociological study of solitary male monkeys, *Primates,* 7, 141–204.
Nishida, T., 1968, The social group of wild chimpanzees in the Mahali Mountains, *Primates,* 9, 167–227.
Nissen, H. W., 1931, A field study of the chimpanzee: Observations of chimpanzee behavior and environment in West French Guinea, *Comp. Psychol. Monogr.,* 8(1), 1–122.
Nissen, H. W., and Crawford, M. P., 1936, A preliminary study of food-sharing behavior in young chimpanzees, *J. Comp. Psychol.,* 12, 383–419.
Olver, R. R., and Hornsby, J. R., 1966, On equivalence, IN *Studies in cognitive growth,* eds. J. S. Bruner *et al.,* Wiley, New York, pp. 68–85.
Oppenheimer, J. R., 1968, Behavior and ecology of the whitefaced monkey, *Cebus capucinus,* on Barro Colorado Island, Ph.D. thesis, University of Illinois.
Oppenheimer, J. R., 1969, Changes in forehead patterns and group composition of the whitefaced monkey (*Cebus capucinus*), IN *Proceedings of the Second International Congress of Primatology I: Behavior,* ed. C. R. Carpenter, Karger, Basel, pp. 36–42.
Orr, W. F., and Cappannari, S. C., 1967, The emergence of language, IN *The psychology of language, thought, and instruction,* ed. J. DeCecco, Holt, New York, pp. 63–68.
Oxnard, C. E., 1967, Some occult lesions in captive primates, *Amer. J. Phys. Anth.,* 26, 93–96.
Papoušek, H., 1967, Experimental studies of appetitional behavior in human newborns and infants, *Early behavior,* eds. H. W. Stevenson, E. H. Hess, and H. L. Rheingold, Wiley, New York, pp. 249–278.
Parker, C. E., 1969, Responsiveness, manipulation, and implementation behavior in chimpanzees, gorillas, and orangutans, IN *Proceedings of the Second International Congress of Primatology I: Behavior,* ed. C. R. Carpenter, Karger, Basel, p. 160.
Parkes, A. S., and Bruce, H. M., 1961, Olfactory stimuli in mammalian reproduction, *Science,* 134, 1049–1054.
Patten, B. M., 1958, *Foundations of embryology,* McGraw-Hill, New York, 578 pp.
Petter, J.-J., 1962, Recherches sur l'écologie et l'éthologie des lémuriens malgaches,

Mém. Mus. Nat. Hist. Naturel, n.s. 27, 1–146.

Petter-Rousseaux, A., 1964, Reproductive physiology and behavior of the Lemuroidea, IN *Evolutionary and genetic biology of the primates II,* ed. J. Buettner-Janusch, Academic, New York, pp. 92–132.

Petter-Rousseaux, A., 1968, Cycles génitaux saisonniers des lémuriens malgaches, IN *Cycles génitaux saisonniers de mammifères sauvages,* ed. R. Canivenc, Masson, Paris, pp. 11–22.

Petter-Rousseaux, A., 1969, Day length influence on breeding season in mouse lemurs, Presented at Eleventh Ethological Congress, 1969.

Piaget, J., 1951, *Play, dreams, and imitation in childhood,* Routledge and Kegan Paul, London, 296 pp.

Piaget, J., 1954, *The construction of reality in the child,* Basic Books, New York, 386 pp.

Piaget, J., 1960, *The psychology of intelligence,* Littlefield, Adams & Co., Peterson, N. J., 182 pp.

Pilbeam, D., 1972, *The ascent of man,* New York, Macmillan.

Pitelka, F. A., 1949, Numbers, breeding schedule, and territoriality in pectoral sandpipers in Northern Alaska, *Condor,* 61, 233–264.

Ploog, D. W., 1967, The behavior of squirrel monkeys (*Saimiri sciureus*) as revealed by sociometry, bioacoustics, and brain stimulation, IN *Social communication among primates,* ed. S. A. Altmann, Chicago U. P., Chicago, pp. 149–184.

Plotnick, R., King, F. A., and Roberts, L., 1968, Effects of competition on the aggressive behavior of squirrel and cebus monkeys, *Behavior,* 32, 315–332.

Poirier, F. E., 1968a, Analysis of a nilgiri langur (*Presbytis johnii*) home range change, *Primates,* 9, 29–44.

Poirier, F. E., 1968b, The nilgiri langur (*Presbytis johnii*) mother–infant dyad, *Primates,* 9, 45–68.

Poirier, F. E., 1968c, Nilgiri langur (*Presbytis johnii*) territorial behavior, *Primates,* 9, 351–364.

Poirier, F. E., 1969a, The nilgiri langur (*Presbytis johnii*) troop: Its composition, structure, formation, and change, *Folia Primat.,* 10, 20–47.

Poirier, F. E., 1969b, Behavioral flexibility and intertroop variation among nilgiri langurs (*Presbytis johnii*) of South India, *Folia Primat.,* 11, 119–133.

Poirier, F. E., 1969c, Nilgiri langur (*Presbytis johnii*) territorial behavior, IN *Proceedings of the Second International Congress of Primatology I: Behavior,* ed. C. R. Carpenter, Karger, Basel, pp. 31–35.

Pope, B. L., 1965, Group size and composition of a wild howler monkey population in Argentina, *Amer. J. Phys. Anth.,* 23, 334.

Pope, B. L., 1966, The population characteristics of howler monkeys (*Alouatta caraya*) in Northern argentina, *Amer. J. Phys. Anth.,* 24, 351–360.

Portmann, A., 1965, Über die Evolution der Tragzeit bei Saügetieren, *Rev. Suisse Zool.,* 72, 658–666.

Pratt, C. L., and Sackett, G. P., 1967, Selection of social partners as a function of peer contact during rearing, *Science,* 155, 1133–1135.

Premack, D., 1970, A functional analysis of language, *J. Exp. Anal. Behav.,* 14, 107–125.

Premack, D., and Schwartz, A., 1966, Preparations for discussing behaviorism with chimpanzee, IN *The genesis of language,* eds. F. Smith and G. A. Miller, MIT Press, Cambridge, Mass., pp. 295–338.

Price-Williams, D. R., Gordon, W., and Ramirez, M., 1968, Manipulation and conservation: A study of children from pottery-making families in Mexico, IN *Eleventh Inter-American Congress of Psychology Proceedings,* Mexico City.

Prost, J. H., and Sussman, R. W., 1969, Monkey locomotion on inclined surfaces, *Amer. J. Phys. Anth.,* 31, 53–58.

Rensch, B., 1957, Aesthetische Faktoren bei Farb- und Formbevorezugungen von Affen, *Z. Tierpsychol.,* 14, 71–99.

Rensch, B., and Döhl, J., 1967, Spontanes Öffnen verschiedener Kistenverschlüsse durch einen Schimpansen, *Z. Tierpsychol.,* 24, 476–489.

Rensch, B., and Döhl, J., 1968, Wahlen zwischen zwei überschaubaren Labyrinthwegen durch einen Schimpansen, *Z. Tierpsychol.,* 25, 216–231.

Rensch, B., and Duecker, K. C., 1966, Manipulier Fähigkeit eines jungen Orangutans und eines jungen Gorillas: Mit Anmerkungen über das spielverhalten, *Z. Tierpsychol.,* 23, 874–892.

Reynolds, V., 1968, Kinship and the family in monkeys, apes, and man, *Man,* n.s. 3, 209–223.

Reynolds, V., and Luscombe, G., 1969, Chimpanzee rank order and the function of displays, IN *Proceedings of the Second International Congress of Primatology I: Behavior,* ed. C. R. Carpenter, Karger, Basel, pp. 81–86.

Reynolds, V., and Reynolds, F., 1965, Chimpanzees of the Budongo forest, IN *Primate behavior,* ed. I. DeVore, Holt, New York, pp. 368–424.

Richard, A., 1970, A comparative study of the activity patterns and behavior of *Alouatta villosa* and *Ateles geoffroyi, Folia Primat.,* 12, 241–263.

Riopelle, A. J., and McChinn, R., 1961, Position habits and discrimination learning by monkeys, *J. Comp. Physiol. Psychol.,* 54, 178–180.

Ripley, S., 1967a, Intertroop encounters among Ceylon gray langurs (*Presbytis entellus*), IN *Social communication among primates,* ed. S. A. Altmann, Chicago U. P., Chicago, pp. 237–254.

Ripley, S., 1967b, The leaping of langurs: A problem in the study of locomotor adaptation, *Amer. J. Phys. Anth.,* 26, 149–170.

Robinson, J., 1969, *Freedom and necessity: An introduction to the study of society,* Allen, London, 128 pp.

Rogers, C. M., and Davenport, R. K., 1969, Sexual behavior of differentially reared chimpanzees, IN *Proceedings of the Second International Congress of Primatology I: Behavior,* ed. C. R. Carpenter, Karger, Basel, pp. 173–177.

Rosenblum, L. A., 1968, Mother–infant relations and early behavioral development in the squirrel monkey, IN *The squirrel monkey,* eds. L. A. Rosenblum and R. W. Cooper, Academic Press, New York, pp. 207–234.

Rosenblum, L. A., Kaufman, I. C., and Stynes, A. J., 1966, Some characteristics of adult social and autogrooming patterns in two species of macaque, *Folia Primat.,* 4, 438–451.

Rowell, T. E., 1962, Agonistic noises of the rhesus monkey (*Macaca mulatta*), *Symp. Zool. Soc. Lond.,* 8, 91–96.

Rowell, T. E., 1963a, Behavior and female reproductive cycles of rhesus macaques, *J. Reprod. Fert.,* 6, 193–203.

Rowell, T. E., 1963b, The social development of some rhesus monkeys, IN *Determinants of infant behavior I,* ed. B. M. Foss, Methuen, London, pp. 35–49.

Rowell, T. E., 1965, Some observations on a hand-reared baboon, IN *Determinants of infant behavior III,* ed. B. M. Foss, Methuen, London, pp. 77–84.

Rowell, T. E., 1966a, Forest-living baboons in Uganda, *J. Zool. Lond.,* 149, 344–364.

Rowell, T. E., 1966b, Hierarchy in the organization of a captive baboon group, *Animal Behav.,* 14, 430–443.

Rowell, T. E., 1967a, A quantitative comparison of the behavior of a wild and a caged baboon group, *Animal Behav.,* 15, 499–589.

Rowell, T. E., 1967b, Female reproductive cycles and the behavior of baboons and rhesus macaques, IN *Social communication among primates,* ed. S. A. Altmann, Chicago U. P., Chicago, pp. 15–32.

Rowell, T. E., 1968a, The effect of temporary separation from their group on the mother–infant relationship of baboons, *Folia Primat.,* 9, 114–122.

Rowell, T. E., 1968b, Grooming by adult baboons in relation to reproductive cycles, *Animal Behav.,* 16, 585–588.

Rowell, T. E., 1969, Long-term changes in a population of Ugandan baboons, *Folia Primat.,* 11, 241–254.

Rowell, T. E., 1970, Baboon menstrual cycles affected by social environment, *J. Reprod. Fert.,* 21, 133–141.

Rowell, T. E., and Hinde, R. A., 1962, Vocal communication by the rhesus monkey (*Macaca mulatta*), *Proc. Zool. Soc. Lond.,* 138, 279–294.

Rumbaugh, D. M., 1968, The learning and sensory capacities of the squirrel monkey in phylogenetic perspective, IN *The squirrel monkey,* eds. L. A. Rosenblum and R. W. Cooper, Academic Press, New York, pp. 256–318.

Rumbaugh, D. M., and McCormack, C., 1969, Attentional skills of great apes compared with those of gibbons and squirrel monkeys, IN *Proceedings of the Second International Congress of Primatology I: Behavior,* ed. C. R. Carpenter, Karger, Basel, pp. 167–172.

Russell, C., and Russell, W. M. S., 1968, *Violence, monkeys, and man,* Macmillan & Co., London, 340 pp.

Sackett, G. P., 1966, Monkeys reared in isolation with pictures as visual input: Evidence for an innate releasing mechanism, *Science,* 154, 1470–1473.

Sackett, G. P., Porter, M., and Holmes, H., 1965, Choice behavior in rhesus monkeys: Effect of stimulation during the first month of life, *Science,* 147, 304–306.

Sackett, G., Griffin, G. A., Pratt, C., Joslyn, W. D., and Ruppenthal, G., 1967, Mother–infant and adult female choice behavior in rhesus monkeys after various rearing experiences, *J. Comp. Physiol. Psychol.,* 63, 376–381.

Sade, D. S., 1967, Determinants of dominance in a group of free-ranging rhesus monkeys, IN *Social communication among primates,* ed. S. A. Altmann, Chicago U. P., Chicago, pp. 99–115.

Sade, D. S., 1968, Inhibition of son–mother mating among free-ranging rhesus monkeys, *Sci. Psychoanal.*, 12, 18–37.

Sarles, H. B., 1969, The study of language and communication across species, *Curr. Anth.*, pp. 211–220.

Sauer, G. F., 1967, Mother–infant relationship in galagos and the oral child transport among primates, *Folia Primat.*. 7, 127–149.

Sauer, G. F., and Sauer, E. M., 1963, The Southwest African bushbaby of the *Galago senegalensis* group, *J. S. W. Afr. Sci. Soc.*, 16, 5–36.

Schaffer, H. R., 1966, The onset of fear of strangers and the incongruity hypothesis, *J. Child Psychol. Psychiat.*, 7, 95–106.

Schaffer, H. R., and Parry, M. H., 1969, Perceptual-motor behavior in infancy as a function of age and stimulus familiarity, *Brit. J. Psychol.*, 60, 1–9.

Schaffer, H. R., and Emerson, P. E., 1964, The development of social attachments in infancy, *Monogr. Soc. Res. Child. Develop.*, 29, 3, No. 94.

Schaller, G. B., 1963, *The mountain gorilla,* Chicago U. P., Chicago, 431 pp.

Schaller, G. B., 1967, *The deer and the tiger,* Chicago U. P., Chicago, 370 pp.

Schenkel, R., and Schenkel-Hulliger, L., 1967, On the sociology of free-ranging colobus (*Colobus guereza caudatus*) Thomas 1885, IN *Neue Ergebnisse der Primatologie,* eds. D. Stark, R. Schneider, and H.-J. Kuhn, Fischer, Stuttgart, pp. 185–194.

Schiller, P. H., 1951, Figural preferences in the drawings of a chimpanzee, *J. Comp. Physiol. Psychol.*, 44, 101–111.

Schiller, P. H., 1957, Manipulative patterns in the chimpanzee, IN *Instinctive behavior,* ed. C. H. Schiller, International Universities Press, New York, pp. 264–287.

Schmidt, U., and Seitz, E., 1967, Waschen mit Harn zum Zweck der Thermoregulation bei Totenkopfaffen (*Saimiri sciureus* L.), *Anth. Anz.*, 30, 162–165.

Schultze-Westrum, T., 1965, Innerartliche Verständigung durch Dufte beim Gleitbeutler *Petaurus breviceps papuanus* Thomas (Marsupialia, Phalangerida), *Z. Vergl. Physiol.* 50, 151–200.

Scott, J. P., 1968, *Early experience and the organization of behavior,* Belmont, Maine, Brooks Cole, 117 pp.

Seay, B., Alexander, B. K., and Harlow, H. F., 1964, Maternal behavior of socially deprived rhesus monkeys, *J. Abnorm. Soc. Psychol.*, 69, 345–357.

Seitz, E., 1969, Die Bedeutung geruchlicher Orientierung beim Plumplori *Nycticebus coucang* Boddaert 1785 (Prosimii, Lorisdae), *Z. Tierpsychol.*, 26, 73–103.

Simonds, P. B., 1965, The bonnet macaque in South India, IN *Primate behavior,* ed. I. DeVore, Holt, New York, pp. 175–196.

Singh, S. D., 1965, The effects of human environment upon the reactions to novel situations in the rhesus, *Behavior,* 26, 243–250.

Singh, S. D., 1966a, Effect of human environment on cognitive behavior in the rhesus monkey, *J. Comp. Physiol. Psychol.*, 61, 280–283.

Singh, S. D., 1966b, The effects of human environment on the social behavior of rhesus monkeys, *Primates,* 7, 33–40.

Singh, S. D., 1968, Social interactions between the rural and urban monkeys, *Macaca mulatta, Primates,* 9, 69–74.

Skinner, B. F., 1957, *Verbal behavior,* Appleton, New York, 596 pp.

Skinner, B. F., 1966, The phylogeny and ontogeny of behavior, *Science,* 153, 1205–1213.

Smith, W. J., 1968, Message-meaning analysis, IN *Animal communication,* ed. T. Sebeok, Indiana U. P., Bloomington.

Smith, W. J., 1969, Messages of vertebrate communication, *Science,* 165, 145–150.

Southwick, C. H., 1962, Patterns of intergroup social behavior in primates, with special reference to rhesus and howling monkeys, *Ann. N.Y. Acad. Sci.*, 102, 436–454.

Southwick, C. H., 1967, An experimental study of intragroup agonistic behavior in rhesus monkeys (*Macaca mulatta*), *Behavior,* 28, 182–209.

Southwick, C. H., and Siddiqi, M. R., 1967, The role of social tradition in the maintenance of dominance in a wild rhesus group, *Primates,* 8, 341–354.

Southwick, C. H., Beg, M. A., and Siddiqi, M. R., 1965, Rhesus monkeys in North India, IN *Primate behavior,* ed. I. DeVore, Holt, New York, pp. 111–159.

Spencer-Booth, Y., 1968, The behavior of group companions toward rhesus monkey infants, *Animal Behav.*, 16, 541–557.

Spencer-Booth, Y., and Hinde, R. A., 1969, Tests of behavioral characteristics for rhesus monkeys, *Behavior,* 33, 179–211.

Spencer-Booth, Y., Hinde, R. A., and Bruce, M., 1965, Social companions and the mother–infant relationship in rhesus monkeys, *Nature,* 208, 301.

Spitz, R. A., and Woolf, K. M., 1946, The

smiling response: A contribution to the ontogeny of social relations, *Gen. Psychol. Monogr.*, No. 34.

Spock, B., 1969, *Decent and indecent,* McCall, New York, 210 pp.

Stephens, W. N., 1963, *The family in cross-cultural perspective,* Holt, New York, 460 pp.

Struhsaker, T. T., 1967a, Social structure among vervet monkeys (*Cercopithecus aethiops*), *Behavior,* 29, 83–121.

Struhsaker, T. T., 1967b, Ecology of vervet monkeys (*Cercopithecus aethiops*) in the Masai-Amboseli Game Reserve, Kenya, *Ecology,* 48, 891–904.

Struhsaker, T. T., 1967c, Auditory communication among vervet monkeys (*Cercopithecus aethiops*), IN *Social communication among primates,* ed. S. A. Altmann, Chicago U. P., Chicago, pp. 281–324.

Struhsaker, T. T., 1967d, Behavior of vervet monkeys (*Cercopithecus aethiops*), *Univ. Calif. Publ. Zool.,* pp. 1–64.

Struhsaker, T. T., 1969, Correlates of ecology and social organization among African cercopithecines, *Folia Primat.,* 11, 80–118.

Subramoniam, S., 1957, Some observations on the habits of the slender loris, *Loris tardigradus* (Linnaeus), *J. Bombay Nat. Hist. Soc.,* 54, 387–398.

Sugiyama, Y., 1964, Group composition, population density, and some sociological observations of hanuman langurs (*Presbytis entellus*), *Primates,* 5, 7–38.

Sugiyama, Y., 1965a, Behavioral development and social structure in two troops of hanuman langurs (*Presbytis entellus*), *Primates,* 6, 213–247.

Sugiyama, Y., 1965b, On the social change of hanuman langurs (*Presbytis entellus*) in their natural condition, *Primates,* 6, 381–418.

Sugiyama, Y., 1966, An artificial change in a hanuman langur troop (*Presbytis entellus*), *Primates,* 7, 41–73.

Sugiyama, Y., 1968, Social organization of chimpanzees in the Budongo Forest, Uganda, *Primates,* 9, 225–258.

Sugiyama, Y., Yoshiba, K., and Pathasarathy, M. D., 1965, Home range, mating season, male group, and intertroop relations in hanuman langurs (*Presbytis entellus*), *Primates,* 6, 73–106.

Suzuki, A., 1965, An ecological study of wild Japanese monkeys in snowy areas—focused on their food habits, *Primates,* 6, 31–72.

Suzuki, A., 1966, On the insect-eating habits among wild chimpanzees living in the savanna woodland of Western Tanzania, *Primates,* 7, 481–487.

Suzuki, A., 1969, An ecological study of chimpanzees in a savanna woodland, *Primates,* 10, 103–148.

Tanaka, J., 1965, Social structure of nilgiri langurs, *Primates,* 6, 107–122.

Thorgersen, H. L., 1958, Studies of tactile discrimination by raccoons, *Dissertation Abst.,* 18, 2203–2204.

Thorington, R. W., 1967, Feeding and activity of *Cebus* and *Saimiri* in a Colombian forest, IN *Neue Ergebnisse der Primatologie,* eds. D. Stark R. Schneider, and H.-J. Kuhn, Fischer, Stuttgart.

Thorington, R. W., 1968a, Observations of squirrel monkeys in a Colombian forest, IN *The squirrel monkey,* eds. L. A. Rosenblum and B. W. Cooper, Academic Press, New York, pp. 69–87.

Thorington, R. W., 1968b, Observations of the tamarin, *Saguinus midas, Folia Primat.,* 9, 95–98.

Tinbergen, N., 1951, *The study of instinct,* Oxford U.P., New York.

Tokuda, K., and Jensen, G. D., 1968, The leader's role in controlling aggressive behavior in a monkey group, *Primates,* 9, 319–322.

Tokuda, K., Simons, R. C., and Jensen, G. D., 1968, Sexual behavior in a captive group of pigtailed monkeys (*Macaca nemestrina*), *Primates,* 9, 283–294.

Tsumori, A., 1966, Delayed response of wild Japanese monkeys by the sand-digging method II: Cases of the Takasakiyama troops and the Ohiragama troop, *Primates,* 7, 363–380.

Tsumori, A., 1967, Newly acquired behavior and social interactions of Japanese monkeys, IN *Social communication among primates,* ed. S. A. Altmann, Chicago U. P., Chicago, pp. 207–220.

Tsumori, A., Kawai, M., and Motoyoshi, R., 1965, Delayed response of wild Japanese monkeys by the sand-digging method I, *Primates,* 6, 195–212.

Turner, C. H., Davenport, R. K., and Rogers, C. M., 1969, Effect of early deprivation on social behavior of adolescent chimpanzees, *Amer. J. Psychiat.,* 125, 1531.

Tuttle, R. H., 1967, Knuckle walking and the evolution of hominoid hands, *Amer. J. Phys. Anth.,* 26, 171–206.

Tuttle, R. H., 1969, Knuckle walking and the problem of human origins, *Science,* 166, 953–961.

Udrey, J. R., and Morris, N. M., 1968, Distribution of coitus in the menstrual cycle, *Nature,* 220, 593–596.

Van Wagenen, G., 1967, Fertility of the colony-born male macaque, *Folia Primat.*, 5, 241–246.

Vandenburg, J. G., 1969, Endocrine coordination in monkeys: Male sexual responses to the female, *Physiol. Behav.*, 4, 261–264.

Vessey, S. A., 1968, Interactions between free-ranging groups of rhesus monkeys, *Folia Primat.*, 8, 228–240.

Walker, A., 1967, Patterns of extinction among the subfossil Madagascan lemuroids, IN *Pleistocene extinctions,* eds. P. S. Martin and H. E. Wright, Jr., Yale U. P., New Haven, pp. 425–432.

Walker, A., 1969, The locomotion of lorises, with special reference to the potto, *E. Afr. Wildlife J.*, 7, 1–60.

Walters, R. H., 1968, The effects of social isolation and social interaction on learning and performance in social situations, IN *Environmental influences,* ed. D. C. Glass, Rockefeller U.P., New York, pp. 155–184.

Warren, J. M., 1965, Primate learning in comparative perspective, IN *Behavior of nonhuman primates,* eds. A. M. Schreier, H. F. Harlow, and F. Stollnitz, Academic Press, New York, 249–282.

Washburn, S. L., and DeVore, I., 1961, The social life of baboons, *Sci. Amer.*, 204, 62–71.

Washburn, S. L., and Hamburg, D. A., 1965, The implications of primate research, IN *Primate behavior,* ed. I. DeVore, Holt, New York, pp. 607–622.

Washburn, S. L., and Lancaster, C. S., 1968, The evolution of hunting, IN *Man the hunter,* eds. I. DeVore and R. Lee, Aldine, Chicago.

Weinstein, B., 1945, The evolution of intelligent behavior in rhesus monkeys, *Genet. Psychol. Monogr.*, 31, 3–48.

Weir, R. H., 1962, *Language in the crib,* Mouton, The Hague, 216 pp.

Wheeler, W. M., 1911, The ant colony as an organism, *J. Morphol.*, 22, 307–325.

Wickler, W., 1967, Sociosexual signals and their intraspecific imitation among primates, IN *Primate ethology,* ed. D. Morris, Weidenfield and Nicolson, London, pp. 69–147.

Williams, L., 1967, *Man and monkey,* Andre Deutsch, London, 203 pp.

Winter, P., 1968, Social communication in the squirrel monkey, IN *The squirrel monkey,* eds. L. A. Rosenblum and R. W. Cooper, Academic Press, New York, pp. 235–255.

Wynne-Edwards, V. C., 1962, *Animal dispersion in relation to social behavior,* Oliver & Boyd, Edinburgh, 653 pp.

Yamada, M., 1963, A study of blood relationship in the natural society of the Japanese macaque, *Primates,* 4, 43–66.

Yamada, M., 1966, Five natural troops of Japanese monkeys in Shodoshima Island I: Distribution and social organization, *Primates,* 7, 315–362.

Yerkes, R. M., 1943, *Chimpanzees: A laboratory colony,* Yale U. P., New Haven, 189 pp.

Yerkes, R. M., and Yerkes, A., 1929, *The great apes,* Yale U. P., New Haven, 652 pp.

Yoshiba, K., 1967, An ecological study of hanuman langurs, *Presbytis entellus, Primates,* 8, 127–154.

Zimmerman, R., and Torrey, C. C., 1965, Ontogeny of learning, IN *Behavior of nonhuman primates,* eds. A. M. Schreier, H. F. Harlow, and F. Stollnitz, Academic Press, New York, pp. 405–445.

Zuckerman, S., 1932, *The social life of monkeys and apes,* K. Paul, Trench, Trubner & Co., London, 357 pp.

Zuckerman, S., 1933, *Functional affinities of man, monkeys, and apes,* K. Paul, Trench, Trubner & Co., London, 203 pp.

Index

The designation "f" after a page number refers to a figure (illustration), and "t" to a table. When consecutive pages deal with a topic, the inclusive page numbers are first given, followed by pages that contain figures and/or tables (e.g., "172–82, 173f, 174–77t").

Because of index-length limitations, specific entries have been restricted. If a specific entry cannot be located, check a more general entry (e.g., for "sibling behavior," check "kinship"). *For taxonomy and vernacular names, see Table 1 (pp. 16–22).*

A

B

C

D

E

F

G

H

I

J

K

L

M

N

O

P

Q

R

S

T

U

V

W

Y

Z